CE

The future of road goods transport and distribution is fully explored in this study. The author examines transport policies, distribution methods and operational techniques — and the effects of all these factors on the large and rapidly increasing expenditure on transporting goods by road. He points out some of the difficulties involved in trying to implement more efficient methods to control traffic congestion and concludes that all practicable methods would lead to increased costs for operators of road transport. With the government being unable to help, firms must control road transport expenditure themselves — and are only likely to succeed by reducing road usage. They could do this by increasing consignment size and density; but without changes in distribution methods their efforts would lead to undesirable side effects. The author outlines systems for increasing consignment size and density without these bad side effects and focuses attention on some of the major technical problems involved: the estimation of journey durations, calculation of journey plans, design of information processing and transmission systems, and the financial conditions necessary for the successful application of these techniques. He concludes that there is real scope for massive reductions in expenditure on road goods transport if some of the technical and organisational problems can be overcome.

Transporting Goods by Road

L.S.E. research monographs 10

This series is published jointly with the London School of Economics and Political Science. It aims to make available research of originality and quality from the whole range of the social sciences, including all the fields and disciplines which are studied at the School. The intention is to provide a continuing outlet for serious scholarly work, and relatively quick publication. The books will be of interest to specialists in the various fields, irrespective of whether they are in universities, government departments, industries or elsewhere; as well as to libraries throughout the world.

The following monographs have already been published:

Changes in Subject Choice at School and University
Celia M. Phillips
The Criminal Liability of Corporations in English Law
L.H. Leigh
Industrial Demand for Water: A Study of South East England
Judith Rees
The Politics of Decontrol of Industry
Susan Armitage
Students in Conflict
Tessa Blackstone, Kathleen Gales, Roger Hadley, Wyn Lewis
The Administrative Functions of the French Conseil d'Etat
Margherita Rendel
The Theory of Customs Unions: A General Equilibrium Analysis
Richard G. Lipsey
Criminal Responsibility
Francis G. Jacobs
The Nineteenth Century Foreign Office: An Administrative History
Ray Jones
Russian Police Trade Unionism
D.Pospielovsky

Forthcoming:
Six Studies of Indian Industry
Angus Hone (Editor)

Transporting goods by road

Michael Webb

Fellow in Management Studies,
London School of Economics

London School of Economics and Political Science

Weidenfeld and Nicolson
5 Winsley Street London W1

ISBN 0 297 00352 6

Printed by Redwood Press Ltd., Trowbridge & London.

Contents

Errata

The publishers regret that the following errata
appear in this book:

p.5, line 9: for 'services.' read 'services it should
     be'

p.45, line 23: delete ', if these were also to
     increase at established rates,'

p. 307, line 26: for '$N1 \sim (N/e)^N \sqrt{2\pi N!}$' read
     '$N! \sim (N/e)^N \sqrt{(2\pi N)}$'

p.308, line 37: for '$N/N\text{-}1/2$' read '$N(N\text{-}1)/2$'

p.329: transpose with page 338

p.342, line 3: for 'any two points X and $\overline{Y}$' read
     'any two points X and Y $\underline{\quad}$'

p.343, line 1: for 'XY' read '$\overline{XY}$'

p.396, Figure 42.2: there should be a shaded area
     between 2 and 6 on the vertical axis, extending
     the whole length of the horizontal axis

p.397, line 22: for 'curves' read 'curve'

p.400, lines 1-2: transpose with page 401, lines
     1-2

Tables

Figures

Foreword

Expenditure on road goods transport, £2,500M. in 1967, is already very large. The purpose of this study is to examine what can be done to contain or reverse the established trend of rapid increases in this expenditure.

Road goods transport expenditure could be reduced if increases in consignment size and density permitted the efficient utilization of the capacity and time of larger vehicles, thus reducing road usage.

Firms, and managements, might be able to make these changes without deterioration in the quality of service given if they were prepared:–
1 to change the methods and organization of their transport and distribution functions;
2 to adopt improved methods of planning journeys and of estimating their duration;
3 to develop and introduce information and control systems, based upon journey planning by computer, in order to cope with additional complexity and scale.

The range of policies and activities examined is extremely wide, embracing government policies, firms' marketing, distribution and transport policies, the design of information processing systems, and methods of preparing journey plans for individual vehicles. The reason for this breadth is that the combination is far more significant than the sum of the components.

The technical virtuosity of planning journeys by computer is likely to be of only accidental benefit unless the plans are based on sound estimates of their work content. Even if the planning procedures are incorporated into computer-based information processing and communications systems, few firms are likely to realise appreciable savings from them. The benefits of advanced planning procedures are only likely to be very substantial if transport functions are re-organized to obtain economies of scale, and such reorganization is virtually impossible without advanced procedures.

Considerable financial rewards might not be enough to persuade many firms to exchange familiar, simple systems for new and complex ones, especially if it is believed that changes in government policy could easily slash transport expenditure anyway. However, closer examination of possible government policies suggests that there are no magic wands; firms will themselves have to absorb, or devise means of avoiding, the inevitable, sharp increases in the costs of road usage. Radical changes in firms' road goods transport policies are therefore proposed: to justify the proposals it is necessary to examine some limitations of existing policies, and to demonstrate that those advocated are practicable.

Changes in goods transport policies along the lines advocated could only be brought about by co-operation between a number of specialist groups, or departments, within firms, acting with the approval and support of non-specialist managers. Some of the material presented is new, and the aim has been to render it comprehensible to the non-specialist without destroying its usefulness to the specialist, because lack of communication between different functions can be a major barrier to progress. Specialists taking exception to the appreciations of current knowledge and thought expounded, if they appear to them to be superficial or biased, may be less offended if the communication objective is borne in mind.

It is hoped that this study will be of general interest outside firms. No one, from town planners to housewives, can afford to be entirely indifferent to road goods transport costs, policies, and problems. While this study is not intended to be a text-book, students may find that it broadens and deepens their view of transport and of the activities necessarily associated with it.

Because of the length and scope of the study, parts have been written so that they can be read in isolation. The first chapter is a summary; it should direct the reader to those aspects which interest him and demonstrate how these fit into the whole.

For the sake of simplicity, in view of the change in 1971 to decimal coinage, only three monetary units are used and the shilling is ignored. The units used are £1M., £1, and 1d., and the relationship between them is

$$£1M. = £1,000,000$$

$$£1 = 240d.$$

Because of the possible confusion neither 'penny' nor 'pence' is used.

The author takes this opportunity of offering grateful thanks to innumerable friends and colleagues for their help, and the Foundation for Management Education for supporting a Fellowship in Management Studies at L.S.E.

Part 1

Part 4

Chapter 1

Summary and Conclusions

Road Goods Transport expenditure.

Expenditure on goods transport by road, which is the dominant form of goods transport, is very large; in 1967 it was estimated to have been £2,500M. This was equivalent to 10% of total consumers' expenditure, 45% of consumers' expenditure on food, over 35% of public expenditure on the social services, and more than national expenditure on defence.

The annual rate of increase of expenditure on road goods transport has been approximately 10%. This rate of increase is of the same order as that of public expenditure on the social services, but is 75% higher than the rate of increase of consumers' expenditure.

Between 1957 and 1967, expenditure on road goods transport, expressed as a percentage of gross company trading profits in the U.K., increased from 31% to 53%. If established trends of road goods transport expenditure and gross company trading profits in the U.K. were to continue, expenditure on road goods transport would be the larger by 1975.

The rate of increase of expenditure on road goods transport is much higher than the rate of growth of the economy, transport generating industries, or distribution; thus, it cannot easily be explained in terms of the rate of growth of the activities which are normally thought to give rise to the bulk of transport demand. The unit costs, including taxation, of road goods transport are not increasing any more rapidly than the general run of costs and prices, while it appears that road goods transport productivity is increasing in real terms. Further, while some goods traffic has been converted from rail to road transport, this only partially explains the high growth rate of road goods transport expenditure.

More detailed examination of the reason for the growth in the estimates of expenditure leads to concentration on the estimating procedure rather than on the expenditure. Nevertheless, it may be significant that, although there has been an increase in the number of large vehicles, indicating an increase in productivity, there has been an equivalent increase in the number of very small vehicles. The number of goods vehicles appears to be increasing at a much greater rate in most other countries than it is in Britain.

Ton-mileage is used as the main statistic indicating both transport demand and supply, although it only refers to both if demand and supply are equal. It is a defective measure of transport demands because changes in the relative location of production units and centres of consumption, in the commodity mix, and in the characteristics of individual commodities and their packaging, give rise to changes in the relationship between production and ton-mileage.

Similarly ton-mileage is a poor measure of transport supply, as is shown by the very different performances, in terms of ton-miles, of vehicles performing different functions.

Ton-mileage is also a very poor measure of expenditure on road goods transport. The major part of vehicle operating costs is associated with having vehicles and drivers available for work; costs vary but slightly with the mileage driven, or, as far as is known, with the loads carried.

Road goods transport is a heterogeneous activity, and attempts to ignore this, by utilizing some statistic, such as ton-mileage, as a measure of transport demand, supply and expenditure for explanatory purposes, are likely to be of little benefit, and may prove seriously misleading.

In these circumstances, forecasting expenditure on road goods transport is inevitably difficult because of the difficulty of explaining the established trend. However, the established trend is one of very rapidly increasing expenditure, despite any past improvements in real productivity. Looking ahead, no new factors can be seen which would help to reduce expenditure, although some can be seen whose overall effect is impossible to forecast with certainty. Further, a number of factors can be seen in prospect which will almost certainly lead to an increase in expenditure over and above any which might arise from increased production; these are road congestion, recent legislation, especially the provisions reducing the permitted hours of driving, and the concentration of production and distribution facilities. In these conditions it seems reasonable to expect the established trend of road goods transport expenditure, an increase of the order of 10% per annum, to continue into the future. Yet it is difficult to believe that road goods transport expenditure can increase very much further without provoking major attempts by firms or by public authorities, or both, to curtail it.

Transport Co-ordination as a Government Policy for Reducing
Transport Expenditure.

Road goods transport is only one part of the total inland transport activity.
Co-ordination of all inland transport activities has often been advocated as
a way of solving transport problems. Co-ordination, regulation, and
competition, are by general accord linked as emphasizing different aspects
of approach to the same set of problems. That co-ordination is 'good' is
widely, though not universally, accepted. Many references to co-ordination,
however, fail totally to make clear what it should mean in practice, or
how it should, or could, be achieved; when specific measures are broached
the concensus disappears. This confusion at the operational level reflects
lack of clarity at the conceptual level. Co-ordination is a sentiment rather
than a precise idea, let alone a meaningful, operational, set of policies.

    If attention is confined to road and rail as the main basic forms of
inland transport, all the evidence appears to suggest that, given adequate
utilization, the construction and operating costs of rail are less than those
of road, and that these lower costs reflect a lower utilization of resources.
Furthermore, the costs of public road passenger transport, given adequate
utilization, are less than those of private transport, also reflecting lower
resource utilization.

    In contrast, the out-of-pocket expenses of an extra car journey are less
than the equivalent bus fare which, in turn, is less than, or equal to, the
equivalent train fare. The pricing mechanism is distorted, since relative
prices do not reflect the utilization of resources.

    Price distortion is increased by the effects of road congestion, since
the slower speeds caused by congestion increase the cost of road usage.

    Neglecting the effects of rail congestion, which exists but appears to be
very localized, the extent of price distortion can best be summarized
as follows:
a) the ratio of the resource costs of rail, bus, and car travel is of the
order of 2:3:4;
b) in urban areas the ratio of the public costs of marginal journeys
typically lies between 1:2:8 and 1:6:72, according to the degree of
congestion;
c) the ratio of the costs faced by travellers for extra journeys appears to
be between 3:3:4 and 2:1:1.
The degree of price distortion is substantial; travellers do not face the
relative real costs of alternative modes when making their choice. Goods
transport prices are also distorted.

The net rate of taxation of road usage is of the order of 13% of expenditure, which is a comparatively low rate of indirect taxation; its effect on transport price distortion is minor.

Only a small proportion of public transport costs are variable; most are fixed if the service is to be maintained. Fares reflect average costs; because of the very low average utilization of most public transport capacity, fixed costs represent a major part of the fares. In contrast, it is normal to pay most of the fixed costs of private transport when the facility is acquired: only the variable costs enter into decisions over individual journeys. Most of the resource price distortion may be attributed to the variable costs of private transport being compared with the average costs of public transport which are inflated by low utilization. The price distortion is rendered more noticeable because there are many non-price reasons for private transport, if the fixed charges can be afforded.

Price distortion may be magnified many times by the effects of road congestion. But neither traffic management, nor parking or other administrative restrictions are likely to relieve congestion or restrict its growth to any very great extent. The deterrent effect of congestion has some effect on the incidence and severity of congestion, while the costs of road usage, which includes an element of taxation, must contribute to limiting traffic. Available evidence suggests that road building on a scale to relieve congestion, or even avoid deterioration, is impracticable, primarily because it would be too expensive. Severe traffic constraint is likely to become a permanent feature of the way of life.

Transport demands in excess of capacity may be suppressed, or attempts may be made to satisfy them in some other way. If road capacity is inadequate for all the potential journeys it may be possible to satisfy some of these by rail, or by denser usage of road capacity made possible by larger batches. But because of terminal handling requirements there is relatively little scope for transfer of goods traffic from road to rail. Car transport contributes most to congestion: passengers are physically more amenable to conversion to rail transport or concentration into bus or larger car loads: some car journeys are the easiest road journeys to eliminate: consequently, car traffic should contribute most to the relief of road congestion and bear the brunt of restrictions. Furthermore, restrictions on car usage will need to be less severe for a given level of congestion, and will be more acceptable, the better the rail services. Road and rail, public and private transport, are aspects of the one inland transport problem, and should be treated as such.

The cost inflicted on all other users of a congested road by an extra vehicle is of the same order as the vehicle's share of the cost of a heavily used new road built to relieve congestion. It is economically efficient to tax road users to the extent of the costs their usage inflicts on others, and the revenue could be used as a direct criterion for the need for road construction to relieve congestion. Congestion taxation appears to offer to road transport, and to be the only measure that does, the possibility of operational efficiency through quick and reliable journeys, but the price would be high. To those displaced from private transport services. possible to offer better and cheaper public transport services.

The need to treat different inland transport problems as aspects of one integral problem arises from the impossibility of dispensing with any significant part of existing transport facilities. To ensure efficient usage of all the existing facilities which must be retained, users should choose between alternative modes according to their valuation of the services and the relative true cost of these; this would follow if price distortion were replaced by price co-ordination. It would entail a complete reversal of generally accepted attitudes in which railway 'subsidies' loom large, and which amount to an implied denial that there is essentially only one inland transport problem. It has never even been demonstrated that British Railways could make a consistent profit. British Railways could be made 'profitable' under price co-ordination if the basic price were set sufficiently high; the cost might be the unnecessary suppression of a large number of transport demands, and therefore greater resentment of the policy as a whole.

Price co-ordination would restore rational price competition between transport modes, but, unless public transport services are of an acceptable quality, the main effect might not be a transfer of traffic from private to public transport, or more concentrated vehicle utilization, but rather an increase in transport charges with only moderate compensation in the form of additional operating efficiency. Public transport services could be improved in quality by operational co-ordination.

Proposals for both transport price and operational co-ordination are tantamount to proposals for a voluntary transport revolution. The need for a transport revolution can be shown by the economic distortions and by the existence of positive feedback, or vicious circles, in transport. The vicious circles most widely recognized occur in the impact of road congestion on public bus services; congestion reduces the quality of service given by buses and increases bus costs due to slower journeys; both of these effects of congestion encourage bus passengers to convert to private transport and thus increase congestion.

It is possible that government policy could help reduce road goods transport expenditure, but it is unlikely, because of the political implications, and it would be economically dangerous if the policy were introduced quickly. Road goods transporters have little to gain from road construction; their interests do not coincide with those of the majority of private motorists.

Firms' Policies for Reducing Road Goods Transport Expenditure: Economies of Scale.

Firms should be prepared to face for themselves all the problems posed by the rapid growth of road goods transport expenditure. Fortunately, as regards planning, in the unlikely event of the adoption of congestion taxation one of the effects will be similar to that of continuous acute congestion; the cost of road usage will be very high. Thus, to reduce expenditure, one objective should be to reduce the relative amount of road usage. Large vehicles are cheaper to operate per unit of capacity than small vehicles, and require less vehicle mileage to perform the same work, if their additional capacity can be utilized. Increases in consignment size or density would reduce the relative amount of road usage, and usually make it possible to exploit the lower unit costs of larger vehicles in addition. There is ample scope for increases in consignment size and density. Larger organizations might be expected to benefit from lower unit costs of administration and maintenance; more significantly, however, it might be expected that larger organizations would be able to support more commercial activity and exploit this to achieve higher effective consignment size or density.

There is, however, little evidence that larger organizations achieve better results than smaller ones in practice. A number of barriers to economies of scale exist which hinder both the establishment of a transport market and the realization of the potential efficiency of a large undertaking. Drivers and owners of small transport undertakings prefer their independence. The market is fragmented geographically and by the large variety of special service requirements. Many transport operations are vertically integrated into firms' own operations. The large number of very small consignments, each requiring services of very little value, poses very severe technical and financial problems related to communication and operational planning. Before economies of scale in road goods transport can be realized it is necessary to overcome, at least partially, some of these barriers.

Functional Organization for Economies of Scale.

The problems of achieving economies of scale can be illustrated by more detailed examination of the wholesale distribution function. There are economies of scale in stock holding and handling, and in the associated administrative systems, which are reflected in a trend to reduce the number, but increase the size, of warehouses. But, in general, a larger area is served from a larger warehouse and this leads to an increase in transport costs. Equally, increases in consignment size or density in wholesale deliveries are liable to be associated with a transfer of stocks from the wholesaler to retailer, and by reduction of the service given to retailers in terms of choice over the timing and frequency of deliveries.

The conflicting demands of customer service and of economies of scale in stockholding and transport could be resolved by the adoption of a different functional organization. Stockholding could be concentrated even further, preferably at the factory; goods for many outlets from many sources could be transhipped at local distribution centres where they would be sorted and loaded onto shared vehicles for delivery. The potential savings of such a system could be as much as 3% of gross retail trade.

Manufacturers and multiple retailers are tending to take over much of the wholesale physical distribution function. Independent retailers, in conjunction with wholesalers, are participating in voluntary chains which are similar in effect to the multiple retail chains. Manufacturers are limited in consignment size by their product range; the chains are limited in consignment density by the density of the retail outlets within the chain. However, there are some organizations, a few on a national scale, which attempt to provide a distribution service, and these may be forerunners of the potential system described. In contrast, another rapidly developing wholesale trend is cash-and-carry which is the antithesis of the system described, since it involves local stocks and collections of single, small consignments in small vehicles. It could be suggested that cash-and-carry is a proper, but specialized, result of the application of marginal costing principles by both wholesaler and retailer, and that, since this view of retailers' marginal costs is essentially confined to small independent retailers, who belong to a declining breed, any trend towards cash-and-carry may be essentially transient. But the record, and forecasts, of cash-and-carry trading hardly encourage acceptance of this view.

Cash-and-carry is not just a fringe development in wholesaling, but is a major factor underlying the main trends of retail distribution. Furthermore a declining number of retail establishments is dealing with an increasing trade; one result is the increasing importance of motorized shopping journeys. The trend towards concentration in retailing has been associated with increases in retailing productivity; customers like the trend. But the congestion costs arising from the increased traffic may be greater than the benefits arising from the increased productivity. If customers were to be faced with the real costs of their journeys, as with congestion taxation, the trend towards cash-and-carry might be halted or reversed; in the circumstances, it might prove difficult to reconcile economies of retail scale with transport efficiency. Home delivery services, which would themselves be subject to economies of consignment size and density, might enable retailing concentration and economies of scale to be reconciled with transport efficiency. Once again, however, a key to the reconciliation of the conflicting demands of retailing and transport efficiency would be the adoption of new forms of functional organization.

An Introduction to Journey Planning.

It is possible to view road goods transport as a craft, or cottage, industry. Consumers have not yet been offered a full range of good quality, mass-produced road goods transport services at a price which is low relative to that of the craft product. It is possible to contrast the general acceptability of the service and costs offered by the letter mail services with the rather limited use of any single public goods haulage service. But giving high standards of service to large numbers of consignments involves very complex control and communications systems. In particular, transport tasks have to be planned in such a way that they can and will be performed; this is the function of journey planning and has been referred to as operational co-ordination. Journey planning is the operational problem of matching transport supplies and demands efficiently. In the longer term, matching supplies and demands efficiently is the problem underlying goods transport planning and forecasting. As the scale of transport operations increases, so the complexity of the journey planning task increases dramatically; manual journey planning becomes very difficult and of declining efficiency within the size of transport situations met in practice. This is a barrier to economies of scale.

There is an almost infinite variety of journey planning problems. Particular factors which may influence the form of the problem are the organizational context, with its commercial, service and financial objectives, and the limitations imposed upon the plans produced by laws and regulations, vehicle characteristics, customer requirements and drivers' skills and limitations. Even if the function served is defined (for example, wholesale delivery) the range and variety of journey planning problems is apparently endless; nearly all such problems are complicated by the need to consider them in the detailed administrative and data processing context of the firm.

When attention is focussed on one very different problem, that of planning duty schedules for the drivers of a vehicle fleet whose task is performing the individual services demanded by a timetable, each detail of the conditions of service of the drivers increases the complexity of preparing efficient schedules, and the involvement with the administrative and data processing context reappears in the need to keep the timetable requirements up to date and produce actual duty schedules for each driver for all the services and other tasks to be performed each shift.

Estimation of Journey Duration and the Planned Idle Time.

In general, to give adequate commercial service and maintain fleet efficiency, when a vehicle is dispatched on a planned task, that task must be performed. To enable the vehicles utilized to be as large as reasonably possible, the duration of the planned journeys should be as long as possible; for most purposes this is one day. Journey plans are usually prepared subject to a duration limit; on the one hand the planned tasks should rarely, if ever, exceed the duration limit in practice, on the other, if the planned tasks take less than the available duration it is difficult, if not impossible, to utilize the spare time productively. When the time taken to perform a given task varies, as is the general rule, especially for journeys in congested areas, the work allocated to a journey plan will be limited by consideration of whether the duration is likely to exceed that permitted under the worst reasonable conditions anticipated. But the average duration, and therefore the productive utilization of the available duration, will be less than the maximum possible; the difference is the planned idle time. For a number of reasons the planned idle time is often not perceived; when it is perceived it is rarely recognised as a managerial responsibility. In particular, the planned idle time increases as the journey duration estimation procedure decreases in precision, since the journey plan must contain adequate allowances for all the uncertainties of duration.

The duration of most journeys is estimated on the basis of separate estimates of the distance and speed. The actual speed of each performance of a particular journey will deviate from the average for that journey, while the average for that journey will deviate from any general 'average speed' in the area. Using data from Central London, but producing results that are probably typical of journeys in congested areas, it appears likely that the planned idle time is at least 50% of the average duration; this implies that it is virtually impossible to obtain more than two-thirds utilization of the time available for driving; poor methods of estimation would lead to lower levels of utilization.

In comparison, even crude methods of estimating the road distance of a given route are far more accurate, and, given the inaccuracy of estimates of speed, it is, in general, not worth using refined methods. The adjusted crow flight method of estimating road distances, and that using 'real road distances' between the centres of zones, produce results of the same order of accuracy for most purposes. In general, the adjusted crow flight method appears to be preferable because it is simpler and not significantly less accurate. Unfortunately, a much greater source of inaccuracy creeps into distance estimation, arising from the problems of specifying the route which will be followed; there appear to be many reasons for departures from the planned route.

There may well be planned idle time associated with the performance of tasks other than driving, e.g. waiting for attention and unloading, due to imprecise estimates of their time requirements, which may in turn be due to the variability of these time requirements. An increase in the regularity and predictability of journeys may reduce the total time planned for, and allocated to, a journey as much as, or more than, an increase in the average speed. But additional precise constraints on the time at which parts of the journey must be performed, or a reduction of the maximum duration, almost certainly increases the proportion of planned idle time. These implications go apparently unrecognized in the introduction of shift working, reduction of the permitted driving hours, introduction of evening deliveries, and in recommendations that customers should be encouraged to make irregular purchases of milk rather than receive regular deliveries.

Without proper methods for the estimation of journey duration, efficient transport operation is unlikely; while attempts to achieve efficient operation are likely to put unreasonable stresses on drivers. Knowledge of the proper methods, without their application, may call attention to many sources of inefficiency, particularly with regard to variability, that might not otherwise be apparent. Application of such methods to estimate accurately the duration of journeys already planned may be neither particularly difficult nor particularly rewarding. To exploit the available time to the maximum financially possible, i.e. to obtain an efficient operation based upon efficient operational plans, it is necessary to plan journeys and estimate their duration at the same time; to do this planning and estimation techniques based upon computers will almost invariably be necessary.

Calculation of Journey Plans.

When planning journeys for most goods transport activities the cost, duration, or length of the journeys planned depends upon the sequence of the tasks in each journey; any computational method should allocate tasks to the most appropriate journey and find the most efficient sequence within each journey; at the same time, the journeys planned must conform to the restrictions imposed. There are so many possible solutions to any one problem that, when plans are prepared manually, it is impossible for any significant proportion of the possible solutions to be examined; yet the solutions produced are practicable, even if not perfect.

If the most common method of planning wholesale delivery journeys, the pigeon-holing method, is formulated as a set of logical rules, which emphasize proximity, and applied to test problems, the results obtained, while not very bad, nevertheless look as if they could be improved by simple adjustment, and are probably worse than the plans most people would draw on maps for the same problems. Proximity is not the only factor which needs to be taken into account when journeys are planned.

In contrast, the most common rigorous mathematical optimization techniques, such as linear and dynamic programming, can only be applied with difficulty to a simplification of journey planning problems known as the travelling salesman problem, and then only to very small sample problems. The fundamental difficulty is that there is an almost infinite, and certainly 'astronomical', number of possible solutions to such combinatorial problems, and no computationally quick, general rules have been established for either selecting the best from amongst the mass or establishing that any solution identified is the best. In even the most effective, rigorous methods of finding the shortest tour around a given set of cities, all the possible tours are effectively tested to find the best; the full computational requirements of exhaustive enumeration are reduced by rules which enable most of the possible tours to be rejected at an early stage of formation by implicit, rather than explicit, tests. No more purposive methods of seeking for the best solution have been developed. The computational requirements increase so rapidly with the size of the problem that they remain impracticable. In one of the best-documented of these methods, the computational requirement increases tenfold for each addition of 10 cities; on the basis of the established performance of this method it would be estimated that to find the shortest tour around 100 cities would take 8 million minutes! Forecast improvements in computer speed and cost-effectiveness imply little practical change.

Because the computing requirements of rigorous methods are so high that application is limited to extremely small problems, efforts have been directed to finding 'good' solutions quickly without attempting to prove that these are the 'best'. A large number of such methods have been published; in many of them a major part of the procedure depends upon testing a prescribed set of variations and permutations of several, random, initial tours; the quality of the results and the computing time requirement vary in opposite directions, being influenced by the complexity of the variation and permutation procedure. The computing time requirements of all these methods increase rapidly with problem size; in general, only the simplest and roughest of these procedures appears to offer the prospect of computing costs low enough to be applied in practice to any but the most specialized journey planning problems, and only small problems appear to be amenable to any kind of solution.

When computational methods of optimization are applied it is often assumed that the optimum can be defined solely in terms of the application; by implication the computing costs are assumed to be comparatively negligible. With combinatorial problems such as journey planning, however, it would be relatively easy to spend very much more on finding the solution offering the lowest planned transport cost than the cost saving it would represent. The minimum combined transport and computing cost would be the result of a compromise, and would involve less computation and journey plans which did not offer the lowest planned transport cost. Because of the uncertainties of estimation of journey distance and duration the solution offering the lowest planned transport cost is not, in any case, necessarily that offering the lowest actual cost;

other solutions, superficially more costly, might turn out to be better in practice. Thus, a sensible, practical objective of computational methods for journey planning might be to find very quickly a solution near enough to the optimal to be within the band of estimation uncertainty around the lowest planned transport cost.

Manual methods of planning journeys are very different from the approximate methods described. Rather than using a prescribed set of variations to improve several, random, initial sets of plans, the tendency is to concentrate on producing good journey plans from the start; these journey plans are produced one by one and section by section, and are rarely modified significantly once produced. Similar computational methods, called directed search methods, can be developed and give results sufficiently close to the minimum planned transport costs, to be satisfactory for many journey planning purposes. Directed search methods have received most publicity in connection with the use of the savings criterion to plan wholesale delivery journeys; but the strategy is not confined to this criterion and application. However the computing costs are still not insignificant and appear liable to increase as the square of the size of the problem, which would tend to prevent widespread application. Even with simple and effective methods of calculation it is necessary to pay detailed attention to possible computing strategies for applying the given method if the objective is practical application.

In the most widely used method of using the savings criterion to plan wholesale delivery journeys, called the savings file method, an attempt is made to reduce the computational load by preparing in advance a file containing the results of computations, which, if circumstances allow, can be used repeatedly. This stratagem is not, however, without its own difficulties. The savings file, which is inherently proportional in size to the square of the problem size, has to be transferred from the backing store into the computer, and the contents of the file have to be matched with the required deliveries. If the stratagem were to be applied without further modifications one computational load would have been exchanged for another, and the computing time requirements of the new method would increase more quickly than the square of the size of the problem. To avoid this complication it is common practice to identify customers with zones, to maintain data about zones, not customers, on the savings file, and to control the size of the savings file and the computing time by judicious choice of the number of zones used. If the number of zones is reduced too far, however, the quality of the plans produced would decline due to greater uncertainties in the estimation of journey distance.

An alternative group of methods of using the savings criterion to plan wholesale delivery journeys depends upon the use of what is called the convergent limit approach. In this, the delivery data are organized in such a way as to enable a very good candidate for the next stage of route formation to be identified quickly, and tests are derived from this candidate which, together with the data organization, enable possible better candidates to be identified with simple, quick tests, and the bulk of the other possibilities to be eliminated implicitly by proxy limit tests. The tests used to guide and limit the search converge rapidly. The computing time requirements of programs using this approach may be very small and may increase at a rate little faster than the size of the problem. The convergent limit approach appears to be both simpler and faster than the savings file method for all but exceptional applications.

However, the savings criterion itself does not provide an ideal answer t all problems of planning wholesale delivery journeys, and some of these have yet to be faced, let alone solved. This is not an area where general methods of solution are available or likely. Even when the design of convergent limit methods to use the savings criterion is considered, relatively slight changes in the structure of the problem may change the computational efficiency of any one method, and change the design whic is likely to give the most efficient computation.

Some of these points can be illustrated by the application of a directec search, convergent limit method to a very different type of application, that of preparing duty schedules for the drivers of a substantial fleet conveying mail in bulk according to a timetable in the London area. But a directed search computational method employing a convergent limit approach has been successfully applied to it.

Administrative and Financial Aspects of Journey Planning by Computer.

Goods transport activities can rarely be divorced from administrative systems. Examination of possible designs for integrated systems, based on computers, associated with wholesale delivery by manufacturers serves to illustrate the type of considerations and problems which may be involved Systems can be envisaged which make use of either local or central computers, or both, according to the requirements: but to interpose remote processing between two local activities, e.g. order receipt and dispatch, imposes severe demands on the system.

A number of factors other than considerations of data-processing economy largely determine the choice between distinctly different systems for order taking, dispatching and sales accounting. Orders are usually taken by salesmen in person or by telephone, or by the receipt of written orders; the mode of order-taking is usually determined for marketing reasons. To arrange for delivery within three days of the order being determined, it is necessary either for order processing prior to delivery to be carried out locally, or for some stages of information transfer to be carried out by wire, in person, or by special conveyance; the acceptable period between order and delivery is also usually fixed for marketing reasons.

Most companies use post-invoicing systems, i.e. prepare invoices after goods ordered are picked from stock. Apart from facilitating rapid deliveries when orders are placed locally, post-invoicing systems are likely to be preferred when the orders are placed irregularly or infrequently, and when there are frequent credits and discrepancies between items ordered and delivered. Pre-invoicing systems may be preferred if orders are received centrally and are placed frequently and regularly, and if both credits and discrepancies between order and delivery are rare.

A significant proportion of orders is only likely to be communicated by telephone conversations if order offices are situated locally, because of the cost of long-distance telephone calls. If much data has to be transmitted over long distances very rapidly to ensure rapid delivery while using a distant computer, then methods that utilize the information transfer capacity of telephone channels more efficiently than conversations are likely to be preferred.

If orders are received as documents, whether from salesmen or customers, by post, the economies of batch processing methods are such as to make large centralized systems attractive.

The need to convert data into a machine readable form is a major handicap to data-processing systems: conversion is liable to be expensive and slow. A major advantage offered by real-time systems is an increase in the speed and accuracy of data conversion together with a reduction of its cost. The most attractive alternatives are automatic conversion systems, which are most appropriate to centralized batch processing systems. Whatever the method of data entry, special provision needs to be made for error detection and correction.

In practice, it may be impossible to design an administrative system which incorporates only one processing method; it is usually necessary to provide a number of alternative processing methods for the convenience of both the organization and its customers. Even when it is not necessary

to design a number of different processing methods into a system, it is
likely to be preferable because, despite its economy, a simple system is
likely to be very inflexible.

Consequently, different administrative computer systems for wholesale
distribution are liable to overlap extensively in both strategy and tactics,
even if not in detailed execution. There may therefore be scope for very
large economies of scale in design, implementation and maintenance if
co-operative systems were to be established. Expressed in another way, the
marginal costs of the minor variations of detail which distinguish the
requirements of different companies may be extremely high.

A computer system with the sole objective of producing better routes
for vehicles is only likely to break even on operating costs alone if the
delivery cost exceeds £0.25 per delivery, the transport operating cost at
each depot is in excess of £20,000 per annum, and either an adequate
company owned computer, or a large multi-access computer operated
by a bureau at time-hire rates, is available. Only very large depots,
operating relatively expensive vehicles, each performing few deliveries
per day, offer significant profits from the planning of shorter or quicker
routes by computer in isolation from other procedures.

If a computer system is used to plan journeys on the basis of better
methods of estimating journey duration, so that planned idle time is
reduced, the scope for saving is enhanced. However, this would normally
need the explicit co-operation of drivers, who would usually expect some
form of productivity bonus in return.

The marginal case for introducing and integrating journey planning by
computer into an existing computer-based administrative system is likely
to be more attractive, since there is unlikely to be any significant increase
in total administrative and computer costs; all the transport benefits
would be net benefits.

There are believed to be substantial economies of scale in computers
and in development activities, such as the design and implementation of
computer systems and the preparation of better methods of estimating the
duration of planned journeys. There are also substantial economies of scale
in road transport and its associated depot and stockholding activities, if
suitable functional organizations and administrative, planning, control and
communications methods are adopted.

It appears probable that dramatic reductions in the cost of transport
and associated activities could be achieved if comprehensive changes,
designed to this end, were made. Much development work remains to be
done, but there are no obvious reasons, given adequate support, why it

should not be successful.

Part 2

Road goods transport expenditure

Chapter 2

The level and growth of road goods transport expenditure

Expenditure on the transport of goods by road, according to official estimates, has been increasing at 10% per annum; in 1967 the estimated level of expenditure was £2,500M. (**2.1**). In table 2.1 expenditure on road goods transport and its growth over the decade 1957-67 at current values is compared with consumers' expenditure and public expenditure respectively.

Table 2.1 Comparison of expenditure on road goods transport with consumers' and public expenditure

	level 1967 £M.	ratio = $\frac{\text{level 1967}}{\text{level 1957}}$
expenditure on road goods transport (*2.1*)	2,500	2.63
total consumers' expenditure (*2.2*)	25,323	1.74
total expenditure by public authorities (*2.3*)	17,544	2.21

In table 2.2 consumers' expenditure and its growth is analyzed in greater detail.

Table 2.2 Consumers' expenditure and its growth 1957-67 (*2.2*)

	level 1967	ratio = $\frac{\text{level 1967}}{\text{level 1957}}$
food	5,522	1.39
alcoholic drinks	1,585	1.75
tobacco	1,512	1.54
housing	2,976	2.33
clothing	2,139	1.49
durable goods	2,021	2.01
other	9,568	1.91
total	25,323	1.74

while public expenditure is analyzed similarly in table 2.3.

Table 2.3 Public authorities' expenditure and its growth 1957-67 (*2.3*)

	level 1967 £M.	ratio = $\dfrac{\text{level 19}}{\text{level 19}}$
defence	2,412	1.52
housing and environmental services	1,863	2.52
social services	6,711	2.52
debt interest	1,771	1.86
other	4,787	2.38
total	17,544	2.21

It may be seen from these tables that expenditure on road goods transport is relatively large, being equivalent to 10% of consumers' expenditure, 45% of consumers' expenditure on food, and more than public expenditure on defence. The rate of growth appears to be relatively very high, being higher than the rate of growth of expenditure on any of the classifications given. To find a higher rate of growth it is necessary to look at, for example, consumers' expenditure on the running costs of motor vehicles, which quadrupled over the decade under discussion.

The size and rate of increase of the expenditure may be illustrated in another way. In 1957, gross company trading profits from operations in the U.K., before providing for depreciation, stock appreciation or taxation were £3,075M (*2.4*). In the same year the estimated expenditure on road goods transport was £950M, equivalent to approximately 31% of the trading profits. By 1967 gross company trading profits had risen to £4,694M; but by this time estimated expenditure on road goods transport had risen to £2,500M, equivalent to 53% of trading profits.

Expenditure on road goods transport also appears to be increasing rather faster than the different categories of industrial and commercial activity which are thought to generate most demands for transport; this is illustrated in table 2.4.

Table 2.4 Expenditure on road goods transport compared with production of transport generating activities (*2.1, 2.5*)

activity	production value 1967 £M.	ratio = $\dfrac{\text{production 1967}}{\text{production 1957}}$
agriculture, forestry and fishing	1,121	1.30
mining and quarrying	713	1.00
manufacturing	11,385	1.65
construction	2,395	2.12
gas, electricity and water	1,110	2.34
distributive trades	3,759	1.58
expenditure on road goods transport	2,500	2.63

The effects of relative movements in prices and costs may be separated from other effects if the growth of production at constant factor cost and of transport statistics is compared, as in table 2.5.

Table 2.5 Growth of production at constant factor cost and road goods transport statistics 1957-67 (*2.6 - 2.8*)

	ratio = $\dfrac{\text{level 1967}}{\text{level 1957}}$
agriculture, forestry and fishing	1.29
mining and quarrying	0.82
manufacturing	1.33
construction	1.44
gas, electricity and water	1.63
distributive trades	1.31
tons carried by road goods transport	1.55
ton-mileage performed by road goods transport	1.88
mileage by road goods transport	1.65
licensed goods vehicles	1.30

The value of production at constant prices only indicates changes of the weight of produce insofar as the weight/value ratio, at constant prices, has remained constant. If the value of production had declined relative to the weight, use of the value as a measure of production might lead to the ton-mileage required being under-estimated. However, a more likely trend is that, with technical development, the value of production is increasing relative to weight, in which case the ton-mileage required might be exaggerated.

Despite the reservation about possible lack of correspondence between weight and value at constant costs, these figures appear to support the hypothesis that road goods transport is expanding at a greater rate than the goods transport generating activities.

It might be suspected that the disproportionate growth of road goods transport should be attributed to conversion of transport to road from, in particular, rail. The growth of tonnage carried by, and ton-mileage performed by, all forms of goods transport in Great Britain is shown in table 2.6.

Table 2.6 Growth of goods transport in Great Britain 1957-67 (*2.9*)

	$\text{ratio} = \dfrac{\text{level 1967}}{\text{level 1957}}$
tons carried	1.38
ton-miles performed	1.36

Examination of this table, and comparison with the growth of categories of production shown in table 2.5, might tend to confirm a suspicion that the extraordinary growth of road goods transport has taken place at the expense of other modes.

However, it has been shown that, between 1952 and 1962, most of the decline in rail freight was attributable to a decline in coal and coke consumption and conveyance, and a reduction in the transport requirement of the steel industry relative to output, these two industries being responsible for more than 60% of rail freight. The decline of the coal industry between 1957 and 1967 is clearly shown in table 2.5. 'The rapid growth of road transport in recent years appears to arise more from growth in activities which depend on the services of road transport than from actual switches in traffic from rail to road.' (**2.10**) If this is so then the growth in road goods transport is only explained by the growth of production or output of industries normally dependent upon road transport if, on the whole, the value of unit weight of the products of these industries is declining.

Furthermore, expenditure on road and rail goods transport together in

1967 was 2.16 times the level in 1957 (**2.1, 2.11**). This relative growth was greater than those of the categories of production, except gas, electricity and water, quoted in table 2.4, and supports a contention that, during this decade, relative expenditure on goods transport increased. This argument suggests that, while there may have been some conversion of goods transport from rail to road, the relative increase in expenditure on road goods transport is not entirely explained by this conversion, and is in excess of what would have been anticipated on account of both the conversion and the growth of goods transport generating activities.

The number of road goods vehicles has only increased during the decade by 30%, while expenditure has increased by 163%. This might appear to be evidence of severe cost inflation. Reference to appropriate editions of the Tables of Operating Costs (**2.12**), the basic vehicle operating cost information used in the estimation of goods transport expenditure, shows that the increase in cost of vehicles of the same capacity operating the same number of miles has been of the order of 50%; the increase in fuel tax between 1957 and 1967 was just over 40%. The increased expenditure per vehicle implied in the estimates and statistics cannot be ascribed to an abnormally high rate of cost inflation, including increased taxation, in vehicle operation. Indeed, the sharpest increases in vehicle operating costs appear to be in the standing charges, with rent and rates, interest, and, for larger vehicles, insurance, making the most notable contributions, while running costs show only a small increase. (These are broad generalizations concealing detailed variations depending upon the size and type of vehicle and distance driven).

One notable feature of the figures in table 2.5 is that the number of road goods vehicles increased much more slowly than the tonnage carried, or the mileage or ton-mileage performed. This would appear to be evidence of increased real productivity. The increased tonnage could have been carried by larger vehicles driving the same distance, or by the same vehicles performing more journeys, and therefore driving a greater mileage, if the average length of haul had remained the same. In practice, as shown by the increase in the ton-mileage relative to the tonnage, the average length of haul increased by approximately 21%, and, as the increase in the mileage driven was less than that of the ton-mileage, it follows that some of the increase in vehicle performance was associated with the carriage of larger loads, probably by larger vehicles. The proportion of general haulage vehicles of unladen weight over 3 tons has increased from 13% to 26%, supporting this diagnosis (**2.13**). But an increase of 20% in capacity and 20% in mileage, which would explain the increases in vehicle performance in terms of tonnage carried and ton-mileage performed, would not account for all the increase in mileage; further, it would hardly account for an increase in vehicle operating costs of as much as 15% (**2.12**) and would leave much of the increased expenditure per vehicle not accounted for by cost inflation still unexplained.

The trend towards an increased proportion of vehicles of more than 3 tons unladen weight is accompanied by an increase in the proportion of vehicles not over 1½ tons unladen weight from 53% to 58%; the proportion of vehicles between 1½ and 3 tons unladen weight declined sharply. Thus the increase in vehicle performance and the proportion of large vehicles has also been accompanied by an increase in the proportion of small vehicles, the absolute increase of these two categories over the period under consideration being almost identical at 270,000 vehicles. It may be among the reasons for this increased number of small vehicles that the explanation for the increased expenditure not otherwise accounted for should be sought.

This argument could be taken further by attributing quantitatively the increase in expenditure to various causes; but there are objections. The estimates of expenditure are based upon statistics similar to those being used; the argument would be circuitous and only serve to give detailed reasons for changes in the estimates. There are large uncertainties about, for example, the extent of the conversion of freight from rail to road, and even how conversion could be defined, which would remain unresolved. Quantitative estimates of the reasons for increases in the estimates do not seem to be particularly useful unless they give a guide to the reasons for a real increase in expenditure. Finally, it will be shown later that details of this method of estimation are themselves open to serious criticism.

The rate of growth in expenditure on road goods transport is not simply explained by cost inflation, including the effects of taxation, or by the growth of output of industries and trades closely linked with road transport, since these appear to be growing more slowly. Some of the growth may be attributable to conversion of traffic from rail to road; but much of this would be expected to be associated with the increased number of large vehicles and improved vehicle performance. There remains an unexplained increased number and proportion of smaller vehicles to which a significant part of the increased expenditure must be attributed.

The discussion has been based on the developments over the decade from 1957 to 1967. The general picture would not be changed significantly by examination of the data for other years, or for moderately shorter periods.

The rapid growth of road goods transport does not appear to be peculiar to Britain. Taking the number of vehicles as a guide, these have been increasing at a rate of 2.8% per annum in Britain, 3.6% per annum in the U.S.A., and 6.2% per annum in Europe, taken as a whole (2.14).

Chapter 3

Ton-mileage as a measure of transport demand and supply

In order to make meaningful analyses of the supply or demand of transport, or an examination of the interaction of supply and demand, it is general practice to introduce common units of account. The generally preferred unit of account is the ton-mile; tons carried and miles performed are used to a lesser extent, usually for purposes of amplification. Expenditure is rarely used, largely because it is usually estimated on the basis of observations of numbers of vehicles, traffic flows and vehicle operating costs, rather than on the basis of expenditure reported by organizations.

Ton-mileage is preferred to tonnage and mileage as a measure of transport demand and supply because it reflects the effect of both the quantity transported and the length of haul. Ton-mileage is, as a statistic, easy to collect and estimate, and does not suffer, as does expenditure, from price changes. An additional appeal of ton-mileage is that it is easily used in calculations.

Transport Demand.
It would be convenient for many purposes, e.g. forecasting future transport demands, if there were a simple relationship between aggregate measures of production and ton-mileage. Unfortunately,

'An examination of the relationship between the Gross Domestic Product, expressed at constant prices, and total inland transport, measured in tons and ton-miles, in the period 1952-62 has revealed that whereas there is a strong correlation between G.D.P. and tonnages transported, the correlation between G.D.P. and ton-miles performed is rather poor; during some periods ton-mileage increases at a faster rate than G.D.P., at other times slower. A study of the relationship between transport and a transport weighted G.D.P. (weighted to allow for the different demands that various industries make on inland transport) gives rather better results, but for the purpose of measuring short-term changes in transport growth (i.e. the annual changes for the 4 or 5 years between survey years) this method yields estimates which at best are only fairly good.

A further drawback to using this method is that unless figures are available for the other modes of inland transport, the correlations have to be made between G.D.P. and road transport alone, and extrapolations based on this relationship cannot take into account changes in the competitive situation between road and other forms of inland transport.' (3.1)

While this quotation is taken from a discussion of the relative merits of methods which could be used to produce statistics for the years between road goods transport surveys, the comments may be applied, probably with added force since longer periods and fewer cross-checks would be possible, to forecasts of transport demand.

A similar warning may be derived from the contrast between American and Russian transport experience; according to Hunter (3.2), transport ton-mileage is increasing approximately 40% faster than Gross National Product in the Soviet Union, and nearly 40% slower than Gross National Product in the United States.

A number of possible reasons may be advanced for the lack of close relationships between measures of production and ton-mileage. Statistics of production are not confined to the production of goods, indeed more than 50% of Gross National Product in 1967 was of services (3.3), including transport. The proportion of Gross National Product comprised by services appears to be increasing in all the 'developed' countries.

Turning to the production of goods, the different transport demands of different commodity groupings are shown in table 3.1.

A change in the balance of production of different commodities could have a substantial effect on transport demands; it is reasonable to infer that changes in the balance of products within commodity groups could, similarly, have a substantial effect.

Theoretically, transport requirements might be expected to change as a result of the development of industrialization and mass production. If specialization of function, and increased capital utilization per worker, has been associated with the concentration of production facilities, then it has also probably been obtained at the expense of an increased average haul between factories and consumers. On this basis increases in production following increased productivity might be associated with disproportionately greater increases in ton-mileage.

Table 3.1 Transport demands and characteristics of different commodity groups (3.4, 3.5)

	weight produced or imported (m. tons)	total weight transported by inland transport (m. tons)	weight transported per ton produced or imported (tons/ton)	weight carried by road transport (m. tons)	average length of hau by road transport (miles)
cereals	12 - 16	17	1.4 - 1.1	15.7	33
fresh fruits, vegetables, nuts and flowers	10	35	3.5	34.4	33
meat and poultry	4	13	3.3	12.3	35
fish	1	4	4.0	3.8	41
live animals	5	10	2.0	10.2	32
dairy produce, eggs	13	49	3.8	48.7	24
beverages	7	34	4.9	33.1	30
flour	4	8	2.0	7.7	44
animal feeding stuffs	12 - 16	30	2.5 - 1.9	28.8	32
other foods, tobacco	17	75	4.4	73.1	34
oil seeds, nuts and kernels, animal and vegetable oils and fats	2	2	1.0	2.1	64
wood, timber and cork	8	26	3.3	24.8	28
crude and manufactured fertilizers	6	12	2.0	10.0	31
crude minerals other than ore	212	273	1.3	260.2	14
iron ore and scrap iron	33	30	.9	10.1	23
non-ferrous metal ores	2	5	2.5	5.1	29
textile fibres and waste	.3	8	2.7	7.5	39
other crude materials	–	18	–	17.6	27
coal and coke	209	318	1.5	150.2	14
petroleum and petroleum products; gas	47	95	2.0	55.3	31
tars from coal and natural gas	3	6	2.0	5.5	25
chemicals and plastic materials	–	28	–	25.8	55
lime	–	13	–	6.4	26
cement	14	18	1.3	15.5	32
building materials	–	110	–	108.5	26
iron and steel					

	weight produced or imported (m. tons)	total weight transported by inland transport (m. tons)	weight transported per ton produced or imported (tons/ton)	weight carried by road transport (m. tons)	average length of haul by road transport (miles)
finished and semi-finished products	20	53	2.7	39.9	52
non-ferrous metals	3	10	3.3	9.8	48
metal manufactures	–	21	–	20.9	37
electrical and non-electrical machinery; transport equipment	–	44	–	44.1	50
miscellaneous manufactured articles	–	55	–	53.9	43
furniture removals	–	–	–	2.9	34
unallocable loads; mixed loads	–	–	–	85.0	22
empty containers	–	–	–	15.8	37
laundry and dry cleaning	–	–	–	3.2	31

On the other hand, there may be contrary trends, arising, for example, from locational factors. Better location of factories in relation to their markets and sources of raw materials would be expected to reduce transport requirements; and similar effects might result from population movements, particularly migration to the cities and depopulation of the remote rural areas.

It is possible to illustrate these qualitative suggestions by some quantitative data. Between 1952 and 1962, while the tonnage of coal and coke carried by rail decreased by 15% (**3.6**), the average length of haul of coal and coke by rail declined from 60 to 50 miles. This decline in the average length of haul occurred although, by the end of the period, there was a large quantity of coal and coke carried over very short distances, averaging 14 miles, by road (**3.5**). The implication is that there was a relative increase either in the production of coal close to the consuming areas, or in the consumption of coal close to the production areas, although in absolute terms both production and consumption declined; and during this period a number of electricity generating stations were built in coal fields in order to reduce transportation charges.

The same phenomena, though not so marked, may be observed in statistics of the transport of minerals: a 25% decrease in the tonnage conveyed by rail was associated with a 31% decrease in the ton-mileage, reflecting a decrease of 7% in the average length of haul to 77 miles, despite substantial transport of minerals by road over an average haul of 14 miles (3.6).

While the average length of haul of coal and minerals was decreasing, it is possible to infer the opposite for manufactured articles. Thus, over the same period, a 29% drop in the tonnage of merchandise carried by rail was associated with a 24% decrease in the ton-mileage. The average length of haul of merchandise being carried by rail increased by over 8% to 144 miles (3.6). As far as goods carried by road are concerned, over the same period the tonnage carried increased by 47%, while the ton-mileage performed increased by nearly 79% (3.7); since approximately 50% of the tonnage carried by road goods transport can be identified (in table 3.1) as being manufactured or processed, these figures may be taken as evidence, but not conclusive evidence, that the length of haul of manufactured goods increased over the period concerned, in accordance with expectations based on the concentration of production facilities. However, the evidence is not as strong as it may appear since rail was losing some merchandise traffic, primarily in the 80-150 mile range, to road competition.

Commodities, as transported, do not remain the same. Changes in packaging or methods of handling may increase or decrease transport requirements; for example, pallets and containers increase the weight and volume to be carried, while the introduction of light, non-returnable glass bottles, and substitution of plastic for glass bottles, reduces the weight carried to and from the consumer. Some differences in the packaging of, and methods of handling, different commodities may be reflected in the variations of the ratios of weight transported to weight produced shown in table 3.1. New designs of manufactured products may be lighter due to the more sparing use of material, or the use of lighter materials.

There is no inherent reason why the relationship between production and ton-mileage should remain constant except when conditions in general are constant. Changes of population, distribution of population, industrial location, methods of distribution, product packaging and design, and consumer demand and preferences may all be expected to influence the relationship between production and ton-mileage. Any apparent constancy about the relationship can easily be attributed to relatively slow rates of change. Since most forecasting and planning activities are usually under-taken in the anticipation of change, assumptions about specific relationships between production and ton-mileage should be examined with care, and the sensitivity of any particular results deduced to possible changes in the relationships tested; this applies whether the forecasting and planning activities are for firms or for larger aggregates.

Transport Supply.

If it is assumed that transport supply and demand are more or less in balance, then it is convenient to use the same set of observations as a measure of both. But if they are not in balance then the ton-mileage performed should only be regarded as a measure of either transport demand or transport supply, whichever is smaller. Measures of unsatisfied demand or surplus supply are hard to obtain, and would not necessarily be expressed in terms of ton-mileage. For example, surplus supply might be most naturally expressed in terms of unemployed men and vehicles.

Putting aside these reservations, however, an examination of the obvious measures of transport supply is relevant. Table 3.2 shows the average operating performances of vehicles according to size and type of haulier's licence (3.8).

Why should the average annual mileage increase with the size of the vehicle? Why do 'A' licensed vehicles cover greater mileages than 'B' or 'C' licensed vehicles of the same size? Why is the average ton-mileage performed, the preferred measure of transport work, so much lower for 'C' licensed vehicles than for 'A' licensed vehicles with the same unladen weight? In the face of obvious, and unexplained, irregularities of this nature, any use of transport statistics, whether for explanation, prediction, or control, involves very heavy reliance upon good fortune in the form of the continued and constant influence of unrecognized factors.

If reference is made to figures gathered in 1962 (**3.10, 3.11**), some help can be obtained. It was found that nearly 10% of licensed vehicles were being utilized for work other than the transport of goods. These vehicles were employed as mobile showrooms and libraries, mobile cranes or for similar functions requiring equipment fixed to a vehicle; other vehicles were licensed as goods vehicles, but were used during the survey solely for carrying personnel. Another 1% of goods vehicles were utilized exclusively for site work, and did not appear on the public roads at all. Furthermore, replies to the survey indicated that approximately 11% of licensed vehicles were idle, the reasons given being repairs, holidays, or lack of work.

Table 3.2 Estimated average mileage, tonnage and ton-mileage performed in 1962 by vehicles employed on goods transport on the public highway (3.9)

licence category	unladen weight over	unladen weight not over	average performance miles	average performance tons	average performance ton-miles
A		1 ton	12,400	360	3,700
	1 ton	2 tons	11,100	920	8,200
	2 tons	2½ tons	9,500	1,220	16,300
	2½ tons	3 tons	13,600	1,520	36,700
	3 tons	5 tons	26,100	2,640	124,700
	5 tons		34,200	3,630	293,000
Contract A		1 ton	14,600	220	4,500
	1 ton	2 tons	16,400	550	11,800
	2 tons	2½ tons	13,200	1,300	20,900
	2½ tons	3 tons	15,500	2,000	41,000
	3 tons	5 tons	25,900	3,440	106,500
	5 tons		35,100	4,650	245,100
B		1 ton	7,500	140	1,800
	1 ton	2 tons	8,700	360	4,400
	2 tons	2½ tons	8,300	1,480	13,000
	2½ tons	3 tons	10,800	2,070	26,000
	3 tons	5 tons	19,400	4,450	71,700
	5 tons		28,700	5,440	169,600
C		1 ton	7,000	90	1,500
	1 ton	2 tons	8,400	230	3,900
	2 tons	2½ tons	9,100	770	11,400
	2½ tons	3 tons	11,300	1,100	21,500
	3 tons	5 tons	16,400	2,460	50,900
	5 tons		22,600	3,980	132,200

Altogether 22% of all vehicles with hauliers licences were not used, according to replies received, for carrying goods during the four weeks of the survey.

The figures collected concerning the type of work carried out by 'C' licensed vehicles, representing over 86% of licensed vehicles, throw further light on the relative performances of vehicles utilized for different purposes (**3.12, 3.13**). The average quantity of work, measured in ton-miles, performed annually by each of the 170,000 vehicles engaged in 'wholesale delivery' was over 30,000; the 385,000 vehicles engaged in 'retail delivery' performed less than 8,000 ton-miles apiece, almost exactly one quarter of the quantity of work carried out by 'wholesale delivery' vehicles; the 133,000 vehicles engaged on 'maintenance and repair work' performed less than 2,500 ton-miles each. It is a reasonable inference that the vehicles employed on 'maintenance and repair work' are not employed primarily to carry out transport work, if this is defined as ton-mileage. In contrast, the 41,000 vehicles employed on 'delivery of materials and fuel to factories' performed 62,000 ton-miles apiece, more than twice as much as the vehicles involved in 'wholesale delivery', and eight times as much as the vehicles involved in 'retail delivery'. The 118,000 vehicles engaged on 'carriage of materials to and from building sites', and the 4,000 vehicles engaged on 'carrying export goods to the docks', carried out similar quantities of work to the vehicles engaged on 'wholesale delivery'. On the other hand, there were 235,000 'C' licensed vehicles engaged on 'other work' which only performed 10,000 ton-miles apiece. Judged from this information it would be reasonable to suggest that:

1 the 11% of 'C' licensed vehicles concerned with 'maintenance and repair work' were hardly concerned with the transport of goods and, when they were, only as a secondary function;

2 the 31% of 'C' licensed vehicles employed on 'retail delivery' were engaged in a different sort of transport work to the others, presumably dictated by the small size of consignments;

3 a substantial proportion of the 19% of 'C' licensed vehicles employed on 'other work', because they also performed a comparatively small amount of transport work as judged by the ton-mileage, were only secondarily engaged in the carriage of goods;

4 the real work, as far as transport of goods measured in ton-mileage is concerned, was performed by the vehicles concerned with 'wholesale delivery', 'carriage of materials to building sites', and 'delivery of materials and fuel to factories', or by just over 27% of the total number of 'C' licensed vehicles;

5 the remaining 12% of 'C' licensed vehicles were idle.

Any suggestion that the categories of work, e.g. 'wholesale delivery', for which figures were collected, represent a uniform or homogeneous classification does not survive further examination of the survey results.

Thus, the 11,000 vehicles owned by petroleum wholesale distributors perform over 80,000 ton-miles per annum apiece, as compared with the average performance of 30,000 ton-miles per vehicle for vehicles employed on 'wholesale delivery' (3.14, 3.15).

It is clear that different types of transport utilization are associated with very different vehicle performances in terms of ton-miles; very similar conclusions would have been drawn if performances expressed in terms of tons carried or miles driven per vehicle had been examined. Thus, if ton-mileage is used as a measure of transport supply, then there is only a link between that measure and the number of vehicles and their size if the function served is taken into account, and even then the link is uncertain.

Chapter 4

Ton-mileage as a measure of road goods transport expenditure

The most common unit of account between different activities is that of money, and this is so despite the problems of price changes and acknowledged difficulties in attributing financial values to phenomena which do not have easily measurable costs, or are not freely traded in a market. The value of any non-monetary unit of account within any restricted sphere of activity therefore depends to a large extent on the existence of a close relationship between that unit and money.

Recognition of the importance of transport and, in particular, the product of the weight and distance, or the ton-mileage, in the location of economic activity, dates from 1826 (**4.1**), or earlier; the use of ton-mileage as a transport measure has a venerable history. The value of ton-mileage as a measure of transport was disputed in 1948, if not earlier, when it was asserted that transport costs, and in particular road transport costs, were non-linear with regard to both distance of carriage, and quantity carried (**4.2**); this assertion has been supported since (e.g. **4.3**).

When the use of ton-mileage as a measure of road transport 'work' was advocated and supported for the provision of transport statistics, it was acknowledged that it was not a measure of road transport costs (**4.4, 4.5**); the main advantage described was that it reflected the effect of both weight and distance; however, a major consideration in the use of ton-mileage as a measure of transport work appears to have been the relative ease of collecting the appropriate statistics, together, possibly, with some lack of a viable alternative suggestion. It has been recognized (e.g. **4.6**) that the incidence of journeys involving multiple deliveries or collections (intermediate journeys), complicates both the collection of statistics and interpretation of the ton-mileage as a measure of work.

The relationship between the cost per capacity ton-mile, the size of vehicle and the distance driven, is illustrated using notional operating cost information (**4.7**), in table 4.1.

Table 4.1 Capacity ton-mileage costs according to vehicle size and
distance driven

vehicle capacity (tons)	costs in d./ton (200 miles/week)	capacity/mile (400 miles/week)
1	27.6	16.5
2	15.2	9.2
3	10.5	6.3
4	8.2	5.0
6	6.3	3.9
8	5.3	3.3
11	–	2.8
14	–	2.6
16	–	2.5

Costs appear to be closely dependent upon the size and mix of vehicles
chosen. It is probable that the link between ton-mileage and cost is
a function of the vehicles being utilized, and that ton-mileage on its own
is no guide to cost.

According to the operating cost information (4.7), doubling the annual
ton-mileage performed by a transport fleet by doubling the number of
vehicles and maintaining the same level of performance would double the
cost. Doubling the ton-mileage either by doubling the size of
individual vehicles and maintaining the mileage constant, or by doubling
the mileage performed by the same vehicles, would result in an increase
in costs of the order of only 20%.

Drawing on notional operating cost information again, and on the
average performances of vehicles of different size operating under
different licences (table 3.2), the same point may be made in another
way. The highest average performance reported in the 1962 survey was by
'A' licensed vehicles of over 5 tons unladen weight; these performed, on
average, 293,000 ton-miles per year and were driven almost 700 miles per
week. The lowest performance was by 'C' licensed vehicles of under 1 ton
unladen weight; these performed, on average, 1,500 ton-miles per year,
and were driven approximately 140 miles per week. These two performances,

in terms of ton-miles, are in a ratio of almost 200:1. The notional operating cost of a vehicle of 1 ton capacity being driven 140 miles per week would be approximately £22 per week; for a 22 ton capacity vehicle being driven 700 miles per week the operating cost would be approximately £105 per week. Thus, the cost ratio is of the order of 5:1.

The numbers of vehicles of different capacity in use in 1962 (**4.8**), shown in table 4.2, may be compared with the different operating performances shown by vehicles performing different functions and under different licensing conditions and the different notional unit costs.

Table 4.2 Numbers of licensed goods vehicles analyzed by carrying capacity in 1962

carrying capacity in tons		number
over	not over	
	1	795,500
1	2	136,900
2	3	95,300
3	5	144,100
5	7	108,600
7	10	90,700
10	13	19,100
13	16	25,100
16		3,200

There is more to the transport of goods than the performance of ton-mileage.

The structure of road goods transport costs may be amplified by examining in more detail a breakdown of notional vehicle operating costs in 1967. This is shown in table 4.3.

Table 4.3 Typical vehicle operating costs (based on 3 ton capacity
diesel vehicle driven 200 miles per week (4.7))

object of expenditure	cost (£/week)	% total cost
licences	1.15	4
wages	13.35 a	51
rent and rates	1.3	5
insurance	1.95	7
interest	1.7	7
fuel	2.2	8
lubricants	0.2	1
tyres	0.7	3
maintenance	2.25	8
depreciation	1.45	6
	26.25	100

a) These are basic wages; average wages of public road haulage drivers were
approximately 50% greater (4.9) in 1967, and appear to have been close
to average weekly wages. There is no reason to assume that own-account
vehicle drivers would be satisfied with significantly less.

The major component of these operating costs is labour cost, and this is
generally true of road goods transport. Any conclusions about how
operating costs will vary with work done or ton-mileage performed must
depend heavily on the way in which labour costs vary.

   In the short term, labour expenses are mostly, if not completely, fixed.
In some fleets drivers operate under agreements by which the wages are
completely determined, while, even when payment is based on hourly rates,
the basic wage, or the wage for the basic working week, is usually the
agreed minimum wage. Furthermore, the supervision of drivers is so
difficult that in many cases drivers effectively determine the amount of
overtime worked. The evidence for this is blatantly obvious at some
depots, where it is standard practice for vehicles to be parked just outside
the depot between the time actual work has been completed, and the time
to clock off, which is usually just before the end of the legally permitted

working day; while it can also be seen in the statistics collected by the Prices and Incomes Board (4.9) where it appears that the average number of hours worked is not very much short of the maximum number of hours that a driver is allowed to work in a week.

In the longer term, labour expenses are clearly variable, in that it is possible to reduce the number of men employed, either quickly by making some redundant, or more slowly by not replacing natural wastage. However, there are a number of factors operating against a hiring and firing policy, quite apart from possible distaste for such a policy. Drivers normally need some training in company procedures, while knowledge of the products, and very often of the customers and their whims, can be essential to the provision of good service. In addition to these factors, which are inherent in the transport situation and provide an incentive to maintain continuity of employment despite short-term fluctuations of work load, there may also be a requirement for special redundancy payments to employees.

Similarly, expenditure on licences, rent, rates, insurance and interest can all be varied in the longer term, and can sometimes be changed very quickly in the short term. But to reverse such a change in the short term is usually expensive; consequently it is, for most purposes, more meaningful to regard these expenditures as fixed in the short term.

Depreciation and maintenance are usually regarded as being proportional to use and therefore totally variable, even in the short term. However, there are circumstances in which depreciation and maintenance are not fully variable. Even if a vehicle is completely unused there is some depreciation due to obsolescence and some maintenance may be required. More seriously, maintenance labour costs may be no more variable than other labour costs, or maintenance may be sub-contracted under conditions which restrict the short-term variability of maintenance costs; similarly, goods vehicles may be bought under fleet purchasing arrangements with guaranteed re-sale or exchange values which restrict the variability of depreciation costs.

Under almost any conditions a substantial proportion of total operating cost is fixed in the short term irrespective of usage. Furthermore, the variable portion of costs is assumed to vary according to time (primarily labour) or mileage (primarily fuel, lubricants, tyres and, where applicable, depreciation and maintenance), the two being closely related. Costs may vary a little as the load being carried varies, within the capacity of the vehicle, but this variation is generally ignored as being insignificant. In these circumstances a close relationship between ton-mileage and operating cost, at least in the short term, cannot be expected.

It seems likely that the number of vehicles employed is a better predictor of road goods transport expenditure than the ton-mileage performed. Insofar as the number of vehicles is a good guide to transport costs and expenditure, it may be assumed that vehicle hours is also a good guide, and that vehicle miles may not be too much worse.

Ton-mileage has been used as a measure of transport demand, supply, and expenditure at the micro-economic, as well as macro-economic, level; at the level of the firm, or part of the firm, as well as the industry or nation. The desired location of transport depots has, for example, been determined by determining the location which would be associated with the lowest ton-mileage requirement to do a given job; indeed this is the basis of most of the sophisticated methods which have appeared in the technical literature. But very little attempt has been made to examine or justify this assumption.

Firms' transport costs can be directly proportional to the ton-mileage if all transport work is sub-contracted at rates which are proportional to the ton-mileage. As against this, however, it is generally desirable that charges should reflect costs, in order to maintain the economic basis for making proper decisions, and it is inevitable that in the long run charges should be equal to, or in excess of, costs. But in any case a very large proportion of goods vehicles in European countries are utilized by the owners primarily or solely for the carriage of their own goods. In Britain 86% of vehicles are operated on own-account; comparative figures for other countries are given in table 4.4.

Table 4.4 Proportion of goods vehicles operated on own-account (**4.10**)

country	total goods vehicles	percentage operated on own-account
Austria	104,000	85
Czechoslovakia	94,900	78
France	2,360,600	93
Greece	81,200	79
Ireland	46,400	86
Italy	1,057,800	83
Poland	212,700	61
U.K.	1,739,000	86
W. Germany	1,015,000	83
Yugoslavia	109,100	91

Note: for the sake of internal consistency all the above have been taken from one source, and relate to 1967; nevertheless, difficulties of definition remain, e.g., over what constitutes a goods vehicle and how they should be counted, over the treatment of vehicles which do not appear on the roads, especially farm vehicles, and of vehicles run by different public authorities, and over what vehicles are operated on own-account; consequently these figures are only roughly comparable.

For vehicles operated on own-account, at least, it is necessary to take into account the costs incurred. Thus, in general, transport depots should be located so as to minimize transport costs; locating transport depots in such a way as to minimize ton-mileage implies an assumption that costs and ton-mileage are closely related.

Wholesale delivery is one of the major transport activities; expenditure has been estimated as being over £400M per annum (4.11). Most wholesale deliveries take place in multiple delivery, or intermediate, journeys. The relationship between ton-mileage and transport cost, numbers of vehicles, vehicle hours, or vehicle miles is less obvious for intermediate journeys than for trunk haulage of loads from a single origin to a single destination, or end-to-end journeys. Yet the use of ton-mileage as a method of locating depots for wholesale delivery journeys has been widely advocated or taken for granted (e.g. 4.12-4.16).

However, in one study (4.17) of wholesale warehouse and depot location the relationship between vehicle time, used as a measure of cost, and other variables was examined. It was concluded that, for that purpose, the sum of the straight line distances of the deliveries from the depot was more closely related to vehicle time than the other variables tested, including ton-mileage. In another study (4.18) it was found that the relationship between ton-mileage and vehicle-mileage was unstable, and sometimes very poor, and that similar conclusions applied to the relationship between the sum of the straight line distances of the deliveries from the depot and vehicle-mileage. It was also shown in the second study that the locations showing the minimum vehicle-mileage and ton-mileage for a given task did not coincide and could be quite widely separated. A third study (4.19) has re-emphasized the importance of the radial distance of the deliveries from the depot; the delivery load was found to be of only secondary importance. It must be concluded that, at the detailed level, ton-mileage and vehicle-mileage or vehicle time are not closely related.

A current (1969) study of firms' transport costs has, so far, shown only a slight relationship between vehicle size and costs. The main relationship found is that between mileage and cost. Costs per mile show, however, a very large dispersion (4.20).

Thus there are observational as well as *a priori* grounds for doubting the value of ton-mileage as an indicator of transport cost. It is concluded that the ton-mileage performed, tonnage carried and mileage run, are only related in a comparatively superficial way to the transport cost involved. The variables, or factors, which are most strongly associated with transport cost, are the numbers of vehicles and associated personnel required, with the mileage being largely determined by the number of vehicles. And it is the way in which transport demand is related to vehicle and personnel requirements that is fundamental to the expenditure associated with the performance of a given set of tasks.

Road transport is often thought of as being a part of the overall problem of transport of goods in bulk, on a par with the transport of goods by pipeline, train, or ship; and it is convenient to use ton-mileage as a common transport measure. In these bulk haulage operations, transport work, as measured by the ton-mileage, may bear a closer relationship to cost than it does in road transport. But it is doubtful whether ton-mileage is closely related to cost for any changes less than several times unit capacity whatever the mode of transport, because of the high fixed cost of the necessary assets, high semi-fixed cost of having the assets available for any work whatsoever, and relatively low marginal cost of increasing the amount transported, up to the limits of the capacity available.

Chapter 5

A forecast of road goods transport expenditure

The importance of forecasting future road goods transport expenditure is not confined to the implied forecast of the resources which will be required, but extends to provision of the essential information upon which decisions should be based as to whether it will be necessary to make attempts to restrict or reduce expenditure in the future, how serious these attempts will have to be, and when, if at all, action should commence. Furthermore, if it appears necessary to make attempts to restrict or reduce expenditure, identification of the reasons for the size and rate of increase may make it easier to devise effective policies for application by national or local authorities, or firms, and increase the likelihood that the policies adopted will be consistent. The time taken to prepare, test, and implement new policies, and to adapt existing practices and policies to them, is so long, especially when investment or technical development is involved, that decisions need to be taken a long time in advance. Hence the need for forecasts, even tentative forecasts.

Because established trends are often a good guide to future trends, and some information is available about established trends, examination of these may offer a useful starting point.

It was noted in chapter 2 that estimated expenditure on road goods transport is very large in both absolute and relative terms, and has been increasing remarkably rapidly. The compound rate of increase of 10% per annum has been so large relatively that, if continued, the 1967 level of gross company trading profits, if these were also to increase at established rates, would be exceeded by 1975, and the 1967 Gross National Product by 1995. Clearly, it would be intolerable if the established rate of increase were to continue for long. The rate of increase of resources devoted to road goods transport that would be tolerable in the long run might be of the same order as increases in resource availability, or the increase of Gross National Product; at present resource consumption by road goods transport appears to be increasing 75% faster than the rate at which new resources are becoming available.

Increasing costs, prices, and taxation have played their part in increasing road goods transport expenditure, but probably no more than in the economy as a whole. The number of vehicles has increased, but only in line with the general progress of the economy, The statistics of tons carried, vehicle-mileage, and even more markedly, ton-mileage, have been increasing more rapidly. But it is shown in chapters 3 and 4 that these statistics are poor measures of transport demand, supply, or cost, and especially so when these and the environment are changing rapidly.

Unfortunately, the estimates of road goods transport expenditure are based upon these statistics. If doubt is cast upon the value of these statistics then doubt is also cast upon the estimates of expenditure themselves. Furthermore, tracing the changes in the statistics only serves to trace the reasons for changing the estimates. To detect that the estimate of expenditure increased because the estimate of vehicle mileage increased does not contribute to understanding of why the expenditure, or the vehicle-mileage, increased.

The estimates of expenditure on road goods transport (5.1) are based upon information about the number of licensed vehicles of different sizes, vehicle performances according to the results of past surveys reconciled with current traffic counts, and vehicle operating costs based on observed costs. The operating cost information is prepared as a guide to operators for costs and charges, and a major anomaly is introduced when it is used for estimating expenditure. The labour cost includes only basic wages (5.2). Average wages are probably of the order of 50% greater than basic wages (5.3); annual expenditure on labour may therefore be under-estimated by as much as £500M. The operating cost information appears t have been interpreted somewhat arbitrarily: garage and management costs of public haulage vehicles have been included, but those of private vehicle excluded; the wages of the drivers of many private goods vehicles have been excluded because they are not primarily employed to drive, or for goods transport, but the number excluded appears to be arbitrary.

Without further examination of the method of estimation it can be concluded that the estimates produced are unlikely to be very accurate. However, the estimates have been based on the number of vehicles and some operating costs, and are probably of the right order of magnitude. The conclusion that expenditure on road goods transport is large and increasing very rapidly is almost certainly valid.

Search for reasons underlying the rapid increase in expenditure is not helped by the variety of activities which are included in road goods transport because the vehicles concerned have goods licences. This heterogeneity of road goods transport, explored briefly in chapter 3, highlights the lack of, and need for, simple and meaningful measures of transport demand, supply and cost. It is possible that the trends are different for different activities.

In this context the most that can be achieved is some plausible hypotheses about road goods transport expenditure, and to link these both with such statistical evidence as is available, and with the largely subjective and intuitive understanding of the development of the environment and mechanisms involved.

There is little reason to doubt that road goods transport expenditure is large and has been increasing rapidly, and there must be a pre-disposition to expect the established trend to continue in the absence of strong reasons to the contrary. However, to quote from the Greater London Plan (**5.4**):

'Road freight transport costs are likely to rise in absolute terms during the 1970's. This is due to the large labour component, growing congestion costs resulting from the limitations of London's road system, more stringent safety regulations being introduced, and government policy which results in higher road costs for commercial vehicles . . . The most numerous move-ments of freight in London are in wholesale and retail delivery. These move-ments are mainly to meet the demands of the consumer, although they cover most of London's major service industries. Freight movements will continue to grow to the extent that consumer demand also increases. Delivery demands per head of population are likely to increase as living standards rise, so that wholesale and retail deliveries are likely to increase . . . . '

The references to London were only necessary because of the context; insofar as the points are true for London, they are true for Britain. Some of these factors, however, need clarification and amplification.

Most drivers need not be reminded that congestion is spreading and, in most areas, becoming more acute. The centres of conurbations have been subject to congestion for a long time, but now congestion is noticeable in most urban areas, on many main roads in rural areas, and even on 'country lanes'. During the decade ending in 1968, estimated traffic on all roads in Great Britain increased at a compound rate of over 7% per annum (**5.5**). Whether roads are urban or rural, classified or unclassified, seems to make little difference to the total rate of traffic increase (**5.6**). This traffic trend is an indication of the forces giving rise to an increase in the severity and spread of congestion.

The duration of many urban road journeys is more than double what it would be in the absence of congestion; the duration has also become highly unpredictable. Over 40% of goods vehicle-mileage is performed in urban areas where the effects of congestion are already more noticeable. All road users, whether goods vehicles, ambulances, car commuters, tourists or commercial travellers, are subject to the effects of congestion and incur losses as a result. It was estimated that losses due to congestion in Greater London in 1966 were £100M. (5.7). This estimate only included losses due to extra vehicle running costs and the value of the lost working time of those travelling as part of their employment owing to the reduction of speeds below 25 m.p.h. If the estimated congestion cost in 1966 in London were to apply to Britain in proportion to the population, the cost would be £600M. - £700M. annually, and there is no natural barrier to increases beyond this. Without laying particular stress on the accuracy of this estimate, or on the congestion cost in one area relative to another, it is clear that congestion is already expensive.

Goods vehicles are responsible for approximately 20% of total vehicle-mileage (5.8). Less than 20% of total vehicle miles appears to be travelled by cars being used in the course of employment (5.9). Thus it is probable that a proportion approaching 50% of this estimate of congestion losses has contributed directly to increased road goods transport expenditure.

Inclusion of only extra running costs and loss of working time directly attributable to driving speeds slower than 25 m.p.h. in an estimate of congestion losses results in the neglect of other very serious losses caused by congestion. For example, where goods vehicles work to a planned daily cycle, the effect of reduced speeds is unlikely to be reflected primarily, if at all, in a longer journey duration, but rather in the tasks being divided between a larger number of journeys and vehicles. Dividing a task between a larger number of journeys and vehicles is usually associated with the performance of an increased vehicle-mileage due to an increase in the number of journeys to and from the depot. The effect of congestion may be expected to extend beyond an increase in driving time due to the reduced speed, to include an increase in the number of, probably smaller, vehicles, and an increase in the mileage driven. This secondary effect of congestion may result in extra costs every bit as large as those attributed directly to the slower speeds. Changes in the statistics of vehicle numbers, sizes and mileage have occurred which are compatible with this expectation.

It may be concluded that the contribution of congestion to expenditure on roads goods transport is already significant, and that, if traffic increases more rapidly than road capacity, the resulting increase in the spread and severity of congestion will result in further significant increases in expenditure.

A number of recent Government proposals, some of which have been expressed in the form of legislation, seem more or less likely to increase road goods transport costs. Thus, there was a proposal to impose additional taxes on heavy vehicles to compensate for the high level of road costs supposed to be incurred specifically on their behalf (5.10). In practice, taxes for all vehicles were increased and the proposal has not yet been implemented. The 1968 Transport Act includes provisions reducing the maximum amount of time which may be spent driving in such a way that effective hours worked will probably be reduced, but it is most unlikely that gross wages will be reduced. Further provisions of the Act are intended to impose higher minimum standards of vehicle maintenance; these will probably result in an increase in maintenance and total expenditure, although it is possible that overall costs could be reduced by better maintenance. The effects of other provisions of the Act, such as alterations to the goods vehicle licensing system, on transport costs are more debatable; the freeing of many vehicles from restrictions on use was intended to enable the efficiency of use to be increased (5.11 - 5.13), but the author has doubts about the outcome (chapter 10).

The quality of services performed by road goods transport is changing, but these changes, and their effects on transport costs, are hard to specify or measure. Some forms of retail delivery, e.g., of groceries, have virtually disappeared, often being replaced by collection by private car; an analogous move is the development of cash-and-carry wholesaling. In contrast, in some other trades there have been increases in the number and speed of deliveries as a result of competition; sometimes service quality has also improved in other respects, e.g. in terms of time or scheduled visits, due both to commercial pressures and to side effects of congestion and traffic management or parking schemes. There have also been increases in services performed, using licensed goods vehicles, which are not very closely related to goods transport; for example, many household maintenance and repair services, from window-cleaning, via the on-site repair of consumer durables, to painting and decorating, now use vans. It should be noted that among the expected results of an increase in service quality would be increases in the number of smaller vehicles and in vehicle mileage, i.e. effects similar to those of congestion. There is no obvious basis for a conclusion about the net effect of changes in the quality of service on road goods transport expenditure.

Changes in the relative locations of industrial, commercial and distributive facilities, and of residential areas, may have some impact on transport demands. The net effect of these changes is more likely to be a reduction of the distance goods need to be transported the more rapid the rate of change, since new transport facilities are likely to be better related to existing needs than old. The resultant locational pattern may also require goods to be carried less distance the more concentrated it is. However, reduced distance of conveyance may not be reflected in reduced costs if other phenomena associated with concentration, such as road congestion or high land values, appear. No evidence is known to the author which throws light on the direction or magnitude of overall changes in transport expenditure due to locational changes.

Closely allied to locational changes are those due to the concentration of manufacturing and distributing facilities. When two factories are replaced by one, typically to obtain economies of scale, the average haul between the factory and consumers would be expected to increase in the absence of changes of consumption patterns or relative locational effects. Similarly, a reduction in the number of wholesale distribution depots would normally be expected to result in increased haulage between the wholesale depots and retail customers. The motive for the concentration of warehouse facilities which is undoubtedly taking place, is to obtain economies of scale in stockholding, selection and handling of goods, and in the associated administrative procedures, by mechanization and computerization (5.14). Economies of scale in stockholding and handling may be obtained at the expense of an increase in transport demands. As mentioned in chapter 3, average lengths of haul in road transport, and the carriage of manufactured goods by rail, have increased, which is consistent with this hypothesis.

To summarize, the projection of established trends, the natural development of traffic and road congestion, the expected effects of legislation, and the concentration of production and distribution facilities all combine to support a forecast that expenditure on road goods transport will increase, if present conditions continue, at a rate greater than the increase in Gross National Product, or resource availability. This prediction is qualitative rather than quantitative partly because of difficulties of measurement and estimation. However, failure to ascribe a single, suitably dramatic, figure to the rate of growth in expenditure should not be allowed to obscure the serious implications of growth at rates as high as may be expected in the absence of serious and effective steps to check expenditure. It may safely be concluded that, if the established rate of growth of 10% p.a. were to be maintained, the overall level of expenditure would become intolerable within the next decade or two, while many organizations would be forced to change, even reverse, existing policies of location and methods of distribution even sooner.

It is the author's conviction that increasingly severe steps will be taken to curtail the growth of road goods transport expenditure, which is an additional reason for avoiding a quantitative estimate of the rate of increase.

Part 3

Transport co-ordination as a government policy for reducing transport expenditure

Chapter 6

Transport co-ordination: the conventional concepts

Road goods transport is not an isolated activity, nor is its interaction with other activities confined to those immediately associated with the origins and destinations of the goods carried. Competition between road and rail goods transport for the performance of the same transport services has attracted much attention. Competition between various types of road transport for the use of the same road facilities is a major feature of the growth of congestion. Further, because of the importance of competition between road passenger and goods transport for the use of the same roads, the competition between road and rail for the provision of passenger transport is also relevant to road goods transport. Other forms of inland transport will be ignored in the discussion which follows, partly because they are of minor importance in Britain, in contrast to Western Europe where the inland waterways play a major role, and partly because a suitable test of any theoretical framework developed would be whether these ancillary modes could be assimilated without strain.

Discussions of competition between road and rail transport are frequently based upon the conventional, in a market economy, view that the general good is best served by free competition. However, it is also often assumed that, in transport matters at least, some degree of co-operation or co-ordination is desirable in the general interest.

A simple exposition of the case for integration and co-ordination in transport is given in the introduction to the White Paper on Transport Policy, 1966 (6.1):

1. The rapid development and mass production of the motor vehicle over the past twenty years has brought immense benefits to millions of people: increased mobility, a fuller social life, family enjoyment, new experiences. It has also produced new, quick and convenient means of moving goods. But at the same time it has brought severe discomforts: congestion in the streets of our towns; the misery of the journey to work for commuters; noise, fumes and danger as the setting of our lives; a rising trend of casualties on our roads and a threat to our environment in both town and

countryside which, if it continues unchecked, will ensure that the pleasure and benefit for which we use the car will increasingly elude us. The aim of a rational transport policy must be to solve this paradox.

2. The nation has not yet begun to face up to the implications of the motor age. Each of us still believes he can find his own individual means of escape from the accompanying unpleasantness; for example, by finding a house further afield and buying a car — or cars — to enable him and his family to get to it. In the context of such impulses transport policy would have only one aim: to build more routes for the private car. And it would find its economic justification in the fact that goods would be moving by the same routes.

3. The problem of the motor vehicle has been intensified because it has been thrust, unplanned, on the environment we have inherited from a very different age. We have been slow to realise that the expansion of motor traffic on the present scale calls either for a completely new kind of physical environment or for a willingness to adapt its use to the sort of conditions in which we want to live. Countries which became "motorised" earlier than Britain are just beginning to face up to this truth.

4. Even if we had as a nation consciously chosen the first of these two courses, which we have not, it would be at present beyond our means. New towns can be built to the requirements of the motor age though, even then, they will not necessarily be the sort of towns we want if they are built on the assumption of total dependence on private transport. But most of us live in towns built a century or more ago and the cost of adapting them to take hundreds of thousands of cars is prohibitive. Some adaptation must clearly be made but, inevitably, it can only be slow.

5. The same problem faces us on inter-urban roads. Today Britain is spending more on new and improved roads than at any time in her history: the amount for 1966 will be nine times what it was even ten years ago. Yet so explosive has been the expansion of traffic that by 1972 fifty per cent more miles of our major trunk roads will be heavily overloaded than are today — the legacy of years of neglect.

6. In such a situation, two courses are clearly necessary. The first is to give the country's transport needs the priority they require, not only in the allocation of money, but in their relationship to other developments. Until very recently we have not even attempted to plan as a whole the factors which create our environment — industry, housing and transport — or to plan different forms of transport in relation to each other. Indeed, until the necessary national and regional planning machinery was created, this was impossible.

7. Since Britain's resources are limited, it is imperative that they should be used to the best effect: in other words, industries should not be built without their communications, ports without the means of moving the goods to and from them, or houses without adequate roads. Transport must be planned as part of the national effort as a whole and of the regional contributions to that effort.

8. The second requirement is to face up to the role of public transport. Our towns and cities will never be able to cope with their traffic, or the transport needs of millions of people, without strengthening, improving and expanding their public transport services. Nor can we afford to underestimate, as we have been doing, the valuable contribution which the railways can make in moving goods and passengers from town to town and people to and from work. Clearly these services must adapt themselves to new technological developments, but to get more people and goods moved with less use of road space is vital to the solution of our transport problems.

9. New thinking is required, not only about types and combinations of public transport, but also about how they should be financed. To attempt to solve these problems in exclusively commercial terms is to bring the Victorian mentality to the solution of modern needs. Those who manage or work on London Transport, British Railways and provincial bus services are struggling to reconcile two mutually contradictory objectives: to provide an adequate service for the public and to pay their way. As a result they are finding it increasingly difficult to do either. The solution will call for radical changes in the 1962 Transport Act.

10. It will also call for structural changes. If the public sector of transport is to play its important role effectively, its different elements can no longer operate in isolation. But the new forms of organization must take account of modern developments. On the freight side this calls for a nationally planned and integrated road-rail service designed to take full advantage of the new techniques for handling freight. Passenger services, on the other hand, must be adapted to local needs. The urgent need for integration of road and rail services is now emerging from the practical experience of transport problems in different localities. The ways of ensuring this integration, and the forms it should take must be decided in consultation with the Regional Economic Planning Councils and local authorities. Account will also need to be taken of the role of internal air services in the total transport picture.

11. The key to solving Britain's transport problems, therefore, lies in planning designed to reconcile our many-sided needs, national and regional,

economic and social. If we are to live within our means, while developing modern, efficient transport systems and drawing full enjoyment from the motor car, we must put all our resources to their best use as part of a coherent and integrated whole.

This concern for co-ordination of road and rail transport is not confined to Great Britain; for example, in France, between 1934 and 1968, there were twenty-six laws or regulations, 156 decrees, and 621 ministerial circulars, devoted to this subject (6.2).

The following definitions of co-ordination are quoted in a recent book by Fischer on transport in the European Economic Community, and may be regarded as typical of thought there:—

a   Co-ordination is a general term 'which may be applied to all measures tending to organize competition between transport facilities'; and co-ordination ought to 'promote the coherent operation of transport modes and result in the best distribution of traffic from the economic point of view'. (6.3)

b   'Co-ordinating transport is choosing investments and utilizing assets to the maximum advantage of the community'. (6.4)

c   Co-ordinating transport 'is creating those conditions favourable to fruitful co-operation between all transport sectors in the service of the user, but within the framework of economic and social costs which is most beneficial for the community'. (6.5)

Fischer concludes (6.6):—
To co-ordinate is to organize competition between the different transport modes in order to eliminate the traditional anarchy of competition and to render the burden of transport activities as light as possible both for the user and for the community as a whole.

In Britain, a Royal Commission on transport, appointed in 1928, examined, as a distinct sphere of activity, that concerning the general co-ordination and development of all available means of transport, with particular reference to the rapid growth of road haulage. The recommendations (6.7) concerning this aspect of their investigations included the following:

1   that heavy goods vehicles (over four tons unladen weight) should pay considerably more duty for each successive extra ton weight, as a means of discouraging the use of heavy vehicles and of protecting the railways from further loss of traffic, in the national interest;

2 that road haulage should be licensed so as to put the industry onto an organized basis and as an essential precedent to any attempt to co-ordinate transport generally;
3 that it should be a condition of issue of carriers' licences that the authorizing traffic commissioners should have regard to the fitness of the vehicle concerned and the wages and conditions of employees of the applicant for a licence.

A conference of railway and road haulage representatives, convened in 1932 by the Minister of Transport, and known as the Salter Conference, gave as the main reason for advocating a system of quantitative restriction of road haulage the 'evil effects of excessive competition'. It was believed that excessive competition was leading to excessive bankruptcy rates.

The more recent Geddes Committee on road haulage licensing rejected the view that bankruptcy rates in road haulage were excessive, and also that restricting the entry into road haulage by licensing system reduced the rate of bankruptcy (**6.8**). This committee considered that the main possible objectives of government policy in regulating road transport of goods were:
1 the promotion of the safety of the public;
2 the promotion of efficiency in road transport operations;
3 the reduction of any harmful effects of road transport on amenity and environment;
4 the promotion of increased use of available road facilities for movement of goods;
5 the reduction or control of congestion on the roads.
Co-ordination was not regarded as an aim separate and distinct from those already set out. Rather, the term 'co-ordination' was taken to refer to a policy embracing the several policy aims considered, with emphasis most commonly being placed on a policy of influencing the distribution of traffic towards the greater use of rail (**6.9**).

Co-ordination, regulation, and competition, are by general accord linked as emphasizing different aspects of approach to the same set of problems. That co-ordination is good is widely, though not universally, accepted. Many references to co-ordination, however, fail totally to make clear what it should mean in practice, or how it should, or could, be achieved; when specific measures are broached the concensus disappears. This confusion at the detailed and operational level reflects lack of clarity at the conceptual level. Co-ordination is a sentiment rather than a precise idea, let alone a meaningful, operational, set of policies.

Chapter 7

Road and rail costs

Suggestions have been made that the most effective way to 'co-ordinate' road and rail transport in Britain would be to convert railways into motorways. Many discussions of the problems of creating road facilities to satisfy demands make little or no reference to rail as a possible alternative. It often appears to be taken for granted that new road facilities are of prime importance in their own right, and that any competition or conflict between road and rail transport will, or should, always be settled in favour of road. To hold this view it is only necessary to believe that most transport users prefer, and will continue to prefer, road to rail transport in the face of their relative costs. Such a belief is supported by the established trends of road and rail traffic. However, these trends are based upon the current absolute and relative costs of these modes of transport, and there has been sufficient controversy about these to merit re-examination. If the costs of different transport modes to the user do not correspond to the real costs of usage, then the observed trends of usage may be of little use as guides to real consumer preferences, or to economic behaviour.

Railway Track and Motorway Lane Capacities

To compare road and rail transport costs when the basic facilities are, or are likely to be, fully employed, it is convenient to utilize estimates of road and rail capacities, or relative capacities. As there are many problems of definition and identification, and data has to be drawn from diverse sources, such estimates are bound to be comparatively inaccurate, and only broad and rough conclusions should therefore be based upon them.

A direct comparison can be made between estimates of road and rail capacities utilized in the evaluation of the Channel Tunnel and Bridge proposals (**7.1**). The capacity of a motorway lane was estimated to be 1,000 vehicles per hour at a speed of 50 m.p.h., the speed being chosen to be comparable with that of rail. A single railway track was assumed to be capable of carrying 3,000 vehicles, together with their contents, and three additional trains for either goods or passengers, per hour. These estimates appear to imply that the capacity of a railway track is roughly four times that of a motorway lane.

Sauvy (7.2) quotes an estimate that the capacity of a double-track railway would be 160,000 units per day, while that of a dual two-lane motorway would be 76,000 units per day. Once again the implication is that the capacity of a railway track is approximately four times that of a motorway lane.

The two levels of motorway capacity, 'design' and 'limiting', assumed in planning roads for London are 16,500 and 18,750 vehicles per lane per day respectively (7.3). These estimates are in broad agreement with those quoted by Sauvy.

London Transport's estimate of the peak capacity of the Victoria Line, a new double-track underground railway, is 50,000 passengers per hour (7.4). Some sources quote lower figures than these, e.g., Hall (7.5) suggests that the peak capacity might be up to 30,000 passengers per hour. The difference probably represents differing definitions of capacity. To reduce tunnelling costs, underground trains are typically smaller in diameter, and of shorter length, than surface trains.

The peak capacity of a motorway lane may also be defined in different ways; vehicle flow capacity and speed are related, while vehicle types and utilization could also have an effect on the flow of goods or passengers for a given vehicle flow. The peak vehicle flow on a motorway is probably around 2,000 cars per lane per hour (7.6). Higher peaks have been observed for the traffic moving in one direction only (7.7); these very high flows are associated with congestion and low speeds. At typical levels of utilization, which in urban areas during peak hours appear to be around 1.5 occupants per car (7.8), these peak car flows represent passenger flows of the order of 3,000 passengers per lane per hour. The peak capacity of an underground railway track may be between five and eight times that of a motorway lane devoted to cars. The average car utilization would need to be as high as between 1.9 and 3 occupants to restore the four to one ratio of railway track to motorway lane capacity. In this case it would appear that the ratio of the capacities may be in excess of four to one.

While these examples appear to justify an assumption that the track to lane capacity ratio is of the order of four to one, two reservations should be noted:—

1 An example of relative goods capacity has not been quoted because a suitable one has not been found. The real difficulty is making estimates of possible freight train frequency and net load under meaningful and relevant commercial environments and operating practices. For what it is

worth, Soviet railways, which have been under pressure to extend their freight capacity (most other railways under capacity pressure, e.g. the Indian, have a larger proportion of passenger transport), appear to have achieved average flows in excess of 8,000 tons per hour per track on some routes (**7.9**); in 1968, licensed goods vehicles in Britain (**7.10**) carried an average load of 2 tons (more strictly, performed 2 ton-miles per mile driven and if the peak flow were 1,000 such vehicles per lane per hour, allowing for a congestion effect twice that of cars, then the peak capacity of a motorway lane would be 2,000 tons per hour.

2 If use of roads were restricted to heavily utilized, large vehicles, the potential peak road capacity would be much higher. A passenger flow per lane per hour equal to that estimated for a track of the Victoria Line could be attained by a flow of 700 buses per hour, allowing for the greater congestion effect of larger vehicles, carrying between 21 and 35 passengers each. Similarly the Soviet railways goods flows could be attained by 700 vehicles per hour, carrying 11½ tons each.

Road and Rail Capital Costs

Sauvy (**7.2**) quotes an estimate that the cost of construction of a double-track railway to a standard that would permit speeds of 125 m.p.h. would cost 4.2 million francs per kilometre, and quotes an estimate from the French Fifth Plan that the average cost of dual two-lane motorways over the simplest routes would be 3.65 million francs per kilometre. On the basis of these estimates, and the capacity estimates already quoted, he concludes that motorway capital costs per unit of capacity are 80% higher than those of rail. He adds that the estimate for motorway costs should be increased to 4 million francs per kilometre.

Translating costs like these, especially when parities are changing, is liable to be misleading. However, if translated at a notional parity of thirteen francs equivalent to one pound sterling, these estimates represent estimates of £520,000 per mile for the railway, and £450,000 per mile for the motorway according to the Fifth Plan estimate, which Sauvy would prefer to revise to £500,000 per mile. The author understands that at least one firm of British consulting engineers uses similar figures as rule of thumb guide-lines. Furthermore, the typical cost of a dual two-lane rural motorway has been officially quoted as £550,000 per mile (**7.11**), which again corresponds approximately with the estimates quoted by Sauvy. Further details of rural motorway costs in Britain are given by Tanner (**7.7**).

Urban transport facilities are more expensive. Munby suggested in 1962 that a motorway might cost as much as £12M. per mile on expensive inner urban land (**7.12**). The Western Avenue extension, the first stretch of real urban motorway to be built in Inner London, is costing approximately £12M. per mile. The cost of dual four-lane motorways in Paris has been estimated at 25 million francs per kilometre at the periphery and 200 million francs per kilometre in the centre, equivalent to approximately £3M. and £24M. per mile respectively (**7.13**).

Published details of the Greater London Council's estimates of the cost of one of the road plans it has examined provide further information (**7.14**). The costs per lane-mile of different sections of motorway, without access roads, are shown in table 7.1.

Table 7.1 Average motorway link costs in £M. per lane-mile (1966 prices)

road	approximate distance from centre (miles)	land and property costs (£M.)	construction costs (£M.)	total (£M.)
Ringway 1	4	0.423	0.927	1.350
Inner radials		0.439	0.670	1.109
Ringway 2	7	0.205	0.498	0.703
Outer radials		0.084	0.260	0.344
Ringway 3	12	0.029	0.201	0.230

To these costs have to be added those for interchanges and access points. The average cost of an interchange between motorways varies between £5M. on Ringway 3 to £15M. on Ringway 1. For local access points the average costs are between £2M. and £9M. The overall effect of the access and interchange points in the road plan examined was to double, approximately, the effective lane-mile cost.

More recent (1969), and more detailed, estimates for two sections of this plan being prepared for tenders add to this picture. An estimate for 2¾ miles of dual two-lane motorway through the inner western suburbs, the West Cross Motorway, part of Ringway 1 being built initially to half capacity, is approximately £36M., or £13M. per mile (**7.15**). Preliminary estimates for eleven miles of mainly dual four-lane motorway, forming part of Ringway 2 through the south-eastern suburbs, are £158M., or £14M. per mile (**7.16**).

Estimates of the cost of the proposed motorway programme have been revised upwards in 1970 (**7.17**) by over 40% on account of 'improved environmental standards', additional 'provision for compensation or other expenditure in respect of fringe properties' and 'inflation' (over a period of three years). In addition, Thomson (**7.18**) maintains that these estimates ignore cost elements that should be included, e.g. interest on capital and the cost of disruption during the building process.

Confining attention to the published estimates, however, it appears that the effective cost per lane-mile of motorways in the area between three and eight miles of the centre of London, including access and interchange facilities, is between £1.5M. and £3.5M.

The capital cost of the Victoria Underground Line in London, which was opened in 1969, was approximately £70M. for 10½ miles of double-track underground railway plus servicing and station facilities, and the associated rolling stock. An extension of 3½ miles is expected to cost a further £19M. (**7.19**). Two estimates, published in 1969, for new underground lines in London, the Fleet and Wimbledon Lines, indicate an expected cost of £7M. to £8M. per mile (**7.20, 7.21**); this figure also includes rolling stock and equipment costs in the same way as the figures quoted for the Victoria Line. These lines pass, or will pass, under Central London. The figures suggest a capital cost for underground railway track, together with equipment, of £3.5M. - £4M. per mile.

Costs of underground lines in other cities may be lower. One estimate for lines similar to the Victoria Line in either Leeds or Manchester is £3.5M. per mile (**7.22**). The cost of the first stage of the Manchester Rapid Transit system has been estimated at £5M. per mile (**7.23**). These figures suggest that underground railway costs in favourable conditions may be as low as £1.75M. - £2.5M. per track-mile. In Paris, however, experience appears to have been relatively disastrous, double-track railway costs being equivalent to dual four-lane motorway costs and as high as £12M. per mile in the centre (**7.14**).

To bring the urban motorway and underground railway capital costs into a roughly comparable basis, it is necessary to include an estimate for the motorway rolling stock costs. As a rough guide, cars are assumed to cost, on average, £500 each, and London double decker buses £8,000 each. Thus the capital cost, including rolling stock, of a motorway lane carrying 2,000 cars per hour is estimated to be between £2.5M. and £4.5M. per mile; for a lane carrying 700 buses per hour, the capital cost is estimated to be between £7M. and £9M. per mile. But it should be noted that these rolling stock costs may underestimate the differences between rail and road costs to some extent, since in general, road rolling stock requires to be replaced more frequently than that of rail.

To summarize, the unit capacity costs of construction of rural motorways is approximately twice that of railways; the unit capacity costs of construction and associated rolling stock of urban motorways appears to be more than four times that of urban railways, if the Paris figures are ignored; even if urban motorways were to be reserved for buses their unit capacity cost would be approximately twice those of rail.

These conclusions are subject to reservations, many of which have been noted, and to one major limitation, which is that of size. All the rail estimates used have been for the construction of double-track railways. No suitable estimates of the construction costs of single-track railways have been found, although they may exist; few railways have been built or planned in the Western World recently.

Road and Rail Marginal Operating Costs
Marginal operating costs, if rolling stock and track capacity is already available, largely depend upon the marginal utilization of two types of resource, energy and labour. Sauvy (**7.24**) gives figures, repeated in table 7.2, for the marginal energy and labour requirements for the performance of an extra thousand passenger-kilometres.

Table 7.2 Labour and energy requirements for the performance of an extra 1,000 passenger-kilometres

mode	energy in kilogrammes of coal equivalent	labour man-hours
bus (45 passengers)	8	1.8
private car (5 passengers)	18	0.87
train with electric locomotive (Paris/Marseille)	13	0.65
train with diesel locomotive (Paris/Belfort)	7.5	0.85
diesel multiple-unit trains (Paris/St. Etienne)	10.3	1.57

It seems likely that one of the factors involved in the different energy requirements between electric and diesel locomotives is the running speeds; this difference may also be reflected in the reverse direction by the differences in labour utilization. As Sauvy comments on the different requirements of bus and train, the price of fuel is tending to drop relative to that of labour.

The labour requirements of private car transport do not include driving this advantage is not found in the transport of goods by road, except possibly for limited amounts of own-account transport. Sauvy then gives figures, repeated in table 7.3, of resource utilization for the performance of an extra thousand ton-kilometres.

Table 7.3 Labour and energy requirements for the performance of an extra thousand ton-kilometres

mode	energy in kilogrammes of coal equivalent	labour man-hours
a train consisting of wagons of 29 tons capacity, returning empty		
electric locomotive (Paris/Lyon)	11.7	0.82
diesel locomotive (Nantes/Bordeaux)	6	1.13
road		
lorry (15 ton capacity, average capacity utilization 0.7, with 2 drivers)	49	9.4
tractor and trailer (20 ton capacity, average load utilization 0.8, with 1 driver)	36	4.8

Sauvy comments that the differences are considerable, and concludes that for all large-scale transport over a sufficiently long distance the running energy and labour requirements are less by train.

It is easy to accept that the marginal energy requirements of rail transpo are less than those of road because of lower friction, and smoothed and gentler gradients, and even that marginal labour requirements of an extra train are less than those of the equivalent number of extra vehicle journeys The implication is that the operating costs of rail are lower than those of road at some level of utilization, unless the limit of rail capacity is reached before this level is reached. The fixed labour requirements of rail, such as those for signalling and track maintenance, may be so high that, in practice the average costs of rail will always be higher than those of road transport.

Road and Rail Labour Productivity
The level of labour productivity that can be obtained in rail transport under
the appropriate conditions may be illustrated by Soviet Railways operating
performances. In 1963 Soviet Railways performed 560,000 freight ton-miles
and 60,000 passenger-miles, making together 620,000 transport units, per
worker (**7.25**); this was achieved by a greater degree of shift working and
more uniform train speeds than is common in most other countries. In
France, in the same year, if ancillary workers are excluded, the railways
performed 260,000 transport units per worker, and public road transport
performed 140,000 transport units per worker (**7.26**). In Britain, public
road passenger transport concerns performed 140,000 passenger-miles per
worker in 1966 (**7.27, 7.28**), whilst public goods haulage concerns
performed less than 90,000 ton-miles per worker in 1967 (**7.27, 7.29**).
British Railways performed 100,000 transport units per employee in
1967 (**7.30**); their employees, in contrast to those of public road transport,
include all those engaged on the maintenance of track and signalling, and
most of those engaged on maintenance of all other assets. Some measure
of what might be achievable by road transport may be taken from the
performance of the largest 'A' licensed vehicles, which are engaged mainly
in long distance haulage; in 1962 these vehicles performed an average of
293,000 ton-miles each (table 3.2), which is more than would be
performed per worker, and still less than half of the Soviet Railways
performance per worker. Thus, it would appear that the potential average
transport performance per worker is higher for rail than road transport; a
higher performance is often realized by rail transport, although it has to be
recognized that the average performances quoted are a poor guide because
of the variable composition of traffic. However, further evidence may be
gained from operating cost information.

Road and Rail Average Operating Costs
The estimated incremental operating cost due to the Victoria Line is
between £2M. and £2.5M. per annum (**7.20**), excluding interest on capital
or, counting a week as six working days, approximately £8,000 per working
day. If 60% of this cost were to be assigned to the four peak hours, which
corresponds to the distribution of traffic observed (**7.31**), then the cost
during the peak hours would be of the order of £1,200 per hour. The peak
hour passenger-mileage capacity is 50,000 passengers for 10½ miles, or
525,000 passenger-miles. The feasible passenger-mileage realization during
the peak hour might be of the order of 45% of the ultimate capacity (the
average length of an underground journey is 4.6 miles, or nearly 45% of the

length of the Victoria Line (**7.32**)), or, say, 240,000 passenger-miles, giving an average operating cost of the order of 1.2d. per passenger-mile, excluding interest charges, despite the very poor pattern of utilization.

Average bus receipts which, given the structure of the bus industry, cannot be very far different from average costs, are estimated to have been approximately 39d. per mile in 1967 (**7.33**). Average receipts per passenger mile were approximately 2.4d. (**7.34**); if tax and interest is deducted the receipts represented approximately 1.8d. per passenger-mile. The notional operating cost, excluding interest and tax, of a 60-seater bus working a single shift and performing 400 miles per week, is of the order of 36d. per mile (**7.35**); at 45% capacity utilization this represents 1.3d. per passenger-mile.

Average expenditure on cars in 1967 is estimated to have been approximately 7.5d. per vehicle-mile; this represented approximately 4.0d per passenger-mile (**7.34**); without interest and tax these estimates would be approximately 5.5d. per vehicle-mile and 2.9d. per passenger-mile. Using 1967 notional operating cost information (**7.35**) for a 1,000 cc. car performing 200 miles per week the cost would be 10.4d. including interest and tax, or 7.5d., excluding these, per vehicle-mile. Assuming the same levels of utilization, the notional cost, excluding interest and taxation, would be 4.0d. per passenger-mile.

Thus, it appears that, given adequate utilization, the average cost per passenger-mile of an underground railway line is less than that of road passenger transport. The level of utilization at which the rail costs have been shown to be lower is comparatively low, being 45% during the four peak hours, and 9% during twelve non-peak hours of operation. Thus, the lower marginal operating costs of rail can be reflected in lower average operating costs well within railway capacity, and at feasible levels of railway utilization.

Cost Comparison

All this evidence suggests that both the capital and operating costs of rail transport may be very much lower than those of road if the utilization of rail capacity is adequate; it also suggests that, given adequate utilization, the costs of bus transport may be very much lower than those of cars.

Meyer, Kain, and Wohl (**7.36**) came to the conclusion, as a result of far more detailed calculations, that the passenger flow needed to be between 5,000 and 10,000 passengers per hour before either bus or train became cheaper than car. However, the cost parameters they used were mainly based on American experience in the 1950s, and appear strange to

British eyes at the beginning of the 1970s.

Recent studies in Britain on the relative costs of transport modes for a new town were presented in a summarized form (**7.37**), from which figure 7.4 has been adapted.

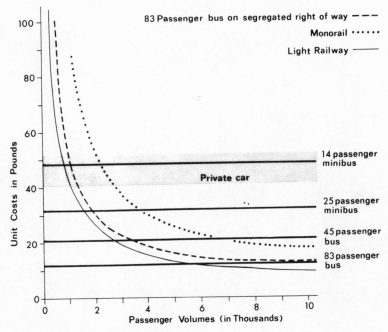

Fig. 7.4 Unit costs of transport modes

This shows the break-even point between the costs of car and rail transport to be at peak flows of approximately 1,000 passengers per hour, and that between big buses and rail to be at peak flows of approximately 6,000 passengers per hour. However, the calculations on which these results are based appear to have excluded the cost of land. In the isolated context of plans for a new town of specified area and population this has some justification; but as the specified population density is approximately half that of existing cities, and as much as 20% of the land area is being allocated to roads, in contrast with, for example, the overall average of 11% in Greater London, these specifications and plans appear to be ignoring general economic pressures. If land costs were taken into account, the more concentrated forms of transport would appear relatively less costly than is shown in figure 7.4. The lower costs of the more concentrated forms of transport under adequate load reflect a lower use of resources.

Chapter 8

Price distortion

It was established, in the last chapter, that the capital and operating costs of rail are less than those of road transport, providing the utilization of facilities is adequate, and also, given adequate utilization, that the capital and operating costs of public road passenger transport are less than those of private transport.

Inter-city passenger travel is supposed to be particularly suitable for rail transport; the second class single rail fare between London and Glasgow, a relatively heavily used railway line, was £5.2 in 1969, whereas the road coach fare was £2.75. This relationship between coach and train fares is typical. In 1968 a comparison was made between different forms of transport based on twelve inter-city routes of an average distance of 200 miles (**8.1**); the results are repeated in table 8.1.

Table 8.1 Comparisons between different forms of transport (average distance 200 miles)

	rail	coach	car	air
average journey time	3 hrs. 35 min.	8 hrs.	5 hrs.	2 hrs. 30 min. (centre to centre)
no. services per day	15	6	–	7
standard fare (single)	£4.06 (1st class) £2.71 (2nd class)	£1.5	–	£4.75 (tourist)
total costs	–	–	£7.83	–
running costs	–	–	£3.33	–

Average full second class rail fares in 1967 were of the order of 3.5d. per passenger-mile (**8.2**); the average bus fare, which is heavily weighted by short distance urban services, was 2.4d. per passenger-mile in the same year, while the average cost of car transport to motorists is estimated to have been 4d. per passenger-mile (8.3). The marginal cost of car transport (petrol tyres, lubricants and maintenance) to motorists, which is almost certainly more relevant to their decisions about specific journeys, was approximately 3.4d. per vehicle-mile for a 1,000 cc. car in 1967 (8.4); at average levels of utilization this represents 1.9d. per passenger-mile. In London, underground and bus fares are approximately 3.5d. per mile, if concessionary rates are ignored, whereas out-of-pocket car expenses have been estimated as being 2.1d. per passenger-mile (8.5). The marginal public transport cost to passengers, the fare, is higher than marginal car costs per occupant at average rates of utilization. Thus, current transport charges do not reflect relative real costs; this is price distortion.

The most flagrant example of transport price distortion in Britain, since it appears in published public transport fares, is that between long distance rail and coach fares between the same towns. Long distance coach journeys usually take longer and, fares apart, few would prefer coach to rail travel given equivalent service frequency and fares. It is probable that most coach passengers only choose coach travel because of the much lower fares. Yet the lower coach fares are associated, according to the arguments presented, with a higher marginal resource usage. If all coach passengers travelled by rail whenever feasible, total resource usage would decrease but total fare payments would increase; thus, relative coach and rail fares for the same journey do not offer the advantages claimed for pricing systems, since the price mechanism appears to be operating in such a way as to encourage a decrease in the efficiency of resource utilization.

The type of price distortion described so far, where relative prices do not reflect capital and operating costs, may be regarded as that due to private resource costs. But price distortion may also arise through costs inflicted on others, or public costs, due, for example, to congestion. Other public costs, such as those of amenity and safety are less tangible, though by no means unimportant, and will not be introduced into the argument here.

Road capacity is an elastic concept; an increase in traffic can be accommodated at the expense of a decrease in speed, once traffic has exceeded a threshold limit. If increased traffic decreased capacity, unstable conditions would occur in which increased traffic resulted in decreased flow, which could only lead to a complete traffic standstill. These conditions occur occasionally, indicating that there is a limit to the elasticity of road capacity; there is also experimental and statistical evidence of an elastic limit (8.6). That traffic is not brought to a standstill more often is probably due to the extent to which road space serves as temporary vehicle storage and introduces a sufficient time lag, between the incoming traffic exceeding the ultimate capacity and the resulting standstill, for incoming traffic to have dropped to an acceptable level in most circumstances before the standstill occurs.

Within the range of traffic flow for which road capacity appears elastic, each vehicle may be regarded as inflicting delay and cost on all the others, insofar as, if it were to withdraw, the remaining vehicles would be able to travel faster and complete their journeys more quickly. The congestion costs inflicted by the delays vary according to the existing traffic speed and associated flow, and one published set of estimates of the congestion cost inflicted by marginal vehicles is repeated in table 8.2 (**8.7**).

Table 8.2 Estimated congestion costs

traffic speed (miles per hour)	marginal congestion cost* (d. per vehicle-mile)
6	140
8	72
10	41
12	26
14	16.4
16	10.8
18	7.1
20	4.6

*This is the total cost inflicted on all existing road users by the addition of one further 'average' vehicle to the traffic flow. This table was calculated for London 'off-peak' conditions.

If buses and cars do not carry loads which are in proportion to their congestion effects then the congestion costs of passenger journeys, costs which are inflicted on all other road users by slowing down their journeys, differ markedly according to whether the journey is made by car or bus. If it is assumed that the congestion effect of a bus is 2.75 times that of a car, that the congestion costs per vehicle-mile are 12d. and 33d. for cars and buses respectively, corresponding to a traffic speed of the order of 15 m.p.h., and that cars have 1.5, and buses 33, occupants, then the relative public congestion costs per passenger-mile would be 8d. and 1d. for car and bus journeys respectively. These are very conservative figures. In a report issued in 1969 (8.8), it was estimated that peak hour congestion costs in London were 90d. and 5.5d. per passenger-mile travelled by car and bus respectively.

Taking the Greater London Council figures already quoted, bus fares are 3.5d. and out-of-pocket car expenses are 2.1d. per passenger-mile; the ratio of these is 5:3. According to the figures in chapter 7, the ratio of the relative resource costs is probably of the order of 2:3. Comparison of these ratios gives a measure of the degree of private price distortion between bus and cars. In the presence of a degree of congestion the ratio of the tangible public costs, comprising both resource and congestion costs, of buses and cars is probably of the order of 1:4; at peak hours the ratio may be 1:12. Comparison of the passenger-mileage payments with the full costs of bus and car travel indicate that the degree of public price distortion between these two modes is substantial.

Rail is not without its congestion problems, although most of these are local, due either to relative shortage of capacity at specific junctions or bridges, or due to a more general shortage of capacity to meet peak traffic demands, especially those of commuters. Little is known about railway congestion costs. Furthermore, it appears to be impossible to acknowledge the economic implications, because any selective increase of public transport fares during the peak hours might increase public congestion costs disproportionately as a result of diversion of some traffic to private transport (8.8). Many peak hour public transport journeys are made at concessionary rates. That ordinary off-peak travellers should pay the same or higher fares than peak hour travellers, when the capital and capacity fixed costs are incurred on behalf of the latter, could be regarded as a further form of price distortion.

Ignoring rail congestion effects, which are probably localized, the overall effects of price distortion for passengers may be summarized as follows:

the ratio of the resource costs of rail, bus, and car travel is of the order of 2:3:4;

in urban areas the typical ratio of the tangible public costs may be 1:2:8, but for peak periods in very congested areas it may be as much as 1:6:72;

the ratio of the costs faced by travellers varies approximately between 3:3:4 and 2:1:1, depending upon the structure of the bus fares and whether total or out-of-pocket car costs are considered.

The degree of price distortion is substantial, and although it has been argued in terms of passenger travel, because a common service is more easily specified and priced, nevertheless, price distortion also exists in goods transport.

Chapter 9

Origins and circumstances of resource price distortion

Private resource price distortions were identified, in the last chapter, while avoiding detailed consideration of the implications and effects of taxation As it is frequently asserted that road user taxation is too high, and that th introduces a form of price distortion between road and rail which discriminates against road usage, the level of road taxation will be examined first, before the origins of the distortions are identified.

Revenue from taxes on road users and usage is often compared unfavourably with public expenditure on the roads, since expenditure has been less than revenue continuously since 1933 (**9.1**). In itself, this argument is of little significance, since indirect taxation applied to any activity involves net government revenue. It does draw attention, however to the fact that some road user taxation is not taxation in the normal sens but may be regarded as payment for services rendered, for road maintenan administration, and some road construction. Based on obvious public expenditure on roads, on estimates of taxation revenue from, and of total expenditure on, road usage, the net taxation revenue from road usage appe to have been less than 13% of total expenditure on road usage in 1967 (**9.**: This was not a high rate of indirect taxation, being less than the average ne rate of taxation (i.e. taxation less subsidies) exacted on all consumers' expenditure, which was 17% (**9.3**).

In contrast, it has sometimes been suggested that the value of road services provided for users is underestimated by recorded expenditure, in t no charge is made for the capital value of roads. Very little of the land utilized for roads has been paid for directly by road users. As this land includes, for example, nearly a quarter of Central London, any valuation o it might be expected to be very high. However, roads also provide a service to buildings and their occupants; undoubtedly some of the value of roads not paid for by road users is reflected in the market value of the buildings served, and any estimate of this would be highly notional. Certainly only a small part of the land at present used for roads could be diverted to other uses without effects on the value of land used for other purposes already.

Attempts to identify more precisely the total value of road services supplied to users do not appear to be justified since it may be asserted with some confidence that the net contribution to indirect taxation is not high enough in total to cause serious price distortion, and there is no obvious basis for determining the proper contribution which should be paid.

It is true that rail is subsidized rather than taxed, according to conventional usage, but this would tend to reduce the effects of resource price distortion between road and rail. It is also possible that the distribution of taxation between different road users leads to significant price distortion effects; for example, it has been asserted that heavy goods vehicles do not contribute enough towards taxation revenues to compensate for the damage to road surfaces attributable to them. Since the evidence concerning the amounts of road damage caused by different categories of user appears to be at least partially contradictory, this possibility will be ignored here.

The origins of resource price distortion between private and public transport may be sought in the private transport revolution. Motorized road transport has always been predominantly a private activity. Public road transport is only responsible for a very small proportion of the total number of vehicles, and a minor part of the total expenditure on road transport.

A major characteristic of private transport is that, once the fixed costs, depreciation, interest, licence, fees, and, where appropriate, wages and establishment costs, have been paid, actual transport demands are satisfied at marginal cost, typically the cost of fuel, tyres, lubricants and maintenance. Indeed, Quarmby (9.4) found that he obtained the best explanation of commuter behaviour if motorists were assumed to believe that their marginal costs were confined to those of petrol usage.

In contrast, the fixed costs of public transport are reflected in the fares. The proportion of the break-even fares needed to cover fixed costs depends upon the average level of utilization. At low levels of utilization, either because demand is low, or because demand is very peaked, 70% or more of the costs of operating buses may be fixed costs. Even at very high levels of utilization the fixed costs of buses rarely drop below 40% of the total. A somewhat ambiguous reference (9.5) suggests that 75% of rail costs are fixed.

Consequently, when considering whether to make a particular journey by private or public transport the prices that are compared are the marginal costs on the one hand, and average costs, including a share of the fixed costs, on the other.

There are many reasons, and not solely financial reasons, for joining the private transport club. Private transport for many purposes offers a more comprehensive and flexible service than public transport. It offers continuous availability of rapid and secure door-to-door transport; it may be developed to a high degree of specialization and adaptation for particular purposes, if this is preferred to general flexibility. Private transport may not only confer prestige, it may also reduce the effort required to find out what alternative services are available to fulfil a transport demand, together with their convenience and price, and thence to determine the best. The attraction of private transport is illustrated by the observation that the number of private vehicles is growing continuous in all developed countries.

Once private transport is owned a marked brand loyalty is developed. Because of this brand loyalty, usually supported by a degree of ignorance of public transport services, and often by price differences, public transpo is only able to offer significant competition in special circumstances when offers a markedly better service for specific demands, e.g. long distance travel by air, urban commuter services, furniture removals or bulk liquid carriage. Public transport is also used by private transport owners when their demands temporarily exceed their private transport capacity.

It has often been asserted that there is a very low elasticity of substitut between private and public transport to anything less than extremely large changes in public transport charges, that the usage of public transport is n substantially increased by fare decreases. But this need cause no surprise since the difference between the fares of public transport and marginal cos of private transport are likely to be so large that there is no real price competition between them, and the general characteristics of private transport reinforce the effect of the price differential.

It has often seemed to the author that the mechanism of price competition between public and private passenger transport may be observed most simply in circumstances associated with the occasional use of private cars for company business. It is the custom in most businesses to pay notional average costs for the approved use of a private car. Car owne tend to see this as a highly attractive rate, since a proportion of fixed costs is recovered and is seen as profit. This phenomenon is sufficiently marked for strict regulations to exist in most organizations governing and restrictin the approved use of private cars, at least those of relatively junior employe Where the use of private cars is not approved, they may be used as alternat to public transport, the payment being the public transport fare. In this ca public transport fares for one person may be about the same as car margin costs, and public transport is often preferred. However, if more than one person is travelling, so that combined fares significantly exceed car margin costs, cars are usually preferred.

Much public transport custom is derived from those without private transport facilities. As far as passenger transport is concerned those without cars are usually those who cannot afford the fixed charges. The sensitivity of car purchasing behaviour to relatively minor variations of Government regulations affecting hire-purchase deposits and repayment periods is another illustration of the important role of fixed charges, and the timing of payments, in the choice between transport options.

If resource price distortion between public and private road transport is primarily attributable to the fixed cost component of public transport charges, and the influence of the level of utilization on these, then it would be expected that the higher fixed costs of rail transport, due to the operation and maintenance of track as well as rolling stock, could lead to greater resource price distortion between road and rail transport unless the average level of railway utilization were very high.

The utilization problems of railways may be illustrated by the proportion of the total number of passengers carried by different transport modes which are carried during the four peak hours in London, between 08.00 and 10.00 hours, and 17.00 and 19.00 hours. During these peak periods British Rail commuter services carry 70% of their total passengers, the Underground carries 60% of its passengers, buses carry 45% of theirs, and only 35% of all car passenger trips are made during the peak periods (**9.6**). If the public transport services were operating at full capacity throughout the four peak hours, then the average level of utilization over an eighteen hour operating day would be nearly 32% for British Rail commuter services, 37% for the Underground services, and nearly 50% for the bus services.

Looking at British Railways as a whole, Joy (**9.7**) showed that the average level of utilization of track was low in comparison with other Western European railways. But a comparison of British Railways' performance with that of Soviet railways produces an even more marked contrast. The average utilization of British Railways assets, measured in transport units (ton-miles plus passenger-miles) per unit, compared with that of Soviet Railways, represents approximately 7% for track, less than 5% for locomotives, and 16% for labour (**9.8, 9.9**). The point is supported by the average utilization of London Transport track, which is six times that of British Railways (**9.8**). The Soviet average track performance is rather less than London Transport railways performance during the peak hours. Utilization of rail facilities in Britain is so low that the fixed cost component of fares must be very high, and the relationship between fares and marginal resource usage remote.

The first railways soon disposed of competitive transport modes. In particular, road transport could not compete on cost or speed. As road traffic declined, revenues of the turnpike trusts also declined, as also did the condition of the primary road network which they maintained.

The railways expanded beyond levels justified on financial grounds, partly, at least, to go as far as practicable towards the provision of a comprehensive transport service. Railways became monopolies with special 'common user', obligations, which included fixed tariffs. It was possible to ignore, to some extent, the cost aspects of providing many of the services because, in the absence of effective competition for the main traffics, it was possible to set fares and tariffs to cover average costs, implying cross subsidization of services which, through lack of sufficient potential traffic, had no hope of paying their way. Furthermore, because of the virtual monopoly situation, it was possible to adjust some tariffs to what the traffic would bear without close reference to either average or specific costs.

The development of motorized road transport introduced a fundamental change in the situation. Railways were faced with a competing mode of transport, which offered better and more appropriate service for many transport demands, at average costs which were of the same order of those for rail, and at prices which could be adjusted at will to take advantage of any and every competitive weakness in the published railway tariff structure. Inevitably, some traffic was converted from rail to road; as the initiative lay with road transport, it is reasonable to assume that much of this traffic was the most profitable for road transport to take from rail. Insofar as railway costs and prices were averaged there is no reason to believe that there was a close relationship between profitability and economic efficiency of carrying different traffics by rail. But the railway tariff structure for goods was adjusted to some extent for what the traffic might bear before the advent of competition; consequently, there must have been some traffics where charges and costs bore little relationship to each other. In the circumstances it is reasonable to suspect that the traffic that was profitable for road transport to take from the railways may also have been very profitable railway traffic. In addition, much of any new transport demands generated were satisfied by road services, and railways were deprived of a source of traffic growth.

In the face of the chronic deficits (the financial history is examined by Aldcroft (**9.10**)) of British Railways, the Beeching Report (**9.11**) concluded that

. . . . in many respects, (British Railways) are being used in ways

which emphasize their disadvantages and fail to exploit their advantages
.... it is proposed to build up traffic on the well-loaded through
trains, and to develop the new services necessary for that purpose. At the
same time it is proposed to close down routes which are so lightly loaded as
to have no chance of paying their way, and to discontinue services which
cannot be provided economically by rail.

Thus, it would seem that railway fares are disproportionately high in
comparison with marginal resource usages because fares reflect average costs;
these are very high because of the extremely low average level of utilization
of the railway network. If this is so then one obvious corrective measure,
while retaining the objective of self-supporting railways, would be to prune
the basic railway network, closing, or downgrading, the lines with least
traffic. But to facilitate a significant reduction in fares, and therefore of
price distortion, the cuts would have to be very much more savage than
those included in the Beeching Report (**9.12**), which themselves have proved,
to a considerable degree, politically unacceptable. The situation appears to
have developed in a broadly similar way elsewhere. A particularly vivid and
amusing picture of the development of competition between road and rail
in France is given by Sauvy (**9.13**). Only the Netherlands' Railway appears
to have been spared chronic deficits; but in the Netherlands the railways were
subjected to extensive surgery very early; for example, between 1930 and
1940, approximately 60% of the passenger stations were closed (**9.14**).

Chapter 10

Road congestion

The phenomenon of congestion is a symptom of the availability of insufficient road space to satisfy, without difficulty, all demands made upon it. One possible way of alleviating congestion would be to build more roads, but, since roads cannot be built instantaneously and are a significant investment, consideration of road building as a remedy will be deferred until later in the chapter. Once congestion exists, there is at least a short term problem, even if roads are to be built, of making the best use of existing road space. Methods of controlling the use of road space when is short will therefore be examined first.

Many road management schemes are intended to increase the effective supply of road space in the short term by making more efficient use of the roads available. They may be simple, e.g. one-way streets, or more comple e.g. computer control of linked traffic lights. Schemes which have been adopted to overcome specific and serious bottlenecks, e.g. prohibition of right turns at busy cross-roads, often have a notable effect on local traffic flows. But this example illustrates one of the main disadvantages of most traffic management schemes: because traffic is denied its preferred option journey distances may be increased; the same journeys result in more traff and the same journey durations require increased speeds.

One of the more dramatic examples of the disadvantages, as well as advantages, of traffic management is met with tidal flow schemes, where most or all of the capacity of one or more roads is dedicated to the main direction of traffic flow, and the main direction of travel is reversed with, for example, the tidal flows of commuter traffic. In this type of scheme n only may some journey distances be increased by the emphasis on flows in one direction, but also the complexity of planning an appropriate route m: be increased owing to increased uncertainty about directions of flow. Even one-way streets are confusing to those who do not know them.

The more drastic traffic management schemes may bring dramatic increases in traffic flows, but they may also require greater increases to offset the increased journey distances they cause, quite apart from compensating for the adverse effects on amenity. Little information is available about the net benefits realized from traffic management schemes (10.1), and even less about the trade-off between the advantages and disadvantages of schemes which are more or less far-reaching. But Smeed (10.2) has suggested that the proportion of the road system effectively used by traffic entering towns during the morning peak travel period, and leaving in the evening, is between 23% and 46%. The scope for enhancement of this figure, having regard to road functions other than those of commuting, is clearly limited. It is unlikely that traffic management schemes will prove any more effective in the future than they bave been in the past; they help, at some cost, but do not solve, congestion problems.

If road space is not available in sufficient quantities to satisfy all potential demands completely, then, whether deliberately or not, road space has to be rationed and demands reduced to match supply. There have been many discussions of possible methods of traffic restraint and of their effects (e.g. 10.3).

Road space could be rationed by selecting the transport demands to be satisfied by administrative decision. Thus, 'essential' traffic could be given priority, and limited examples of this type of arrangement are not hard to find. By common consent ambulances and fire engines are conceded right-of-way, while handicapped persons and doctors are given special treatment, for example, over parking. But outside a few relatively clear-cut cases, specific administrative intervention would probably prove impossible and intolerable in most societies.

While direct administrative schemes of rationing road usage are not seriously in evidence, nevertheless, indirect, or non-specific, schemes have been widely advocated and used.

The reduction of congestion has been one of the main objectives of the widespread introduction of parking restrictions in urban areas. It is generally accepted that parking restrictions have helped to reduce the rate of increase of traffic congestion. Furthermore, a major advantage of parking restrictions is that they can be formulated to have a selective effect on car traffic, particularly car commuter traffic, which is a major component of road traffic during peak hours. But there are snags.

Even in an area like Central London, nearly 45% of the available parking places are on private off-street sites (10.4) which are not under public control. Thus, restrictions on parking in public places have to be substantially more severe to attain a given reduction in traffic than they would have to be if all the parking places were subject to the same restrictions; additionally, the incidence of these restrictions on the usage of public parking places is inequitable between those who have, and those who have not, access to private parking places. In time it is to be anticipated that some parking places will become subject to market forces, and the value placed upon th may well come to reflect the value placed on the ability to evade the restrictions.

Road usage and the demand for parking places are not always very clos related. They are most closely related when all the roads to or from a cen area are equally subject to congestion, and most journeys on those roads have their origins or destinations in the central area. They are less closely related when a significant proportion of the total amount of traffic passes through the congested areas without parking; thus, for example, nearly 2C of the traffic in the centre of Gloucester in the early 1960s was long dista traffic passing through Gloucester (**10.5**). A similar condition arises in the large conurbations when congestion spreads beyond the main central area suburban centres, which tend to carry substantial quantities of through traffic.

Parking restrictions are very expensive to enforce. The costs are not on direct, e.g. those of traffic wardens and meters, but also indirect, e.g. the demands made on the time of magistrates courts to deal with offenders.

It is almost impossible to formulate parking restrictions which will hav the desired effect on traffic without harming, or discriminating arbitrarily between, local commercial or residential interests. Indeed, it is a difficult task to formulate parking restrictions to ration available parking space without discriminating between different users; introduction of traffic considerations only serves to make the task more difficult.

It is possible to allow the deterrent effects of congestion to ration road usage in such a way that supply and demand are equal at a given level of congestion, and this may be regarded as a form of indirect administrative rationing. In these circumstances, until the elastic limit of road capacity is reached, all demands are met at the expense of decreased traffic speeds an increased journey times; once the elastic limit is passed, no demands are satisfied, at least until demands are reduced by withdrawal for one reason another. Under this arrangement, all road users within the congested area suffer; but neither the advantages of a given road journey, nor the costs or penalties of an increase in its duration, are equal to different users. Many goods vehicle journeys are, in the short term, virtually essential; the cost o prolonging these journeys is the full cost of idle resources; the same is true for doctors or commercial travellers on business. At the other extreme, in most cases, a pleasure journey by car may be much more easily forgone, o at least more easily substituted by an alternative excursion; but the main c of delay to pleasure journeys may be reflected in relatively unquantifiable aspects such as the lost amenity and the lost recreational opportunity of the same time spent at the end of the journey.

Thus, a 'first come, first served' system of rationing road space, relying upon the deterrent effect of congestion, has three major disadvantages: firstly, it discriminates against those to whom time is most valuable since the increase in journey duration appears to be independent of the valuation placed upon the time lost;

secondly, those who value their time least persist with their demand in the face of extreme congestion; they would persist longest if it were not for the fact that many goods, professional and business journeys are necessary and must be performed almost irrespective of cost;

finally, its use is inevitably associated with nuisance and waste of resources.

In theory, road usage could be rationed by a pricing system, as is the consumption of most other goods and services in short supply. Prices could be increased until demand dropped sufficiently for congestion to disappear. Price rationing would displace from the roads those who set least value upon their usage and ensure better conditions for those who value road usage most.

At present road usage is subjected to a degree of price rationing. The costs of road usage include not only those costs which reflect direct resource utilization, e.g. vehicle capital and fuel costs, but also a variety of taxes and levies directly concerned with resource utilization, e.g. purchase taxes on cars, vehicle licence taxes, fuel taxes, and parking charges. There is no reason to doubt that the cumulative effect of these taxes is to reduce road usage below what it would be in their absence. But there is no evidence that either the level or the form of the taxes have been determined as part of a specific attempt to ration road usage. Most notably, only parking charges, of existing road pricing weapons, can be adjusted simply to take account of local variations of congestion intensity as would be desirable if pricing methods were being used to ration road usage.

Under existing conditions, congestion occurs although pricing reduces some demand for road usage. Administrative methods are also used, e.g. licensing and parking restrictions. But the final balance, in congested areas, is left to the deterrent effects of congestion itself on the basis of first come, first served.

The relative efficiency of different methods of traffic restraint might not be of very great importance if they were only needed to overcome temporary difficulties until either traffic management schemes or new road building ensured adequate supply of road space to meet all demands. As was mentioned in chapter 5, traffic on trunk and classified roads in Britain has been increasing at a compound rate of 7% per annum. To avoid any increase in congestion and eliminate traffic restrictions already in force, would probably need an increase in the supply of road space of between 5% and 10% per annum, depending upon the effect of other transport policies and the general rate of increase of wealth. Traffic management schemes are unlikely to contribute more than a small part of this total. The major contribution would have to be made by the construction of new roads; and it is the construction of new roads which is the favourite solution to transport problems, especially congestion, proffered by the road lobby, bo national and international, and by road users and their organizations. But the lobbyists appear to ignore the weight of evidence (summarized, for example, in the Crowther Report, and expanded in the Buchanan Report (10.6)) which suggests that road building cannot be a complete cure for congestion.

It has been widely asserted that insufficient capital is available to build sufficient roads to cure congestion (e.g. 10.7). This appears to be the conclusion reached in several of the conurbations in Britain (10.8), but it i most easily illustrated by a discussion of the plans for London, since more detailed information about these has been published and discussed than about plans for the other conurbations as yet.

In examining road building requirements in London between 1972 and 1981 a scheme which would fulfil all the forecast traffic demands in 1981 was developed which it was estimated would cost, at 1966 prices, over £2,000M. Another scheme was developed which would fulfil 94% of traffic demands, and it was estimated that this would cost £1,640M. As it was considered unlikely that sufficient capital for this scheme would be available, the scheme eventually advocated was reduced to only 55% of the traffic carrying capacity of the £1,640M. scheme, and it was estimated tha it would cost £860M. (10.9).

Even this cut-down scheme has faced severe criticism on the grounds, among others, that its costs have been under-estimated and its effectivenes over-estimated (e.g. 10.10).

The method of traffic forecasting had the effects of existing traffic restrictions, especially in Central London, built in, and was therefore probably a serious under-estimate of the traffic demand in the absence of restraint in 1981, and also of the degree of traffic restraint required in 198 by any of the schemes examined. Smeed (10.2) has estimated that traffic i

Central London in 1966 only satisfied from 20% to 25% of desires.

Thomson (10.10) has asserted that the method of cost estimation omitted a number of costs which should have been included: not only was the cost of traffic disruption and of interest on capital during road construction ignored in the evaluations, but also the engineering costs were under-estimated because the proposed access and interchange junctions, as well as the main approach roads, will be inadequate to service the capacities of the motorways.

In 1970, the Greater London Council have announced upward revisions of their 1967 estimates of the cost of the construction programme (10.11). In comparison with an original estimate for the G.L.C. primary programme of £625M., the new estimates have been revised upwards by £190M. for 'improved environmental standards', £40M. for 'compensation or other expenditure in respect of "fringe properties" ', and £75M. for 'inflation'; 'however, £40M. will be saved by building the roads to the full width at the outset instead of by a two-stage operation'. The estimate of the cost of the G.L.C. secondary road programme has been increased from £210M. to £240M. 'on account of price increases since 1967'. Further, estimated expenditure on other secondary roads, responsibility for which has been transferred from the various London Boroughs to the G.L.C., has been revised upwards, 'in order to secure a proper balance' between investment in the primary and secondary networks, from £130M. to £310M.

Since the original estimates were made, economic progress has been slower than anticipated and the planned rate of public expenditure has been reduced in consequence. The combined effect of the increased estimate of the expenditure required and the reduced rate of expenditure has been a revision in the expected date of completion of the network from the mid-1980s to the late 1990s.

The cut-down scheme proposed in 1967 was not expected to cure congestion, or remove the need for a high degree of traffic restraint. Most of the proposed urban motorways were expected to be at, or near, capacity usage by 1981 (10.12). Although incomes, employment and population have all been at lower levels than was estimated, it appears probable that the net effect of all these departures from the original estimates will be that congestion, or the degree of restraint required to contain it, will be more severe than was anticipated. The basic conclusion is that road-building schemes of the type proposed in London require too much capital for congestion to be cured.

In addition, it has often been suggested that the effect of building sufficient roads to satisfy demands could be ruinous to amenity; much can be made of amenity problems, such as noise, dirt, planning blight, air pollution and accident risk, generated by more traffic and, in particular, urban motorways (e.g. **10.13, 10.14**). But one of the arguments advanced for the construction of motorways in London is the improvement in amenity to be obtained by the removal of much traffic from residential neighbourhoods. Yet one G.L.C. study suggests that traffic on local roads may not be appreciably reduced (**10.15**). Thomson believes that local traff will be increased (**10.16**).

Examination of the problems of filtering traffic onto and off the propo urban motorways for a large number of relatively short journeys has led Thomson (**10.17**) to suggest that local congestion, at least in the neighbourhood of the access points, may well be increased. Further, taking account of local congestion around the access points, and a G.L.C. estimat that the average journey making use of the urban motorways will be 40% longer in distance than otherwise, Thomson has queried whether there will be any significant reduction of journey duration.

Resistance to the proposed road building programme in London on soci and amenity grounds appear to be increasing. One of the major contributor factors may be the large number of families (estimated to be 20,850 for G.L.C. roads, and a further 3,500 for Ministry of Transport roads (**10.11**)) which will have to be rehoused to provide land space.

It might be possible, in theory at least, for new areas to be built in such a way as to avoid road congestion, as is claimed for the plan for the new to of Milton Keynes (**10.18**): but this neither solves the problems of existing urban areas, nor shows, in this relatively densely populated island, where sufficient space is to be found. Even Milton Keynes, with its population of 250,000 housed at low density and surrounded by a green belt, may turn out to be a twenty-first century Hampstead Garden Suburb, a middle-class town full of commuters, rather than a balanced, self-contained community and if it does, higher levels of car ownership than predicted (1.5 per family may bring congestion despite its favoured start.

Significant amounts of building up or down to increase the available roa space can almost certainly be ruled out if insufficient capital is available for ordinary road building. The proportion of the land area devoted to roads in Central London is less than a quarter, whereas the proportion in the centre of Los Angeles, the archetypal motorized city, is approximately 50%. The population density of the U.S.A. as a whole is approximately 10% of that of Britain. Overall space availability and the existing urban areas are likely to pose some limitations on road building in Britain, and these limitations are likely to be more severe in Britain than in the U.S.A.; the position in

many of the countries of Western Europe is not so very different from that
in Britain.

Finally, there is no evidence anywhere that any road building programme
in a developed country has managed to cure congestion due to motorized
traffic, except on a very temporary basis; there is no evidence that travel
demands reach a natural ceiling, in the absence of restraint, or that there is
any natural limit to the number of vehicles owned. Rather, road traffic
appears to follow its own form of Parkinson's Law: traffic expands to fill
the road space available to it.

Smeed (10.2) is far more optimistic than the author about the possibility
of increasing traffic capacity by new and re-designed roads, and by vehicle
improvements, but compensates for this by his diagnosis that traffic in
Central London only satisfied about 20% of desires in 1966, and that these
desires could double by 1976, certainly before 1986. He concludes that it is
unlikely that it will be possible to satisfy all travel desires in London or other
large towns without a redistribution of homes and workplaces, including
making towns smaller, or at least having smaller town centres.

Thus, road building programmes offer no serious prospect of a cure for
congestion problems within the near future. Traffic restraint is likely to be
a long-term feature of the way of life of 'developed' countries, and it is
therefore important to select the best method if there is any significant
variation in efficiency between alternative methods.

The contribution of categories of transport to congestion may be very
roughly assessed on the basis of the share of urban vehicle-mileage. Cars,
buses, light vans of less than 1.5 unladen weight, and heavy goods vehicles,
perform respectively 77%, 3%, 8% and 9% of urban vehicle-mileage (3% is
performed by motor cycles) (10.19). If the relative contribution per vehicle-
mile of each category to congestion is taken to be one for cars, two for
light vans, three for other goods vehicles, and four for buses, then the
contribution to the total congestion effect is approximately 60% by cars, 10%
by buses and light vans, and 20% by heavy goods vehicles. Taking urban and rural
vehicle-mileage together, the contribution towards congestion, calculated in
the same way, is 50%, 10%, 20%, and 20% by cars, buses, light vans and
heavy goods vehicles respectively.

The effect of restrictions may be such as to suppress some transport
demands entirely; to divert demands so that they are served by other
transport modes, e.g. rail; to divert them so that they are served by
vehicles which make more concentrated, and therefore less demanding, use
of road space; or divert them to less congested periods or routes. The
effective amount of restraint, or reduction in demand, is the same whatever

method of restraint is used.

Suppression of some transport demands is possible; however, it is not very desirable and, if necessary, suppression should be selectively directed those demands which are considered by users to be of least value or importance.

Satisfaction of transport demands by other modes must be assumed to preferable, unless the user thinks otherwise, to suppression. In this connection, only rail, of inland transport modes in Britain, offers significant alternative capacity; the total potential capacity of air transport for some time to come, will probably be relatively small due, for example, to air congestion problems.

Rail transport is only efficient for the carriage of bulk quantities; the minimum distance of conveyance for efficient services depends upon the ease of assembly and dispersal of adequate trainloads. Passengers do much assemble and disperse themselves, so that passenger train services may be efficient, given sufficient density of demand, over relatively short distances Thus, rail transport might be able to cope efficiently with a significant proportion of traffic served at present by car, bus, and coach journeys. Goods traffic must be assembled and dispersed, and bulk is not only required to obtain heavily loaded trains, but also to justify the installation of effective terminal equipment; thus, it would be anticipated that the minimum distance of efficient conveyance for goods by rail would be longer than for passengers. Given the much greater contribution of cars to congestion, and the anticipated lower efficient distance of rail transport for passengers, the main scope for the use of rail transport to alleviate congestion efficiently is likely to be in the substitution of rail for road passenger journeys rather than for goods transport.

However, some provisions of the 1968 Transport Act were intended to bring about the conversion of some long distance goods transport from roa to rail in order, it was claimed, to reduce road congestion. But as

1   there is no intention of applying pressure to convert journeys of less tha 100 miles in length from road to rail,

2   road goods journeys over 100 miles in length account for less than 2% o total vehicle-miles and less than 5% of the total contribution to congestion.

3   most of these long distance journeys are performed on inter-city trunk roads, which are not, in general, subject to such severe congestion as urban roads,

4   many of these journeys are performed overnight when congestion is less.

5   it is accepted that not all large consignments for more than 100 miles ca or should be converted to rail, and

6 experience suggests that ways of evading restrictions of this type can be found by those who are determined to search, it seems safe to infer that these provisions will have little detectable effect on congestion.

Measures aimed at restricting road goods transport in order to force traffic onto the railways, which are common in Western Europe in the form of size or distance limits (10.20), are unlikely to reduce congestion very significantly, partly because of the small proportion of vehicles susceptible, and partly because measures of evasion are usually available. In particular, private vehicles, the vast majority, are often exempted from such restrictions, while the relative freedom of small goods vehicles may even increase congestion by encouraging the use of smaller, rather than larger, vehicles. It is possible that some of the provisions of the 1968 Transport Act, which selectively reduced restrictions on smaller goods vehicles, will decrease, rather than increase, efficiency both directly because of increased usage of small vehicles, and indirectly, because of the resulting congestion effects.

Concentration of goods or passengers into larger batches would reduce the number of vehicles and vehicle-miles, and hence the congestion, required to satisfy the same transport demands. Considerable assembly, dispersal and stockholding problems may be associated with any increase in the concentration of goods consignments; these will be examined in more detail later. Once again, passengers do not offer the same problems. There is scope for a massive reduction in car traffic, without reduction of the number of passenger journeys, if the average number of occupants per car, currently 1.5 in urban areas, were increased, or if, when demand is sufficient, bus services were developed and heavily used.

Thus, car transport, because it contributes most to congestion, because people are physically more amenable to conversion to rail transport or concentration into bus or larger car loads, and because some car journeys are most easily forgone, should contribute most to the amelioration of congestion and bear the brunt of restrictions. In practice car transport already bears the brunt of existing restrictions. But restraint will need to be far more severe in future than it is already. Indeed, G.L.C. documents (10.21) express doubts as to whether existing methods of restraint will be adequate to prevent an increase in congestion even if the planned motorway system is built.

It must be recognized that measures affecting car usage are inevitably political in content. Car ownership has become a target for, and assumed right of, nearly everyone. There is no limit in sight to the desire for car journeys for all purposes, not only commuting. Thus, measures restraining car usage to a substantial extent must be generally comprehensible and acceptable.

In view of the probable need for severe restraint of car usage to relieve congestion it should be noted that:

1 restrictions on road users to relieve congestion by a given amount need be less severe if railways are available to absorb some of the traffic;

2 the better the services offered by public transport, of which railways are a vital element, the less resentment will be felt by those whose road usage is limited or modified, and the less resistance will be offered to restrictions on road usage;

3 public passenger road transport is in decline, and, so long as it is stifled by congestion and labours under the effects of price distortion, the decline must be expected to continue;

4 there is no possibility of the road network being expanded sufficiently carry, whether as public or private transport, a significant portion of the traffic carried at present by rail.

In short, road and rail problems, public and private transport problems, are but different aspects of one transport problem; and treating parts, rather than the whole, is bound to be expensive and difficult, even if it is a all possible.

Chapter 11

Congestion taxation and road investments

Within limits, the flow of traffic along a road can be increased at the expense of a decrease in speed; one implication of the slower journeys is that every addition to the flow of traffic imposes extra costs on all existing road users. The cost of delays imposed on existing traffic by an additional vehicle may be substantial; according to the Smeed Report (**11.1**), from which table 8.2 has been copied, an extra vehicle-mile in Central London during off-peak periods, when average speeds of the order of 12 m.p.h. are typical, increases the total cost to all other road users by about £0.1. A more recent (1969) estimate of peak period congestion costs in London is £0.5 per car-mile (**11.2**).

The case for taxing all vehicles in congested areas to the extent of the costs marginal vehicles impose on others has been made many times (e.g. **11.3-10**), and has tentative ministerial approval (e.g. **11.11**). In essence, it is argued that if each road user is not prepared to pay the equivalent of the costs his use imposes on others, then that use is inefficient; there would be a net gain to the community as a whole if a toll equal to the marginal congestion costs were imposed, since the toll would displace those users who did not value use as highly as the toll, to the benefit of those who value use more highly.

Most practical investment criteria demand an expected surplus of revenue over expenditure associated with a particular investment. If the revenue required to service capital, both interest and depreciation, is 10% per annum, if the cost of building motorways in Inner London is, as suggested in chapter 7, between £1.5m. and £3.5M. per lane-mile, and if usage is equivalent to the design lane capacity of 16,500 vehicles per day for 300 days per year, allowing for weekend and seasonal effects, then the required revenue per vehicle-mile would be between 7.7d. and 16.4d.

The level of congestion taxation after equilibrium usage was established would depend upon the price elasticity of demand, or upon the readiness to forgo vehicle journeys in the face of rising costs; in turn this would probably depend upon the availability of alternative ways of satisfying transport demands. However, in general, expected levels of congestion taxation and the revenues required to justify new road construction would be of the same order of magnitude.

An alternative view of congestion taxation, therefore, is that it could be used to establish and maintain a balance between the supply and demand f road space when it is short. The volume of traffic at any particular price would be established by congestion taxation; when the revenues from congestion taxation from any section of road network reached a level whic justified the capital expenditure required to relieve congestion, road capacity would be extended; the expenditure required would be derived from the revenues from congestion taxation.

Thus, congestion taxes could be used as part of a system of road user charging in which, on the one hand, users of congested roads would pay both the short and long run marginal costs of their usage, and, on the other, the identification and timing of new road investment to relieve congestion would be virtually automatic, and the investments themselves would be effectively self-financing; in this way road investments could be isolated from the fluctuations and competition associated with their presen status as one component of public expenditure. In the short term congestic taxation would serve to control demand to balance the existing supply of road space.

In contrast, expenditure on roads is currently part of general public expenditure and must compete with other projects for finance. In the absence of an obvious measure of the value placed upon the usage of particular roads or routes, there is a problem of choice between alternative projects. To choose between alternative road schemes, estimates are made of the benefits which might be derived from each.

The major part of the benefits may result from the shortened duration and reduced running cost of existing journeys because of the alleviation of congestion, and from any additional journeys made possible or attractive by the new route or additional capacity. Estimation of the total time and cost savings resulting from a road investment is an elaborate exercise, since it involves identifying all the traffic which uses routes which might be affected by the re-distribution of traffic following the investment. Estimation of the traffic generated by improved road conditions, both on and off the new road, depends upon estimates of the increase in road speed due to the new road, and of the increased demand corresponding to the new conditions. The usual method of estimation starts with a model of existing journeys, which may have been derived from an origin-destination survey and from observation of traffic speeds, proceeds to a forecast of future traffic demands both before and after the possible changes in the road network, and a calculation of new journey times under each of the possible conditions. The time savings of established journeys and benefits of generated journeys are then converted into monetary savings, as, also, are other benefits, such as those (hopefully) resulting from greater safety, and these are added to the running cost savings and treated as the revenues to be compared with the expenditures.

A very great degree of sophistication is applied to the calculation of the journey time savings and the amount of traffic generated, sophistication which is expensive in terms of both money and skilled effort. But the time savings, themselves uncertain, are then converted into cash savings which are very uncertain, because of the uncertainty of the conversion factors used, particularly in respect to the value of leisure time (11.12, 11.13). Estimation of generated traffic and its benefits is also uncertain. The complexity of, and arbitrary results produced by, this chain of calculation is manifest.

This method of evaluating potential road construction projects is one of the more common applications of cost-benefit analysis. In estimating the benefits an attempt is made to evaluate the total consumers' surplus, which is the sum of the value of the benefit, no matter how small, received by each and every member of the population. Although well-established in practice, there are a number of serious difficulties associated with the use of cost-benefit analysis to evaluate road construction projects. One symptom of these difficulties is the apparent contradiction between assertions that the G.L.C. road programme is economically attractive and the comparative inability to find finance for it.

Cost-benefit analysis, and its application to the evaluation of road investments, has attracted considerable attention in the literature, both specialist and more general, and a brief examination cannot do justice to the arguments about such a complex subject. However, some examination is inevitable if existing practices are to be questioned.

Theoretically, the case for using estimates of the consumers' surplus to evaluate investment projects depends upon assumptions which rarely hold in practice; this is a common difficulty associated with the practical application of economic concepts. In the context of road building projects specific problems arise in that, for example, roads are only worth building in substantial lumps and the resources employed cannot all be freely converted to and from alternative uses. A more general problem is that consumers' surplus is not used to evaluate very many investments, and in the absence of strict conditions, e.g. divisibility of investments, there is no formal basis for assuming equivalence between consumers' surplus criteria and the more widely used financial tests. Thus, the estimation of benefits by consumers' surplus may be used as the basis of a method of determining preferences between different projects which have been evaluated in this way, e.g. for ranking a number of possible road projects, without giving any justification either for any investment in these projects at all, or for any specific level of investment. The theoretical fallibility of consumers' surplus as an index of the benefits to be derived from car travel was shown by Mishan (11.14) when he demonstrated that a loss, rather than the expected gain, in welfare could result.

Time savings are usually the major source of benefits derived from a road construction project. The valuation of these, particularly savings of leisure time, has been a major pre-occupation. The valuation put upon leisure time has been challenged in principle and not just in detail. Tipping (11.15) has maintained that the value of leisure time is of a different sort of value from that of productive time. Additionally, reductions in travelling time, if paid for by the community instead of by individuals, result in a completely arbitrary redistribution of benefits, however they are valued. If reductions in travelling time were paid for by those receiving the benefits there would be a re-allocation of incomes which reflected the relative values ascribed to different activities.

Prest and Turvey, in their review of cost-benefit analysis (11.16), concluded that the major justification for its use was that there was often no alternative. In the case of road projects intended to relieve congestion, however, congestion taxation offers a theoretical alternative.

Furthermore, because of the natural link with the costs of new investments, Tipping's (11.15) main objection to any precise valuation of either working or leisure time would be largely overcome. There would be some scope for political choice over the price of road usage, and hence over the implicit valuation of time, since the best policy for the community as a whole would not necessarily be to maximize revenue from road taxation.

The immediate effect of congestion taxation, or road pricing, in congested areas would be to raise the cost of vehicle road usage. Although some journeys, presumably those of lowest value, would be given up as a result, the primary effect would be to increase the financial incentive to reduce the number of vehicle journeys, whether by transfers to other transport modes, or by increases in the utilization of the remaining vehicle journeys. The incentive to increase vehicle utilization would probably apply to both goods and passenger traffic, since it would be as difficult to maintain that all goods vehicle journeys are necessary as that all car journeys are unnecessary; discrimination between them, except on the grounds of relative congestion effects, would be difficult to defend.

For those prepared to pay the price, the roads would be much clearer; journeys would be faster, and journey durations would not only be shorter but also less variable; it will be shown in Part 7 that the variability and unpredictability of journey durations due to the variable effects of congestion has a serious effect on transport costs. For those not prepared to pay the price of individual journeys, clear roads should make it possible to improve the speed, reliability and frequency of public transport services, and increased utilization should reduce the importance of the fixed cost component of fares. Thus, congestion taxation offers the prospects of the benefits of congestion-free roads, the removal of tangible public price distortion between transport modes, and the reduction of resource price distortion due to the expected higher utilization of public transport.

None of the other methods of traffic restriction offers any prospect of a cure for congestion within the foreseeable future. Indeed, congestion taxation itself could prove so unpopular as to be no more effective than Canute's command; it would be more likely to succeed, however, the better the services offered by public transport.

It has been objected that the arguments for congestion taxation or road pricing depend, for theoretical support, upon assumptions of economic rationality and equitable income distributions. But these assumptions apply to the justification of all price-rationing systems.

It has also been argued that the provision of road space is a social service, broadly indistinguishable from the provision of education or medical care. Emphasis on comparisons with services that are commonly supplied free by the community is misplaced; food is also necessary, but is commonly supplied through the market, with preferences and tastes being influenced and, for scarce items, rationed by a pricing system. Social payments of various types are provided to ensure that basic quantities of food can be purchased. Price rationing applies mainly to the premium foods in short supply. Charging for road usage would be expected to have a similar effect; an effective pricing system could guide choice between alternative modes of basic transport, and social payments could be made to provide for transport necessities; it could also ration usage of premium transport services, e.g. those that utilize large amounts of road space where this is short.

Quite apart from arguments which rely upon analogies, there are social considerations arising from the conditions of road transport itself which argue for an effective system of road usage charging. If the premium user of road transport does not pay directly and fully for his premium usage, then the community at large does, since it is reflected in road congestion costs which are borne by all road users. Thus, some of the premium costs are reflected in increased costs, due to road congestion, of road goods transport, which are inevitably borne by the consumers of goods. Since the premium users of roads, e.g. car users, tend to belong to the wealthier section of the community, it is this section, and not the poor, which is tending to benefit from the failure to implement a good system of charging for road usage. It has been asserted that a road pricing system would discriminate against the poor. In contrast, Sauvy (**11.17**) has argued quoting much detail in support, that the history of the motor car is one of exploitation and oppression of the poor by the rich, camouflaged by presentation of the privileged as the victims. Further, even within road goods transport, failure to charge for the real cost to the community of road usage is associated with the loss of a spur towards efficient use of roads, and a tendency to supply and demand services which would not be considered worth the true cost. The effect of congestion taxation on economic welfare has been the subject of many publications (e.g. **11.18 - 25**).

However, road pricing, or congestion taxation, is not without its difficulties. Although the Smeed Committee (**11.6**) concluded that road pricing was technically feasible, there have been doubts. Progress appears to be slow (e.g. **11.26**). Part of the problem may be that the criteria accepted by the Smeed Committee, in particular the requirement that the congestion taxes should be able to be assessed accurately in advance, are too demanding. After all, under congested conditions it is difficult to estimate journey durations, and therefore costs, in advance.

The main conceptual advantages of congestion taxation is that traffic restraint and road construction decisions and financing are linked in a cure for road congestion and its associated price distortions.

Congestion taxation appears to offer, and to be the only potential measure that offers the possibility of operational efficiency and quick, reliable journeys to road transport, although at a price.

The discussion of congestion may be summarized by a crude analogy. It is as possible to adapt to congestion as to life with heart and lung problems; congestion taxation offers the prospect of a cure similar to that offered by a permanent regime of dieting and exercise. However, it may be difficult to make the diet palatable and the exercise stimulating; consequently attention to these aspects is as vital as the cure itself, and this is taken up again in the next chapter.

Chapter 12

Transport price and operational co-ordination

It has been argued that inland transport problems should be seen and treated as aspects of one integral problem. This argument is not just a recognition of the competition between independent transport modes, rather it is a recognition that it is virtually impossible to dispense with any of the competing modes. Many parts of the road network are over-utilized, most of the railway network is under-utilized; the prevailing tendency is for the utilization of the roads to increase, and of the railways to decrease. Common sense would suggest that, in the absence of the prospect of sufficient new road construction to relieve all current road congestion, let alone absorb railway traffic, the trend toward increasing road utilization must be halted, and even reversed, sometime.

In the earlier discussion of the relative costs of road and rail transport it was concluded that the evidence suggests that the capital and operating costs of rail transport are lower than those of road, providing the utilization of rail capacity is adequate, and that this reflects a lower use of resources. Thus, for services which could be provided equally well by road or rail, it is rail which offers the economic cost advantage.

But rail transport has high fixed costs, e.g. for signalling and track maintenance, and low variable costs for operating additional trains. According to Sauvy (**12.1**):—

If all the traffic could be carried by road, without further investment, it might be desirable, not always but often, to abolish the railway line entirely to save its fixed costs.

If the railway is maintained, it should be assured as much traffic as possible in order to profit from its low marginal costs. To abolish, or to exploit intensively, such is the choice. What is economically absurd is to retain without using, to add the high variable costs of road transport to the high fixed costs of rail.

But roads have their uses, too:—
a limited capacity roads can be provided very cheaply, and local roads of

this type are believed to be of fundamental importance for local development; thus, intensive agricultural development is believed to depend upon local roads because they provide access to markets, fertilizers, and other facilities (e.g. 12.2);

b   the construction of new railway facilities is only attractive if traffic is expected to reach a minimum level;

c   road transport offers facilities which rail transport does not, e.g. local, doorstep collection and delivery; it is also far more flexible; in many circumstances the premium value of these services justifies the higher costs

It has already been shown in chapter 8 that the charges for different forms of transport do not correspond to costs, that price distortion exists, and that the pricing mechanism appears to be operating in such a way as to encourage a decrease in the efficiency of resource utilization. As a result of the price distortion which exists in passenger transport (and almost certainly in goods transport) the ratio of the charges paid by travellers for marginal train, bus, or car journeys appears to be between 3:3:4 and 2:1:1 although the marginal costs of additional journeys using existing facilities may be in the approximate ratio of 2:3:4 in the absence of congestion, 1:2:8 in typical conditions of urban congestion, or as much as 1:6:72 in conditions of severe congestion. These estimated ratios could be very wrong without undermining the cases that significant price distortion exists.

To remove price distortion, and bring charges for the use of existing facilities into line with marginal costs, which could be implemented by an appropriate form of congestion taxation, would be expected to reduce, if not reverse, the trend towards road transport, and would therefore be in accord with 'common sense'. It would also be in accord with economic sense as shown most thoroughly and comprehensively by Walters (12.3). (Walters did not go so far towards insisting that the same policy should be applied to both road and rail as the author has suggested here; however, Walters was thinking primarily of the developing countries where the congestion problems are of a different type to those common in the developed countries.) The effect of ensuring that prices reflect relative real costs, which will be described as price co-ordination, would be to restore the transport pricing system to its proper economic function, that of rationing resource utilization.

Furthermore, given administrative flexibility, achievement of the desired effects of price co-ordination would not be dependent upon the charges chosen being absolutely correct, but only on the relative values being approximately correct; since, given time, the system would tend to settle to a stable equilibrium; more traffic on one section of the network would lead to higher charges on that section as it approached capacity utilization, and vice versa. Capacity would be added whenever it was established by the revenue, arising from the volume and unit charge relative to the cost of extension, that it was justified.

The need and case for price co-ordination is illustrated very clearly in the report of a recent study of the transport facilities required for commuter traffic into a notional sector of Paris (12.4). The total costs, including costs assigned to leisure time, were least if the motorway was only just larger than the minimum specified as being essential to carry commercial traffic, and if parking and motorway usage charges were high enough to keep the motorway uncongested and the total parking space required to a very low level.

Foster (12.5) declined to take short-run marginal cost pricing for railways seriously because it would imply a permanent subsidy for the railways, which he regarded as politically impossible. Focussing attention on the financial performance of one transport mode in isolation amounts to a denial of the integral nature of the inland transport problem; it also highlights the problem of railway deficits.

British Government policy for the financial objectives and pricing principles of the nationalized industries (12.6) may be summarized as being that prices should be set to cover long-run marginal costs, and also full accounting costs to the extent of earning a specified profit. There is no necessary correspondence between these two objectives, as shown by the arbitrary capital reconstructions of several nationalized industries to enable full accounting costs to be covered. The practice of capital reconstruction is not confined to nationalized industries, nor is it improper or incorrect as such; it does, however, suggest that the covering of accounting costs is a very arbitrary test of efficiency.

As applied specifically to British Railways these objectives were set after extensive re-organization, e.g. transfer of certain freight traffics to the National Freight Corporation and application of special subsidies to lines which were considered socially necessary but unable to 'pay their way', and juggling with the accounts, e.g. in writing off substantial capital debts. It was suggested that, after these revisions, 'breaking even' would be 'a fair measure of the success or failure of the industry's management' (12.7). Unfortunately, it will also be a test as to whether those responsible for the re-organization were generous or not. Whatever the financial results returned, interpretation will remain a matter of opinion.

Two of the main features of the earlier Beeching proposals (12.8) were the closing of under-utilized lines, as part of a major cost cutting exercise, and the development of some promising types of traffic, notably the freight-liner services. The emphasis upon cost-reduction on the one hand, and revenue development on the other, may be regarded as a classic ploy to eliminate a deficit. However, the closure of many lines has been rejected as socially undesirable, and the development of freightliner traffic proved to be a slower task than anticipated, with labour trouble being a serious factor; wage increases have swallowed most of the other operating economies. The problem of the deficit continued, at least until the accounts were adjusted.

In 1968, rather than sanction a general fare increase, the Prices and Incomes Board (12.9) recommended a more commercial pricing policy with a view to charging fares which the traffic would bear. The first tentative steps in the direction of varying fares from the standard rate have included small fare increases on some of the most heavily used routes

Such is the preoccupation with deficits as a, or as the, problem of British Railways that the sale or development of surplus land has been seen as an important way of reducing the deficit. The efficient utilization of any land is clearly desirable from the national point of view, but it is hard to see how proceeds from property help to resolve railway or transport problems. To this observer it appears that the long overdue conversion of the railway management from its technical orientation has gone too far, and that it is now imbued with a vision of British Railways as a financial corporation rather than as an indispensable component of the national transport services.

There have been objections to railway deficits on the grounds that the danger of government or political interference is increased, that they reflect inadequate labour control, which would be cured by financial rectitude, that they reflect inefficiency and commercial failure, and therefore that they strike at morale and managerial self-respect. Unfortunately, outside 'Management Fiction' such simple concepts must be treated with reserve. Many examples can be quoted of firms making profits which are inefficient and have little labour control and bad morale, while some firms with deficits appear to be efficient. Furthermore political interference is not confined to nationalized organizations with deficits, and this applies in other countries as well as in Britain.

In essence, it has not been shown that it is possible for British Railways to make a consistent profit. Already under-utilized, every decrease in utilization reduces revenues with little reduction in cost. Any reduction in services or increase in charges increases the already potent relative attractions of private transport. Independently, increasing affluence is reflected in increasing car ownership, with its tied transport customers. But it is necessary, because of the lack of alternative transport capacity, for a comprehensive railway system to be maintained. Perhaps most of the difficulties of British Railways can be traced to its many objectives, probably incompatible and unachievable in the long term, especially those left implicit.

Although improvement in the quality of railway service is desirable, and in many respects has been forced upon railways by the competition of road transport, it is unlikely that any bulk batch transport system can consistently offer a full range of services that are of better quality than those of private transport. Consequently, the main competitive weapon of the primary forms of public transport must be that of price; but this is hampered by price distortion. As Foster and Beesley reported (12.10), the Victoria Line is not expected to be financially or commercially profitable; but if the prices of public and private urban road transport were raised until each covered its real costs, there could hardly be any doubt that the Victoria Line would be profitable. (That the Victoria Line is not operated by British Railways is beside the point; many commuter and suburban lines which are said to be loss-making are. But the point being made is not necessarily confined to commuter or suburban services.)

One common objection to basing transport prices (or those of any restricted group of activities) on marginal costs is that this might cause distortions in resource utilization between transport and all those other activities, the majority, whose prices are not based upon marginal costs, due to over-expansion of transport activities. In these circumstances, described by economists as those of the 'second best', the ideal pricing policies become very, even impracticably, complex (e.g. 12.11). One reason for rejecting this objection which has been offered (e.g. 12.12) is that total transport demand is nearly fixed, and therefore that there will be little distortion due to diversion of resources from other activities due to the over-expansion of transport. This reason may be of some validity as far as goods transport is concerned, but the growth of passenger transport, especially air and road transport for holidays and recreation (e.g. 12.13) suggests that there are very strong possibilities of substitution between other forms of consumption and passenger travel and that there is a possibility of over-expansion of passenger travel.

According to one survey carried out in 1961 and 1962 (12.14), some 30% of household cars in Britain, which perform 45% of car mileage, receive some degree of subsidy either from an employer or from a remission of taxes for business expenses to the self-employed. Furthermore as mentioned already, there are many non-price reasons for possessing cars and the incidence of payments is such that, once owned, car usage is paid for on a marginal private cost basis. As road traffic becomes congested the private marginal costs borne by motorists are far less than public marginal costs. Users of congested roads are not paying for the resources required to remove the congestion they cause. There is already danger of diverting too many resources to road construction because road users are paying less than the relevant marginal costs.

In contrast, rail and bus users are paying prices which correspond to some rather arbitrary measures of average costs. There is already very substantial distortion of price and usage between public and private transport. Few non-transport activities operate, or would be retained as working assets, at such a low average level of utilization as the railways; consequently, it is likely that the relationship between rail average and marginal costs is such as to distort the pattern of consumption against rail transport.

Thus the second-best objection to marginal pricing in transport would seem to under-estimate the dangers of the existing second-best situation, and the improvement in this that would result from the extension of marginal pricing to all categories of inland transport. There would, it is true, remain some potential for distortion between transport and other sectors, but the economic optimum is well beyond reach, and improvements are desirable even if these are not final and leave difficulties.

However, the condition for transport price co-ordination, or the removal of transport price distortion, is only that relative prices reflect relative marginal costs, not that prices should equal marginal costs. It would be possible to achieve price co-ordination without railway deficits by setting rail charges to cover average costs and adjusting the charges for other modes accordingly. Just as some of the main arguments for avoiding rail deficits are political, so the main argument for marginal cost pricing and the acceptance of rail deficits is also political: the lower transport prices under price co-ordination the more likely it would be that the concomitant restraint of road usage would be acceptable. Restraint of road usage is inevitable; marginal cost pricing merely appears to offer the way of making the best of it.

Sherman (12.15) recognized that part of private resource price distortion which is due to the comparison of average public with marginal private transport costs. He suggested that it could be overcome by allowing public transport passengers to contribute to the fixed costs by means of a club membership fee which entitled members to special fares equal to the marginal costs. Fishman and Wabe (**12.16**) maintained this would not work because few would be prepared to pay two lump sums for fixed transport costs, and that most of those who were only prepared, or could only afford, to pay one, would prefer to purchase membership of the private transport club. In exchange, they suggested the establishment of hire car fleets garaged in neighbourhood transport centres from which both car and bus services would be available at average costs. Such a device might serve to reduce that part of price distortion due to the comparison of average public with marginal private transport costs. However, it would only serve to improve vehicle utilization, and hence reduce congestion and public price distortion, to the extent that the change in the presentation of the relative costs changed usage. There is, in such a proposal, no automatic self-adjusting measure for matching the demand for road usage to the supply of road space.

Price co-ordination would do much to restore price competition between public and private transport, reflecting the real costs incurred, but it would, of itself, do nothing to reduce the gap between the standards of service offered. Unless public transport offers services which are of at least a minimal quality which is widely acceptable, transport price co-ordination would not result in any substantial degree of transfer of traffic from private to public transport, or more concentrated vehicle utilization; rather it would result in an increase in transport charges without much compensation from the improvement of operational efficiency; in these circumstances the main reduction of road congestion would result from reduction of transport demands because of high prices.

It is not difficult to find evidence that some of those responsible for the transport of goods find public transport services, and particularly the rail services, very unsatisfactory (**12.17**), while not all the letters to newspapers complaining about poor railway service to passengers are unreasonable (**12.18**). Complaints about public goods transport services are many and varied, but most concern slow and unreliable service, including high risks of loss, pilferage and damage; to these are often added complaints about managerial indifference to poor service. For many purposes, senders and receivers of goods need to know the times of collection and delivery in advance; further, to prevent loss and to control the timing, particularly at transhipment points, some record of progress while it is taking place would be desirable. It would be reasonable to expect that concentration of consignments, which might follow warehouse concentration or reflect transporters' reactions to either congestion or congestion taxation, would normally be associated with a deterioration of service, particularly in respect of certainty and timing. Improvements in the quality of service offered by public transport, both road and rail, are most likely to be derived from improved operational planning, communications and data processing systems; these improvements may be described as operational co-ordination, a second form of transport co-ordination.

Operational co-ordination is not a new concept; it is, for example, referred to in the introduction to the white paper on Transport Policy (**12.19**) quoted at the beginning of chapter 6 ['. . . . . . different elements (of the nationalized transport concerns) can no longer operate in isolation . . . . . .'] . But the measures proposed in that white paper to achieve operational co-ordination are essentially structural and organizational, with emphasis laid on common ownership or direction. Yet the history of nationalized transport shows that common ownership is not a sufficient condition for operational co-ordination, perhaps becaus the achievement of operational co-ordination depends on solutions to major technical problems being found. Some of the problems of operational co-ordination in road goods transport will be discussed later in this book. Similar problems have been recognized in railways, for example, the difficulties experienced by the Southern Region of British Railways in 1968-9 in trying to implement a new timetable to increase the number of trains in peak periods in their congested and complex commuter network serving London from the South, and the attempts in many countries to utilize computers to produce train timetables and operating schedules, and to trace wagon movements. Experience of the technical problems suggests that solutions to at least some of the problem are possible, but only in an organizational environment in which solutions are seriously desired; structural or organizational change may be necessary to create a favourable environment and the proper context to exploit operational co-ordination to the full.

Proposals for both transport price and operational co-ordination are tantamount to proposals for yet another transport revolution, but this time a voluntary revolution. Does the situation warrant such drastic remedies?

The trend towards private transport is clearly marked historically by th growth in number of private passenger and goods vehicles, by a relative decline in the number of public goods vehicles, by an absolute decline in the number of public passenger vehicles, and by a decline in railway traffic. Symptoms compatible with this trend, reflecting different degrees

of development, are common to all the western developed countries.
Consumer preferences and motivations are such that this trend will
probably continue if existing conditions and policies continue unchanged.

The trend appears to be associated with some misallocation of resources,
in that prices and charges do not reflect resource utilization. This
misallocation of resources might not be too serious if it were not for the
fact that, under existing policies, the trend results in withdrawal of traffic
from public transport, fare increases, and decline of the quantity and
quality of public transport services, all of which aggravate both the trend
and the misallocation of resources. Thus, an element of positive feedback
is introduced which tends to increase the rate of decline of public
transport and to increase the difficulty of reversing the trend if, and
when, desired.

The relative growth of private road transport, and decline of public
transport, is associated with a relative growth in the amount of road traffic
and expenditure compared with other features of the economy. The
growth of road traffic is associated with the spread, and increasing severity,
of road congestion. In congested areas the marginal private costs of road
users are less than the marginal costs imposed on others; there is some
evidence that many road users do not value usage as highly as the
congestion costs they cause.

Current methods of taxing road usage tend to encourage usage in
congested areas, and discourage usage in uncongested areas, relative to the
marginal real costs.

If it were possible to build sufficient new roads to relieve congestion, it
is possible that even this degree of misallocation of resources would be
tolerable. However, in the most congested centres, existing cities, the
cost and dislocation implied by building sufficient roads to adapt fully to
the private transport age is believed to be beyond the realms of practical
tolerance; in these areas the misallocation of resources has manifestly gone
too far. The available evidence is consistent with, but does not conclusively
prove, the hypothesis that it is not possible to relieve congestion in the long
term by building new roads.

In the absence of sufficient new roads to relieve congestion, there has to
be some method of restricting traffic and rationing road space. But most
methods of traffic restriction are of limited potential. In the absence of
road pricing it appears as if the main force limiting the increase in
congestion is, and will remain, the deterrent effect of chronic congestion
itself. But this involves a reversal of normal ideas, for equilibrium is only
reached as a result of those who are least deterred by congestion, which

includes those who place least value on their time, displacing from the roads, where this is feasible, those who are most deterred by congestion, which includes those who place most value on their time.

Those whose road transport demands are 'necessary', which includes many of the functions of road goods transport, must bear the relevant costs of congestion imposed on them; one such cost is that each transport unit can achieve less than would otherwise be achieved in the absence of congestion; consequently transport units are smaller than might otherwise be the case, and the number of vehicles and the amount of road traffic increases. Again this introduces an element of positive feedback into the growth of congestion. It is possible that a large part of the very high rate of increase in expenditure on road goods transport, which has occurred despite a continuous trend of development and increases in the real productivity of some vehicles, may be ascribed to the growth of congestion and may be circumstantial evidence that the misallocation of resources involved is substantial.

In the absence of natural, instead of inverse, economic forces controlling congestion, it has become an economic force of major, and distorting, influence itself. Two examples may serve to illustrate this:

a   as a result of congestion public road passenger transport services have become slower and more unreliable, thus decreasing its attraction for the remaining customers, reinforcing the effects of the trend towards private transport, and introducing yet another element of positive feedback;

b   because of the onset of severe congestion in the established shopping areas there is a well marked trend towards the dispersal of new shopping facilities and the development of out-of-town 'shopping centres' directed at attracting car-borne shoppers for retail forms of cash-and-carry, thus contributing towards extension of the area subject to chronic congestion; congestion has become sufficiently marked in some of the new shopping centres in the United States for there to be reports of attempts to develop bus services to relieve it (12.20).

The distortions introduced into the development of the developed countries may be much deeper; and, again, two examples will be introduced to illustrate this point.

a   In the absence of natural economic forces to control congestion some of the underlying tendencies causing congestion are themselves not subject to this natural restraint. Thus, the drift of industry and population to the centres of established growth continues unconstrained by the high costs of additional congestion imposed on the existing inhabitants, while the existing facilities in the backward areas continue to be under-utilized.

It is hard to believe that some reduction of the effects of disparities in regional growth would not follow from an attempt to translate into financial forces the economic desirability of a more uniform utilization of existing facilities, and the relative resources required to expand in different areas.

b If the analysis presented here is correct, then the extent to which the growth of the British economy, like that of all the 'developed' western economies (including Japan), has been associated with the growth of the automotive industry, is disconcerting evidence of the extent and size of the distortions resulting from the private transport revolution, and of the problems to be faced when it is eventually appreciated that road space is limited.

An attempt has been made to demonstrate that it is possible to visualize a set of government policies which, if implemented, would have a significant chance of reducing, or reversing, the growth of road goods transport expenditure. A number of corollaries flow from the discussion.

1 There does not appear to be room for anything more than minor variations in the set of policies if the objective is to be achieved; it is difficult to envisage any basically different set of policies, especially one along the lines of existing policies, leading to a decrease in road goods transport expenditure.

2 Unless the basic conclusion that it is impossible to build enough roads to satisfy all, or nearly all, traffic demands is wrong, goods transporters have little to gain from road construction, or from lobbying for road construction; nor do their interests coincide with those of the vast majority of private motorists; indeed, the apparently insatiable demands of private motorists appear to be directly contrary to the interest of goods transporters in efficient road usage, which would be better served by concentrated lobbying, e.g. by their collective organizations, for price co-ordination, and by arranging to develop aspects of operational co-ordination.

3 Price co-ordination could only be introduced by government policy, but it would constitute such a reversal of existing policies, require such a change in public opinion, and require so much re-education to achieve it, that it would demand great political skill to achieve acceptance of price co-ordination, and great political courage to even attempt to do so.

4 Some time would be required to influence public opinion to the extent necessary for acceptance of price co-ordination, and it would be prudent, or even essential, to introduce the economic shock that price co-ordination would represent slowly, over a number of years, to give time for adaptation; thus, it is unreasonable to expect such a policy to be fully

operative very quickly.

5 Goods transporters should make plans on the basis of an assumption that price co-ordination is possible, but no more than possible, in the long run, but that the main burden of controlling road goods transport expenditure, in circumstances in which it may be expected to soar if not controlled, will fall upon them.

Part 4

Firms' policies for reducing road goods transport expenditure: economies of scale

Chapter 13

Technical case for the existence of economies of scale

Firms are faced with the prospect of rapid growth of expenditure on road goods transport relative to other costs. While Government policies could be adopted which might help, nevertheless the early introduction of such policies is most unlikely, and introduction at any time is not very probable. Firms must therefore be prepared to face the problems posed by the rapid growth of road goods transport expenditure themselves.

Whether road transport demands are rationed by congestion, on a 'first come, first served' basis, or by pricing, and these seem to be the alternative possibilities with chronic congestion being far more probable, the effect on expenditure will be to increase the cost of road usage, whether through slower speeds or congestion taxation. Thus a major objective for any economy campaign will be to reduce the relative amount of road usage.

Consideration of vehicle operating costs reinforces this conclusion. Providing the capacity of larger vehicles can be utilized, then the unit costs of large vehicles are much less than those of small vehicles; for vehicles of less than 1½ tons capacity, more than 60% of the total, the marginal cost of increased capacity would probably be less than 15% of the cost of the basic capacity; even vehicles of more than seven tons capacity, 10% of the total, have marginal capacity costs of less than 50% of basic (13.1). If it is assumed that small vehicle capacities are not the main restrictions on vehicle usage, since this would represent an obvious but neglected source of cost reduction simply achieved, and if it is assumed that duration, or working time, is the main restriction on vehicle usage, then to utilize larger vehicles effectively it would be necessary to increase either the duration or intensity of utilization. But wages represent approximately 50% of total operating costs. An increase in the working day, or week, would be against current trends, and would be limited by statutory restrictions on drivers' hours. Two or three shift working would make better vehicle utilization possible, but the effect of this would be much reduced by the need to employ additional drivers. Consequently, the main scope for exploiting the lower unit costs of larger vehicles lies in increased intensity of utilization.

Under most circumstances an increase in consignment size would increase the intensity of utilization of the available working time and reduce relative road usage; the driving time would not be affected by the increased size of the consignment, while loading and unloading usually contain a constant parking and administrative element which would not be increased by the increased size. Thus, it should be possible to realize reductions of unit cost associated with the use of larger vehicles if consignment sizes are increased.

Consignments of goods dispatched by manufacturers are very small: 67% of manufacturers' consignments weigh less than 0.25 tons (13.2). Deliveries to shops are also small; the average retail value of wholesale deliveries to shops in London appears to be of the order of £27, while the average number of deliveries exceeds 0.5 per retail employee per day (13.3).

Attempts are made in practice to increase the size of consignments as transported; for example, British Road Services operate a system whereby 'shunting' vehicles collect and deliver consignments, while concentrated consignments are 'tramped' or 'trunked' over the line haul between collection and delivery depots. Nevertheless, the small size of vehicles may be taken as evidence that consignments as transported are small. Even in the public haulage industry, where the proportion of end-to-end journeys is higher and the premium characteristics of road goods transport are relatively less significant, vehicles are relatively small; more than 40% of public haulage vehicles have less than five tons carrying capacity (13.4) Small vehicles also predominate in most European countries (13.5).

Evidence about economies of consignment size was presented by the petrol companies in their evidence to the Monopolies Commission when it was investigating petrol distribution (13.6) and, in particular, the extent to which garages are tied by ownership and contract to sell only one company's brands of petrol. A major plank in the petrol companies' arguments for the existing distribution arrangements was their claim that substantial distribution economies have resulted, and that the benefits of these have been shared by consumers. As a general guide it was claimed that, as a result of these arrangements, the average delivery size had been increased by approximately 2.5 times to an average of between 3 and 3½ tons, and that this increase in delivery size had resulted in a reduction of transport costs of the order of £0.6 per ton (0.5d. per gallon), a reduction of approximately one third of delivery cost.

Brewing companies have also claimed that one of the benefits of tied public houses has been a reduction in distribution costs. It is normal practice for brewing companies to restrict the number of deliveries they will make to individual tied outlets in order to increase the consignment size. But this does present the other side of the picture. To increase delivery size, at least under this type of distribution arrangement, customer service, in the form of delivery frequency, is reduced.

An increase in the effective density of full vehicle load consignments would enable the dead running between consignments to be reduced, thus reducing the relative amount of road usage. Approximately 36% of the mileage performed by all vehicles engaged on end-to-end journeys is run empty (13.7). Over 80% of 'A' licensed vehicles, i.e. vehicles licensed for hire or reward, are general purpose vehicles with platform, sided or box bodies (13.8); yet 27% of the mileage performed by 'A' licensed vehicles on end-to-end journeys is run unloaded (13.7). These figures indicate that road haulage is performed as if the demands for haulage were widely scattered, requiring an extensive proportion of dead running between loaded journeys.

An alternative to empty running between consignments might be short term idling, waiting for further consignments to occur at the present location. In Italy a legal distinction is made between taxi services, carried out by hauliers who wait in public places to be hired, and whose operations are closely circumscribed, and unscheduled services, carried out by hauliers who are not allowed to wait in public places to be hired, but whose operations are, otherwise, far less closely regulated (13.9). Because of the inevitable lack of supervision of drivers and, also, because of the extent to which overtime earnings are accepted as being part of drivers' wages, evidence about the way time is utilized should be treated with considerable reserve. However, taken at a very general level, a very tentative case can be made out for relative under-utilization of working time. Public haulage drivers work, on average, nearly sixty hours per week, or of the order of 3,000 hours per year (13.10). The largest 'A' licensed vehicles are engaged almost entirely on end-to-end journeys, and even the intermediate journeys which they perform are long ones (13.11); nearly 40% of the end-to-end journeys performed by the largest 'A' licensed vehicles (over five tons unladen weight) are more than 100 miles long. The average number of miles performed by each vehicle is just over 34,000 per year (13.12), suggesting an overall average speed of twelve miles per working hour if it is assumed that no vehicle is ever driven on a two or three shift basis. This is about half the average driving speed which would be expected from long journeys, a large proportion of which are carried out over good roads at night; much time is utilized for activities such as loading, unloading, proper rests and meals, administration, and inevitable delays; but it is difficult to believe that as much as 50% of the time can be accounted for by these activities.

Further evidence for the apparent diffusion of consignment demands might be established if significant under-utilization of vehicle capacity could be demonstrated, since this could be attributed to the acceptance of part loads in preference to empty running. In fact, available capacity appears to be almost fully utilized except during the shortest journeys; figures are given in table 13.1 (**13.13**).

Table 13.1 Average tonnage carried on loaded end-to-end journeys by 'A' licensed vehicles

	average load			
	under 25 miles	25 to 49 miles	50 to 99 miles	100 miles and over
unladen weight				
3-5 tons	5.9 tons	7 tons	7.7 tons	7.5 tons
over 5 tons	9.9 tons	11.8 tons	11.2 tons	12.2 tons

The apparent under-utilization of load capacity on the short journeys may be due to the acceptance of part loads in preference to empty running, and therefore may be evidence of the apparent diffusion of consignment demands.

So uniform is the apparent utilization of vehicle capacity on longer journeys shown in this table, given that the vehicles within the unladen weight categories are not homogeneous, that it is tempting to utilize the argument in reverse. It appears as if the consignment size may be determined by the capacity of the vehicles available to perform it; if so, the question arises as to why, given economies of vehicle size, larger vehicles are not more common.

The only evidence of the apparent diffusion of consignment demands associated with end-to-end journeys, is that offered by the substantial proportion of empty running by general purpose vehicles. The only other clear indications are of a qualitative, rather than quantitative, nature, and depend upon reports of drivers waiting and shopping around for further work between journeys.

In wholesale distribution, increased consignment density would appear as increased delivery density; this would imply a reduction of the driving time between each delivery, enabling larger vehicles to be used. There are several qualitative indications that organizations concerned in wholesale delivery regard delivery density as important. Attempts are often made by wholesale distribution organizations to concentrate deliveries into certain areas or sectors into some small part of the time available, e.g. by making rules that deliveries only take place in specified areas on specified days of the week. In practice, such restrictions are often of only limited effect, except in the more remote areas, because of the strength of commercial pressures; although it may be in the more remote areas that an increase in delivery density would have most effect.

Two of the petrol distribution companies in Great Britain have demonstrated their belief in the value of delivery density by merging the distribution fleets, which were specific to their different brands, or groups of brands, into parent company fleets, which carry all the brands retailed by the two organizations separately. Both Esso and Cleveland petrols are conveyed by vehicles of the same fleet. National Benzole, Power, Shell and BP petrols are all delivered by the Shellmex and BP Group Delivery Service.

Nevertheless, the extremely low effective delivery density achieved in practice, even in the most densely populated areas, is illustrated by the observation that the average distance driven between successive wholesale deliveries in London is approximately 2¾ miles (**13.14**).

Road transport undertakings are small. The estimated distribution of public haulage vehicles by size of fleet in Britain in 1963 (**13.15**) is given in table 13.2.

The evidence of a similar survey in France (**13.16**) is repeated in table 13.3. Bayliss (**13.17**) gives details for some other European countries which show that the fleets of public haulage operators in those countries are also small.

In Britain, at least, the small size of fleets is all the more remarkable because the form of regulation has probably favoured larger organizations; either they are more accustomed to presenting the appropriate case to obtain licences, or they should be in a better position to hire competent representatives, or the larger concern might be more able to secure influential clients to testify about their need for an extension of the service offered.

Vehicles operated on own-account are also in small fleets; in Britain the average number of 'C' licence vehicles per operator is 1.9 and, even if attention is restricted to vehicles of over three tons unladen weight (16.5% of 'C' licensed vehicles), 39% are in fleets of 5 vehicles or less, 11% in fleets of between 6 and 10 vehicles and a further 10% are in fleets of between 11 and 20 vehicles (**13.18**).

Table 13.2 Distribution of public haulage vehicles by size of fleet

size of fleet (number of vehicles)	number of vehicles (total)	percentage of all vehicles
1	23,100	11
2	15,700	8
3	11,900	6
4	10,100	5
5	8,300	4
(total 1 to 5)	(69,100)	(34)
6 to 10	28,900	14
11 to 15	18,300	9
16 to 20	12,500	6
21 to 30	15,700	7
31 to 40	9,700	5
41 to 50	5,800	3
51 to 100	10,100	5
101 to 200	6,600	3
over 200 (including nationalized fleets)	28,900	14

As reviewed by Chisholm (**13.19**) and Harrison (**13.20**) there is little or evidence for the realization of economies of scale. Unit costs appear to be unrelated to the size of firm, although they may be very variable. Similar conclusions are being reached in an as yet (1970) unfinished study (**13.21**).

There are relatively few large public road haulage concerns. However, in the UK there is British Road Services, the nationalized haulage concern, which operates over 19,000 vehicles. It is reasonably, but not remarkably, profitable, appears to be relatively efficient, and has been expanding at a moderate pace by normal commercial methods. But it does not appear to be commercially super-efficient, nor does it dominate the market as, by its relative size, it might. Consequently, the evidence it offers is not consistent with a hypothesis of substantial economies of scale.

Table 13.3 Size of public goods transport firms in France

number of vehicles	% of organizations	% vehicles
1	57.1	24.2
2	20.0	16.9
3 or 4	12.3	17.6
5 to 9	7.7	19.5
10 to 19	2.2	11.9
20 to 49	0.6	7.2
50 and over	0.1	2.7

Other large firms are much smaller, but do not seem, as a group, to offer spectacularly high rates of growth or profitability; when they appear to dominate any particular sector of the market, major factors often appear to be contracts with firms which dominate the market in the commodities being carried, or association with other, or additional, services. Harrison (**13.20**) has shown that growth of public haulage companies can be explained in the absence of economies of scale. Observation of the performance of public haulage concerns supports a conclusion that economies of scale are only realized in practice to a very limited extent, if at all.

Use of own-account transport, almost by definition, implies either a denial of the existence of economies of scale or an assertion that the benefits to be anticipated from own-account operation exceed the value of the scale economies sacrificed.

Increases in consignment size or density would reduce relative road usage, and usually make it possible to exploit the lower unit costs of larger vehicles in addition. There is ample scope for increases in consignment size and density. There is little evidence that larger organizations achieve better results than smaller ones in practice.

Chapter 14

Barriers to economies of scale

If it is maintained that economies of scale in road goods transport should be available and achievable, nevertheless, the relative lack of demonstrable evidence, including progress towards increased scale, cannot be disputed; if there are potential economies of scale, then there must either be strong barriers to change, or strong objections to scale, which prevents their realization.

Many drivers are individualists (14.1). They prefer driving because they like the absence of supervision and detailed control of their activities. Many drivers engaged on 'tramping' appear, in addition, to prefer the relative isolation of their activities, isolation from the community in which they live due to their long and irregular absences, isolation, while driving, from working colleagues, and to enjoy, in contrast, the fleeting encounters with those to whom they give lifts and with other drivers in transport cafes and accommodation. Furthermore, drivers appear to enjoy the right of direct access to the boss, which is normal in small road transport firms; a good proportion of drivers appear to prefer the feeling of being individuals in a small firm, even, on occasions, at the expense of longer hours and arbitrary labour relations, to being members of a more regulated organization, with a high degree of security but less scope for individual dealings, such as is represented to most drivers by British Road Services.

The individualism of drivers is reflected in the individualism of many small transport operators. In public haulage operations, many owners of small concerns have themselves been drivers, and continue to drive. They prefer to be self-employed. Many 'C' licensed vehicle operators are also self-employed, for example, as independent retailers, small painters and decorators, or other building and maintenance firms. Ownership of transport may be vital to these activities, but it may also be part of an expression of independence, organizational as well as economic.

Some parts of public road haulage must be regarded as serving markets separate more or less completely by physical factors. Thus, in 1962, there were 1,200 'A' licensed liquid tankers (14.2); not only are these devoted to specialist operations in a bulk liquid haulage market, but also, because of the nature of many liquids and the difficulties of tank cleaning and purification, many of these vehicles may be restricted to parts of the market, e.g., heavy fuel oil, and may only be substituted with difficulty into other parts of the bulk liquid haulage market, e.g., milk. Similar comments apply to other specialized vehicles, such as bulk solid carriers, and insulated or refrigerated vans.

Nevertheless, most public haulage vehicles are not physically specialized or adapted to the carriage of certain materials only; 80% of 'A' licensed vehicles have platform, sided or box bodies (14.2). But many demands for transport include a variety of service demands which, in the particular combination and balance demanded, may be unique. These demands have to be specified, communicated, and priced; a 'market price' may not exist for transport demands which include special service requirements. To seek quotations from many haulage firms for specialized service demands is administratively extremely expensive to both potential customers and suppliers (14.3). For those organizations whose expenditure on transport is a relatively small part of total expenditure there is little incentive to seek beyond their regular suppliers of transport services. For one reason or another the cost of sending consignments by any other mode was not known for approximately 70% of consignments by manufacturers in two recent surveys (14.4); between one-half and two-thirds of the firms surveyed did not know the costs by alternative modes for any of their consignments.

Many small public haulage firms tend to rely very heavily on established customer contacts or contracts, and it might in theory be possible for larger firms to have a larger range of contacts and to achieve economies of marketing scale thereby. But this does not seem to reflect the way in which the industry is organized (14.5). In the vast majority of road transport undertakings, marketing does not exist as an identifiable activity; selling tends to be a spare-time activity of the owner or manager.

Indeed, it has been asserted that a free roads goods transport market hardly exists. A study in the Netherlands (14.6) produced the conclusion that the road haulage market there more nearly resembled a series of local monopolies than an integrated market showing free competition. This conclusion must be seen in the context of the much greater importance and development of public haulage in the Netherlands compared with most other countries. Approximately 32% of goods vehicles in the Netherlands are employed in public haulage; in most other countries the comparable figures are 20% or less, with France, Yugoslavia, Australia and the United States having 10% or less of their goods vehicles engaged in public haulage.

In many countries, including Britain, there are local clearing houses, or haulage markets, which do perform a function in marrying buyers and sellers of road haulage services. But this function is limited, and usually deals only with transport supplies and demands arising in the immediate locality (**14.5**). On the one hand, the very fact that such markets exist demonstrates that, in theory, a road haulage firm need not be large to have access to many customers. On the other hand, the very fragmentary nature of this market system illustrates how much, in practice, haulage firms depend upon their chain of contacts, how little access to a road haulage market can be obtained by those requiring transport services, and how difficult it would be to shop around thoroughly for transport services when needed.

Entry into the road haulage market does not appear to have been entirely free in the past, partly because of the effect of regulations (**14.7**), and partly because of the degree of personal contact involved in marketing equally the failure of large firms to emerge suggests that even if potential economies of scale exist, they are not realized to a substantial extent and that conditions are sufficiently competitive to limit any monopolistic tendencies.

In the face of such market fragmentation, the large or specialized consumer of transport services must be uneasy about the potential cost of ensuring that competitive prices are obtained, or of failure to obtain either competitive prices or the services desired. In contrast, there is the possibility, by providing their own transport services, of obtaining the advantages, real or imagined, of vertical integration; the most notable advantages of vertical integration, in this context, may be security of supply, and economies resulting from adaptation to a specialized set of requirements.

A survey was carried out by the Traders' Road Transport Association (**14.8**), on organizations tending to represent larger own-account transport operators, to establish the reasons given for preferring own-account to public haulage transport. The main reasons given were: speed of delivery and certainty of timing, cost, placing of goods in premises normally served by public transport, avoidance of breakage, damage or pilferage, reduction in packing costs, prompt return of empties, use of special vehicles, provision of special services by driver (sales, collection, etc.) and advertising on the vehicle. The result of this survey emphasizes the importance attached to the availability of services, in comparison with haulage and its cost, in the use of own-account transport. The conclusions of Bayliss and Edwards (**14.9**) on the reasons for modal choice differ in detail, but not in broad outline.

Another reason for the growth of own-account transport, which arises from considerations of cost, rather than service, results from the users' ability to select the traffic to be performed on own-account and pass the remainder on to public transport. The costs of performing a particular service will often be different for a haulier than for a private organization, because of the effects of interaction with other services provided. Thus, some traffic may appear to be relatively less costly by own-account transport than by public haulier, and the occurrence of this phenomenon may be more common the more public hauliers rely on average cost pricing, rather than charging prices which reflect the costs of providing particular services. Only if hauliers were inherently very much more efficient than other transport operators, or charged prices which reflected the cost to users, rather than to themselves, of performing each service, would users be deprived of cost incentives to perform at least some of their own transport work. There is no obvious reason why the typical small haulier should either be very much more efficient than other small transport operators, or should adopt charging practices of the type described. This may explain to some extent why only 35% of manufacturing establishments with own-account vehicles dispatch more than 80% of their tonnage by them (**14.10**).

The general importance of own-account transport is shown by the figures for the proportion of vehicles operated on own-account in different countries given in table 14.1.

Once an own-account fleet has been established it may be difficult to control and check efficiency. Adaptation to highly specialized requirements makes it difficult to compare costs with 'market prices', since relevant prices rarely exist. In practice, many firms operating own-account transport do not differentiate clearly between expenditures on transport for such different functions as raw material collection, movement of intermediate or finished products between or within factories, trunk haulage of finished goods to central distribution warehouses, or local distribution. A further complication is that the ability to perform specialized services may lead to a demand for them which it is difficult, for reasons already given, to cost; where services are provided for customers, it may be difficult to determine whether any real benefits, in commercial terms, are obtained by the provision of special services, and there may also be a reluctance to put the question to a test; consequently, establishment of the relative costs and benefits of the provision of special services by own-account transport is frequently impossible. The problems of measuring efficiency are examined at greater length in chapter 19.

Table 14.1 Proportion of goods vehicles operated on own-account

country	total goods vehicles	percentage operated on own-account
Austria	104,000	85
Czechoslovakia	94,900	78
France	2,360,600	93
Greece	81,200	79
Ireland	46,400	86
Italy	1,057,800	83
Poland	212,700	61
U.K.	1,739,000	86
W. Germany	1,015,000	83
Yugoslavia	109,100	91

Note: For the sake of consistency all the above have been taken from one source, the United Nations' Annual Transport Statistics for Europe 1967, and relate to 1967; nevertheless, difficulties of definition remain, e.g. over what constitutes a goods vehicle and how they should be counted, over the treatment of vehicles which do not appear on the road, especially farm vehicles, and of vehicles run by different public authorities, and over what vehicles are operated on own-account. Consequently these figures are only roughly comparable.

Superficial comparison of a possible road haulage market with the main commodity and service markets illustrates the difficulty of establishing such a market, even if the transport services performed are assumed to be relatively indifferentiated, as the trunk haulage of most consignments amounting to a full vehicle load might be. In 1962 'A' licensed vehicles carried out nearly 24 million loaded end-to-end journeys (14.11); these probably engaged between 50,000 and 65,000 vehicles (14.12), and accounted for expenditure of between £100M. and £200M. or, say, between £4 and £8 per journey. The total number of end-to-end journeys performed by licensed goods vehicles was over 176 million. In addition, there were 161 million intermediate journeys (excluding those assumed to have been performed by 'C' licensed vehicles of under 1 ton unladen weight) carried out by vehicles with goods licences. If the number of journeys is assumed to have remained constant and the expenditure on road goods transport, excluding expenditure on small 'C' licensed vehicles, is of the order of £1,700M., then the cost of the average journey is of the order of £5.

Thus, there are a large number of road haulage consignments and the value of the service supplied to each consignment is very low. There are also a large number of buyers and sellers of road haulage services and, because of the freedom of movement of road haulage vehicles, geographical segmentation would be expected to reduce the efficiency of the market. Consequently, while it is possible to envisage a goods haulage exchange, which would match buyers to sellers to facilitate transport efficiency and a competitive and free market, nevertheless comparison with the number of transactions, transaction sizes and costs of other exchanges would suggest that the administrative cost of such an exchange might be too high, relative to individual consignment costs, if orthodox methods were used; and if many of the services required are specialized this conclusion is reinforced. Not all commodity and service markets impose minimum transaction values, but when they do, the minimum values are usually hundreds or thousands of pounds. Smaller transaction values than these may attract special commission rates, e.g. the minimum commission on ordinary share transactions on the stock exchange was increased from £1 to £2 in 1970, or may be associated with the provision of standardized services where buyers and sellers do not have to be separately matched, e.g., house and car insurance.

There would be an underlying technical problem associated with communications in the establishment of an integrated market, even if there were no other problems. If each journey was associated with separate messages to indicate 'demand', 'vehicle available', 'demand satisfied', and 'vehicle no longer available', and all the messages were handled through a single communication system, then the communication load associated with licensed goods vehicles for end-to-end journeys would average 2 million messages per day. (The number of messages has probably been

under-estimated, while the variety and complexity of the messages has
certainly been over-simplified. The intention is only to give a rough
indication of the order of magnitude of the communications problems.)
The amount of information that would have to be handled concerning
demands for transport services, the availability of transport facilities, and
the problem of matching the two, is extremely large. It will be shown late
that an acceptable level of transaction cost, even for very large systems,
may now be technically feasible. But the order of size of the system
envisaged is one or more orders of magnitude beyond current experience
of the design and implementation of computer and communication
techniques; yet the cost and performance targets are unlikely to be
achieved by any other methods.

Both the fragmentation and communications problems would be
expected to introduce friction into the operation of the market, and in
these circumstances the market would not be expected to reach equilibriu
conditions. In the absence of an efficient market for transport services, it
natural that a large amount of the commerce should be handled on the
basis of established relationships and that, as a result, many public haulag
organizations should be small, depending upon personal contacts for
custom.

In these circumstances it might be anticipated that, at some stage, the
very large British Road Services would develop a natural advantage in that
utilizing information from the extensive branch and depot system, it
should be possible to establish an efficient internal exchange. Much of the
business is already concerned with long, large, and therefore costly,
consignments, and the depots are already connected by a communications
system based on telex. But, as yet, there is no sign that British Road
Services intends to develop in this direction. Transaction messages are not
concentrated, as would be necessary for an internal exchange, and as is
done, for example, in the airline seat booking systems. Indeed, at present
a different approach is dominant in that, as far as practicable, operational
planning and control is applied to traffic which is segregated functionally
and geographically; consignments are categorized by size and dealt with at
each depot according to the categories of traffic.

Decentralization focuses attention on managerial responsibility, which
is usually considered to be desirable. However, the extent of effective
decentralization and local autonomy that can possibly exist in large
transport organizations is often exaggerated. For example, customers
may insist on negotiating package deals whose burdens and benefits may
be distributed very inequitably between different internal spheres

of responsibility; redistribution by administrative or internal negotiation does not really give autonomy, for no manager has the alternative of non-participation. Without a centralized communications and control system it may be impossible to realize all the potential of a large organization; however, such a centralized system could not be installed without changes in managerial functions and responsibilities.

A number of barriers to economies of scale have been identified which hinder both establishment of an integrated transport market and exploitation of the potential efficiency of a large undertaking: personal preferences, natural market fragmentation, vertical integration of transport into the operations of the firm, and technical problems of communication and operational planning. Consequently, the potential existence of economies of scale, even though realization in practice cannot be demonstrated, becomes credible in the light of the examination and explanation of the mechanisms by which they might occur, and why they have not.

Unit costs of larger vehicles are lower than those of smaller vehicles if the increased capacity can be utilized; unit costs of larger consignments, within the limits of economic or feasible vehicle size, are also lower. Increased consignment density, by reducing the road usage and driving time, either empty or part-loaded, between consignments, should be reflected in lower costs. To obtain some part of these potential economies, communication and operational planning mechanisms would be necessary, to enable a large range of market demands to be assembled and allocated to a larger fleet of vehicles; in this way larger marketing and administrative functions might play their part in obtaining economies of scale. Should the administrative function become significant in size and role then the employment of specialized personnel and the exploitation of advanced techniques would become possible and, beyond a certain scale, both necessary and potentially profitable.

Economies of scale have not been realized in the past; their realization in the future may reasonably be expected to depend upon changed conditions. The development of computing and communications systems make it technically feasible to obtain economies of scale in the future where it was impossible previously. It seems likely that traffic and its growth will be restrained in the future, even if only by the effects of severe and chronic congestion, and that, whatever the form of the constraint, it will serve to increase the incentive to seek and exploit any economies of scale that may be available.

In other forms of transport, increases in size or advances in design and

performance of operating units have often been associated with fundamen
changes in the structure and mode of operation of the undertakings invol\
The introduction of Jumbo Jets, for example, is associated with plans for
complete revision of passenger handling facilities at airports and of the
methods of selling seats, although the change is no more than an increase
in aircraft capacity by two or three times. Bigger changes are accompanyi
the introduction of container traffic to the long distance liner trade route
Among these changes are the formation and liquidation of companies and
consortia, a revolution in terminal locations and handling practices, and
the development of marketing functions by ship-owning consortia which
have been regarded as a threat to the continued existence of both forward
and freight insurance agents as separate and independent organizations.
Changes are not necessarily confined to the functions obviously concerne
for example, it has been suggested that it will be cheaper to send
containerized freight from Europe to the West Coat of North America by
rail from the East Coast, rather than by ship via the Panama Canal; if this
forecast proves correct the effects on the Panama Canal, and on some
North American railroads, could be very significant. If these analogies are
relevant, economies of scale in road goods transport may be facilitated by,
or may only be possible if there are, significant organizational changes.

Part 5

Functional organization for economies of scale

Chapter 15

Wholesale distribution

While substantial economies of scale in road goods transport may be available, nevertheless there are some substantial barriers to be overcome, and realization may depend upon changes of functional organization. Furthermore, transport services are normally associated with, and often dependent upon, complex administrative systems; changes in functional organization must affect, and be dependent upon, changes in these. An attempt will therefore be made to examine the possibility of, and incentives for, achieving economies of scale in the wholesale distribution function in more detail, paying special attention to the organizational implications.

Physical distribution from the point of production (or landing) to the point of sale through retail outlets follows a number of distinctive patterns.

Most wholesale deliveries are of comparatively small consignments, the average weight being under 0.5 tons (**15.1**); the value of wholesale deliveries to shops in London was of the order of £27 in 1962 (**15.2**). These averages conceal substantial variations. Two-thirds of consignments by manufacturing industries producing for final demand, e.g. food processing, weigh less than 113 lb. (**15.3**). Most deliveries are performed in multiple-delivery journeys by vehicles which are located at depots which normally have distribution warehouses associated with them. Many distribution depots and warehouses are operated by manufacturers; it is normal for a comparatively narrow range of items to be held in stock and distributed from each manufacturer's distribution depot. Distribution depots are also operated by wholesalers who act as merchants, buying from suppliers (usually manufacturers or importing agents), and selling to retailers; the range of goods carried is normally wide, but is often restricted to the activities of one type of retail outlet, e.g. grocers. Most wholesalers deliver goods ordered from them, but in recent years there has been a growth of cash-and-carry wholesalers, where retailers may select, pay for, and carry away the goods they require. Distribution depots are also operated by retail chain companies supplying goods to shops in the chain. Again the range of items stocked and supplied will be relatively wide, although rarely extending to all the items sold by shops in the chain. Some manufacturing companies distribute their goods through local public warehousing concerns, which provide both a warehousing and a delivery service. Other variations on these themes exis

Between the point of production, or landing, and the distribution warehouse, there may be a trunk haulage phase involving bulk conveyance over substantial distances, except for that part of the goods being distributed in the immediate vicinity of the place of production or landing. Whenever there are sufficient economies of scale in production, in consignments from overseas, the major part of goods distributed pass through a trunk haulage phase before reaching the distribution warehouse Trunk haulage does not always extend as far as delivery to the final distribution warehouse, since many wholesalers turn over insufficient quantities of some of the many items which they stock to justify bulk consignments. Some items, then, may be distributed to some wholesalers by manufacturers, or importers, in multiple-delivery journeys, or they ma bypass this stage of the distribution system by being sent direct to retail wholesale outlets as parcels or other small consignments, via the post or various small consignment distribution services, especially those of British Railways and British Road Services (now operated as a joint service by National Carriers Ltd).

The main function of stocks is to enable supply to be matched to demand when either supply or demand, or both, may be irregular. Some stocks of goods awaiting consumption are associated with irregular rates of production, whether due to such factors as climatic conditions, as for farm produce, or to economic use of production facilities, as in batch production of manufactured goods. Demand for many goods is irregular, and cannot always be matched efficiently to irregular production cycles: the main occasion for the consumption of fireworks in Britain is the annu festival in memory of Guy Fawkes; many goods are produced solely for the Christmas season, while retail sales of many less exotic foods and drinks are multiplied many times in the weeks preceding Christmas; sales of most goods subject to fashion show a single peak, rather than a repeate seasonal one. Stocks are also held in the distribution system to meet less dramatic variations in demand, and to enable goods to be handled and transported over long distances in bulk. These stocks in the distribution chain awaiting consumption are very substantial.

Unfortunately the variety and flexibility of distribution arrangements reflected in difficulties of definition and differentiation when attempts ar made to estimate the size of the activities or of expenditure on them. It is sometimes difficult to correlate definitions used by different sources. Consequently the estimates that follow do not correspond exactly with physical distribution to retail outlets. The data used mostly refer to the wholesale trades (Minimum List Headings 810, 'Wholesale distribution', 831, 'General dealing in builders materials, grain, and agricultural supplies', and 832, 'General dealing in other industrial materials and machinery'). These include, under dealing, some retail activities and also some merchanting activities which include, for example, reclamation of waste materials for industrial use. The estimates have been adjusted in an attempt to eliminate these merchanting activities, but to include the wholesale activities of manufacturers and multiple retailers, which are usually excluded from statistics on wholesaling.

Wholesale distribution stocks are of the order of £1,250M. (of which nearly £800M. are held by 'wholesale distributors'), and stocks held by retail organizations are of the order of £1,400M. (**15.4**). (The figures quoted for stocks are 'book values of stocks held at the end of 1967'). Some part of finished goods stocks held by manufacturers may also properly be allocated to the distribution rather than manufacturing function; food, drink, and tobacco manufactures carry out a large part of their own wholesale distribution (**15.5**), and hold finished goods stocks to the value of £275M. Some part of manufacturers' finished goods stocks, of stocks held by retail organizations, and of the stocks of wholesale distributors are associated with the function of wholesale physical distribution; it is probable, therefore, that the total value of stocks held for this physical distribution function is at least £1,200M. If the cost to companies of capital invested in stock is assumed to be 9% per annum net of tax, or, assuming a 40% tax rate, 15% per annum, before tax (**15.6**), and the other costs of stockholding, e.g. accommodation, deterioration, handling, and administration, are assumed to be of the order of 10% per annum of the value of the stocks (it is common practice in American literature to use a figure of 25% per annum for stockholding costs) then the estimated total annual cost to firms of stocks held for the physical distribution function is of the order of £300M. Moreover, one survey produced results which suggest that distribution depot expenditure, including stockholding, may represent between 2% and 3% of retail turnover (**15.7**). This is consistent with available data on wholesalers' gross margins and costs (**15.9**). On this basis the annual costs to firms of wholesale distribution stockholding would be between £240M. and £360M.

Approximately 170,000 'C' licensed vehicles were engaged in 'wholesale delivery' in 1962 (**15.10**). However, not all wholesale deliveries are carried out by 'C' licensed vehicles. There were 50,000 vehicles with 'A', 'Contract A', or 'B' licences which were engaged solely on intermediate

journeys, and a further 50,000 vehicles were engaged partly on intermediate journeys (**15.11**). According to the results of this survey the
number of vehicles engaged on wholesale deliveries probably lies between
200,000 and 250,000.

In the London Traffic Survey, conducted in the same year, 12% of
vehicles belonged to owners with wholesale industrial classifications. If
the statistics for vehicles, journeys and mileage, corresponding to the
wholesale industrial classifications, are compared with the journeys and
mileage performed for the purpose 'wholesale delivery', then it would
appear that between 15% and 20% of all vehicles, depending mainly upon
the allocation of those idle at any time, were devoted to wholesale
delivery (**15.12**). If the same proportions were to apply nationally, then
between 210,000 and 280,000 vehicles would be devoted to wholesale
delivery.

The average annual cost of vehicles engaged on wholesale delivery is
probably not less than £2,000 (cf. operating and establishment costs for
diesel lorries of 3 tons capacity driving 200 miles per week (**15.13**),
increased by £450 per vehicle per year to allow for average, rather than
basic, wages (**15.14**), assuming that only one man is associated with each
vehicle). But there are some reasons for believing that the average annual
operating cost per vehicle may be in excess of £2,000, e.g. deliveries of
some commodities, particularly drinks, are performed by vehicles with
two or three men, while the estimate is based on the costs of platform
vehicles, whereas most vehicles used are at least slightly more expensive
(box vans) and some are very much more expensive (liquid tankers and
refrigerated vehicles). It will be assumed here, on the basis of the number
of vehicles employed on wholesale deliveries, that the total annual cost to
firms of road transport for wholesale distribution is between £400M. and
£600M. (These figures relate to mid-1967 costs applied to the number of
vehicles in 1962).

Further evidence about the level of expenditure on road transport by
the wholesale trades may be taken from the results of a Board of Trade
Survey in 1965 (**15.9, 15.15**). This enquiry was confined to the wholesale
trades and marketing boards; it therefore excluded the wholesale
distribution activities of manufacturers and multiple retailers. The estimat
expenditure on own-account transport was £230M., and on purchased roa
transport was £105M., a total of £335M. The survey of industrial distribu
practices and costs already cited (**15.7**) suggested that 'outbound transpo
expenditure by manufacturers represented 4% of retail turnover. 'Outbou
transport' expenditure includes far more than that on wholesale distributi
but one-half of this expenditure (i.e. 2% of retail turnover) would represe
approximately £240M. per year. Together, the results of these two survey

also consistent with a total annual expenditure on road transport for wholesale distribution between £400M. and £600M.

Thus, the total annual cost to organizations of road transport and stockholding for wholesale distribution is probably between £650M. and £950M. This may not represent the cost to the community, as opposed to the organizations involved, because of the effects of taxation. The element of taxation easily identified (for 1967, company and transport taxation has increased since) is approximately 10% of transport expenditure, for fuel and licences, and approximately 25% of the cost of stock-keeping, for company taxation, or between £100M. and £150M. in total. However, some of the taxation, at least, may properly be regarded as payments for services rendered, such as provision and maintenance of roads and their associated services, while a further portion may reasonably represent payments for disadvantages, such as congestion costs, noise and air pollution, imposed on others.

Quite apart from the expenditure on stockholding and transport in performing the wholesale distribution function, there are additional expenditures on other closely related systems and functions. Thus, for example, the distribution depot system is intimately bound up with the manufacturing function via stock records and production control, with the accounting function via sales invoicing and accounting, and with the marketing function via order taking and being the source of sales statistics. Manufacturers may spend as much as 3% of retail turnover on the administration of physical distribution (15.7). Is it possible to achieve economies of scale in the physical distribution function without prejudice to the efficiency of the associated systems and functions, and preferably facilitating increased efficiency in these also?

The main functions of distribution warehouses are to ensure constant availability of goods, break bulk, and tranship goods between trunk haulage and local distribution transport. The size of the stock of any item held is determined by the need to match supply and demand, both of which may be irregular, and the extent to which it is necessary or desirable to hold goods as a result of the bulk breaking operation.

In general, the size of the stock of an item held to match supply to demand, when both are subject to independent, random fluctuations, only needs to increase as the square root of the demand; if the demand on a warehouse is quadrupled, the stocks held need only be doubled.

Whatever the detailed form of the incentive for holding stocks on account of the bulk breaking function, it is because supplies are cheaper in bulk than in small consignments, and this reduction in cost must be believed to be larger than the increased costs associated with the increased average stockholding. The average stockholding of an item resulting from breaking bulk from a given consignment size should be the same whatever the throughput; if larger consignments, and therefore large average stocks, are associated with a greater throughput, presumably it is because this is thought to be financially more attractive. The average stock held for breaking bulk should therefore be, in effect, inversely proportional to the throughput.

Costs associated with stock handling should not increase, relative to turnover, unless diseconomies of scale, e.g. because of warehouse congesti appear. Stock deterioration would be expected to be linked to the average time spent in stock, or the ratio of the stockholding to the turnover. Increased turnover in an item may make the introduction of automatic devices for the selection of that item financially attractive. Increased turnover in general may make increased mechanization of goods handling financially attractive, and should also be reflected in a reduction, relative to turnover, of costs associated with warehouse size. Finally, unit administrative costs should not be increased by an increase in the number of transactions; they may be decreased if the increased number of transactions makes more advanced data-processing methods attractive. Thus, at least in theory, there should be economies of scale in stockholdir all the main costs associated with stockholding offer prospects of a decrea relative to increased turnover in the right circumstances, while increases, relative to turnover, should not be expected in any but exceptional circumstances.

A substantial decrease in the total cost would be expected to follow concentration of stockholding for a given turnover into fewer warehouses and, taking the size of stock needed to match supply to demand as a guide the costs of stockholding would be expected to vary approximately as the square root of the number of warehouses. Many companies have reduced, or are reducing, the number of their distribution warehouses (15.8).

Economies of scale in transport have already been discussed; unit operating costs can be reduced by the use of larger vehicles, if they can be utilized effectively as a result, for example, of increases in delivery density or size.

It might be possible to achieve increases in delivery density and size by reducing the frequency of deliveries and ensuring that all neighbouring outlets receive deliveries on the same journey. This is the method used by some manufacturers and distributors, especially when delivering to outlets which they control; but it does imply a reduction in commercial service, whereas at least some distributors believe they are under constant pressure to improve service. A reduction in delivery frequency, if it affects the frequency of delivery of individual items, also implies some transfer of stocks from the wholesale to retail levels, since there is an increase in the bulk to be broken at the retail outlet. If demand is fluctuating randomly, extension of the time between deliveries would also be reflected in an increase in the 'safety' stocks held to ensure that retail stocks were not exhausted more frequently or for a greater proportion of the time.

Delivery density and size could otherwise be increased, without dictating to the retail outlets, and without increase in the size of deliveries of any single item, if a greater range of items were included in each delivery. But the cost of collecting a greater range of items from different depots would largely, if not entirely, offset the economies resulting from increases in delivery density and size and, consequently, it is only attractive to increase the range of items in each delivery if the range of items stocked at individual depots is increased. Increasing the range of items stocked at a depot does not offer significant opportunities for economies of scale in stockholding, except, possibly, in administration and mechanical handling.

Thus, if the distributing organizations are not to dictate to retailers, then economies of scale for distribution transport can only be achieved by increasing the range of items within a single delivery, which implies an increase in the range of items loaded onto the vehicle at the distribution depot. An increase in the range of items held at one distribution depot, however, leads to only very minor economies of scale in stockholding. To achieve the main economies of stockholding scale, it is necessary to increase the throughput of individual items, and this can be achieved by concentration of all the distribution stocks of a single item within a given area at a single depot, and by increasing the area served by a single depot. However, increasing the area served by a single distribution depot will normally lead to an increase in distribution transport costs due to the extra distance driven; the increase in distribution transport cost associated with an increase in distribution area will only rarely be offset to any significant extent by a decrease in trunk haulage costs, partly because the decrease in trunk haulage costs resulting from a relatively small reduction in the distance is very small, and partly because, for geographical reasons, the reduction in the haulage distance will itself usually be small. Thus, while there should be economies of scale associated with both stockholding and distribution transport, it is difficult to obtain these simultaneously (15.8).

It might be possible, however, as a result of changes in the organization of physical distribution, to obtain economies of scale of distribution stockholding and of distribution transport from the same system, but it would be a distribution system that is distinctly different from those in common use at present. The economies of scale associated with turnover of individual items could be achieved if stocks of these items were transferred from the distribution depots and concentrated in one or more central depot. Economies of scale in distribution transport, associated with increasing the size and density of deliveries as a result of carrying more items in individual deliveries, could be achieved if an increased range of items were handled, not necessarily stocked, at individual distribution centres. Thus, the primary function of the distribution centre, as envisaged, would be the transhipment of a much wider range of items between trunk haulage and local distribution transport, rather than holding stocks.

Although the distribution depot commonly performs three functions, ensuring availability of supplies, breaking bulk, and transhipment between trunk haulage and local distribution transport, the main reason for holding stocks at the distribution depot has been that of ensuring availability of supplies, with some additional stocks resulting inevitably from the bulk breaking function. Although most distribution depots are within one or two hours' driving of nearly all the outlets to which they give service, yet in very few distribution organizations is there any real willingness to deliver goods in the time scale made possible by the driving distance. Indeed, only in a few trades has it ever been commercial practice to deliver goods within a day of the order being received. Given the current performance of vehicles, and circumstances in which nearly all local deliveries must take place by road transport, there is no need for stocks of goods to be kept anywhere near as close to customers as they are at present to ensure availability.

One reason for holding stocks in local warehouses is to enable trunk haulage to these warehouses to take place in bulk; stockholding enables a few, large, consignments to replace frequent small ones. However, more frequent, smaller consignments of individual items can be concentrated into bulk shipments of a variety of items, while concentration of all consignments of an individual item to a given population into one shipment would also enable stocks, required to enable trunk haulage to be performed in bulk, to be reduced.

Some goods are frequently required in very small quantities at very short notice, e.g. pharmaceutical chemicals, and it may be difficult to avoid maintaining local stocks of these. For most goods, however, needs for local availability and trunk haulage in bulk could be satisfied without local stockholding.

There are, however, at least two other factors which are sometimes quoted as justifying the maintenance of local wholesale stocks: the first is that, if stocks are maintained locally then it is felt that supply is more secure, and it is true that, in exceptional circumstances, emergency methods of supply will be easier if stocks are held locally, even to the extent of the customer fetching his own supplies; the second reason given for holding stocks locally is that visual inspection is still regarded as playing an important part in the wholesale buying of many items and commodities.

In general, continuity of supply is only improved by large local wholesale stocks in labour disputes. When other, e.g. weather, conditions are such as to render supplies intermittent, stocks are needed at the point of consumption; if wholesale distribution is likely to be intermittent, then so are deliveries or collections from retail establishments. Nevertheless, total retail stocks represent an average of over six weeks' supply, and even if as much as half of this is concentrated in retailers' own depot, as opposed to shop, stocks, the average cover in the shops would be of the order of three weeks' supply. Further, it is only in a few very isolated parts of Western Europe that significant transport disruption extends beyond two days, except in calamities; and local wholesale stocks do not provide much protection from, or consolation for, calamities.

One of the functions of the establishment of branded goods is to establish uniformity of products and remove the need for inspection. This trend is not confined to manufactured items, but has extended to natural commodities which have traditionally passed through markets where both quality and price, as well as supply and demand, have interacted. Retailers, producers' co-operatives, importers and wholesalers are all acting to introduce standards, categories and packs into the natural products, and these efforts are more effective the less perishable the product, and the more production is independent of, or can be isolated from, short term environmental influences. In Britain supplies of apples and eggs are largely sized and graded. More perishable items are gradually moving in the same direction. In the United States, 75% of meat produced passed through local markets in 1948; by 1968 the proportion was reduced to 35% (**15.16**). In Britain, only 20% of the national meat supply is handled by the 30 wholesale markets in the larger cities (**15.17**). Throughout the 'developed' western countries there has been a massive increase in the sales of branded, packaged, frozen foods, providing supplies of perishable fish, meat, fruit and vegetables, some of which are only produced seasonally, at standard qualities and prices throughout the year. Since the early establishment of retail chains, one of their main practices has been to reach back into the chain of supply to establish uniformity of quality, regular availability, and stable prices, and thus to bypass wholesale distribution markets (15.18). Thus, the trend away from holding wholesale stocks locally, in order to facilitate inspection before purchase, started in the last century and has continued strongly ever since; now only in a very small proportion of consumer goods, primarily some fashion goods, meat, and greengroceries, is inspection of actual goods, as opposed to samples, a serious factor in selling to retail outlets.

The potential degree of concentration of distribution stocks depends upon the interaction of two factors: the period commercially accepted between the placing of orders and delivery of the goods, and the economic response time of the delivery system. Commercially acceptable response times are rarely less than twenty-four hours, or delivery on the day after receipt of order; for a substantial proportion of wholesale deliveries the response time currently accepted is much longer than this. The main effect of the distance of distribution stocks from the distribution area on the response time is on the time taken to transfer order information and goods in opposite directions.

In recent years there have been significant developments in the facilities for rapid transfer of information and goods. High speed data transmission over telephone and telex systems has not only become practical technically but has also been brought to a cost performance ratio which makes it viable financially in appropriate circumstances. The development of high speed, containerized, terminal-to-terminal, freight trains (freight-liners), offers, where they exist, very fast, relatively cheap, long-distance freight haulage by rail while, less dramatically, improved roads and larger and faster vehicles have resulted in a significant reduction in the duration of trunk haulage by road. Bulk conveyance of goods over distances between two and three hundred miles overnight is not now remarkable while, over selected routes, significantly higher distances may be achieved regularly. Consequently most stocks may be concentrated within areas of 200 to 300 miles radius without serious reduction in the local physical availability of goods within the customary delivery cycle.

Concentration of the stocks of individual items should make it possible to take advantage of economies of scale in stockholding. There is no inherent reason why concentration should increase the time taken for tasks associated with the picking and selection of ordered items; on the contrary, it is likely that concentration would encourage mechanization of the picking of orders. For other handling procedures, increased turnover would justify an increase in the degree and level of mechanization. The items included in a particular order for wholesale delivery which are stocked at one central warehouse could be selected and assembled as quickly as, and probably more cheaply than, at a series of local warehouses.

The other customary functions of local distribution warehouses are those of breaking bulk of consignments of individual items, and transhipment between modes of transport. However, if goods were being dispatched from a central warehouse to a distribution centre against particular orders for wholesale delivery, then, either individual items might not need to be assembled in bulk at the factory or central warehouse, or bulk might be broken at the central warehouse.

This mode of operation would impose two other handling functions on the local distribution centre; it would be necessary to break the bulk of large consignments from central warehouses, which would contain many assembled part orders, and to sort, physically, the part orders contained in the many consignments so that part orders would be assembled into orders, and orders into loads. In future an increasing proportion of consignments is likely to be conveyed in containers or trailers. One of the great advantages to be obtained from the development of local distribution centres, involving the concentration of a wide range of items and a very heavy turnover, would be the extent to which it would be possible to justify installing equipment for handling and unpacking containers and trailers, and for sorting, assembling and loading small consignments.

Exploitation of delivery density and size would be possible if most local deliveries of a very wide range of goods were dispatched from common distribution centres; but, in addition to highly developed mechanical handling techniques, very powerful and efficient administrative and organizational procedures would be required to plan and control operations and keep records. These procedures would depend upon fast communication systems, e.g. for advanced notice of deliveries before trunk consignments reach distribution centres so that efficient plans can be prepared for delivery journeys and, hence, for the manipulation and sorting of consignments when they arrive. It is difficult to envisage adequate organizational, communications, and record-keeping procedures being possible unless based upon computer systems, which would also be expected to show economies of scale. The unit costs of the main aspects of local distribution centres would therefore be expected to decrease with increase in size.

In 1962 it was estimated that 156 million tons of goods were carried b
170,000 'C' licensed vehicles engaged in wholesale delivery (**15.10, 15.19**)
This represented approximately three tons per head of the population. Th
total weight transported by road for wholesale distribution is higher beca
of the contribution of public haulage. Following the argument advanced
earlier about the number of vehicles involved, the total weight transported
by road for the purpose of wholesale distribution may be of the order of
four tons per person per year, or 220 million tons.

The average population density of the U.K. is approximately 600 pers
per square mile. A third of the population lives in seven conurbations at
average densities of around 9,000 persons per square mile. The various
regions of England and Wales have average population densities which
range between approximately 330 (East Anglia) and 2,200 (North West)
persons per square mile.

If uniform population densities, a working year of 250 days, and an
average distribution centre throughput of 3,000 tons per working day,
average load per journey of 6 tons, and an average rate of wholesale
distribution of 0.5 ton per person per year, are assumed, then the transpo
performance which might be achievable for different population densities
is outlined in table 15.1.

Table 15.1 Notional performance of vehicles working from local
distribution centres

population density persons/ sq. mile	depot distribution area (sq. miles)	radius (miles)	average return journey (miles)	journey delivery area (sq. miles)	total average journey length[a] (miles)	assumed average speed (m.p.h.)	j
300	5,000	39	52	10	65	25	
1,000	1,500	22	29	3	36	20	
9,000	167	7	10	0.33	12	12	

[a]The premiss is given in note **15.20**

(The assumption of 3,000 tons throughput for a distribution centre is
entirely arbitrary. It has been put at a comparatively high figure to
emphasize the belief that substantial bulk will be needed to justify the
utilization of highly mechanized handling and sorting equipment. The

average load has been chosen to be 6 tons because, at this level, the rate of decrease of cost per capacity ton-mile, as capacity increases, is not so very great and because many outlets might not be able to accommodate very much larger vehicles. Finally the rate of wholesale distribution of 0.5 ton per person has been assumed to exclude the awkward and heavy commodities, e.g. fuels, to eliminate any suspicion of double counting of the same material being carried twice, and yet avoid any suggestion that local distribution centres should have local distribution monopolies.)

If unloading times and access were feasible for larger vehicles, then an increase in average size of load would do little to increase the length of the journey or its associated driving time; according to the assumptions utilized here, to double the average load would result in an increase in the journey length and driving time of approximately 10%. Under conditions such as those assumed, the incentive, from the point of view of transport costs, to increase unloading speeds, would be very great.

In the area covered by the London Traffic Survey the average population density was approximately 9,400 persons per square mile (**15.21**). The average distance driven by vehicles engaged in wholesale delivery was over 30 miles per day, including 2¾ miles between successive deliveries (**15.21**). Nearly 40% of the vehicles weighed less than 1.5 tons unladen (**15.22**), and most of these were probably under one ton carrying capacity (**15.23**); on the basis of the size distribution of heavier vehicles in the UK a further 30% were probably of less than five tons carrying capacity. If the annual wholesale distribution load in London was four tons per head, the average suggested nationally, and the proportion of vehicles engaged was between 15% and 20% of the total, then the average load carried per vehicle per year was between 950 and 1,250 tons. The average delivery was between 0.3 and 0.5 tons (assuming between 3.5 and 5 tons delivered per vehicle per day in eleven deliveries), and presumably heavily biased by the large size of fuel deliveries.

Nationally, 'C' licensed vehicles engaged in wholesale distribution, except those engaged in distributing petroleum products, delivered an average of approximately 800 tons per vehicle per year in 1962 (**15.10, 15.19**), while those engaged in wholesale delivery of petroleum products delivered 3,000 tons per annum each (**15.24**). The average wholesale distribution vehicle travelled 63 miles to deliver 3.2 tons per day (assuming 250 operating days per year).

An examination of the figures presented in table 15.1, which are based on an assumption of a degree of concentration of deliveries and delivery density, suggest that there should be no difficulty about a vehicle distributing one 6 ton load each day, and sometimes two, and hence that the average performance could be doubled, even in the less densely popul. regions, under these conditions. In the conurbations, critical factors affec the possibility of greater performance improvement would be the develop of suitable unloading conditions and techniques, the daily number of jour each vehicle could perform and the effective limits on the size of vehicles utilized.

Preliminary (unpublished) estimates, using journey planning models, su that doubling average delivery size and density and average vehicle size wc more than halve wholesale transport costs.

The petrol companies have suggested (**15.25**) that doubling the average delivery size to over three tons reduced delivery costs by approximately £0.6 per ton. If a reduction in delivery cost of £0.6 per ton could be obtained for the 157 million tons goods delivered wholesale by 'C' licensed vehicles annually it would result in a total cost reduction of £94M.; if the reduction were to apply to all the 220 million tons estimate to be delivered wholesale annually, the reduction in cost would be £132M The petrol companies' claimed reduction in cost followed from an increas in delivery size, starting from a delivery size that was already substantial, and excluded any reduction in costs which could be achieved from an increase in delivery density.

The total wholesale distribution road transport costs have been estimat as being between £400M. and £600M. annually. Reduction of these by as much as 50% as a result of increases in delivery density and size would appear to be feasible.

On the basis of the assumptions made earlier about the overall relationship between the size and cost of wholesale stocks, to decrease the value and cost of stocks by 50%, or between £120M. and £180M. per year, it would be necessary to achieve an effective reduction of the numbe of warehouses to a quarter of the present number. If wholesale stocks wer concentrated into 'central' warehouses each carrying supplies for distribution areas of at least 200 miles radius then the number of ware-houses would be reduced well below a quarter of the present number. It appears possible that wholesale stocks, and stockholding expenses, could be reduced by 50%.

A re-organization of wholesale distribution along the lines suggested appears to offer very large reductions in annual stockholding and road transport costs; the potential benefits to firms appear to be between £325M. and £475M., equivalent to as much as 10% of gross company trading profits in the U.K.

Some part of this sum, probably of the order of £50M. to £75M., represents taxation. A portion of this corresponds to services rendered specifically for road building and maintenance. A further portion might represent the reduction of congestion costs inflicted on others; if proportional to the reduction of total vehicle miles this might be worth £10M. to £20M. (However, 'marginal' vehicle miles cause far more than their average share of total congestion costs.) Thus, although taxes saved by firms do not, in general, represent resource savings, nevertheless, in this case it could be held that a significant part of this tax saving would represent real resource savings rather than transfer charges. The resource saving to the economy might be between £300M. and £425M., or of the order of 3% of gross retail trade, or 1½% of consumers' expenditure.

A functional reorganization of wholesale distribution appears to offer the opportunity to reduce costs very substantially. Furthermore, the effect of the reduction in vehicle-mileage on costs would become even more significant than that based on 1967 statistics if the actual cost of road usage were to increase as forecast. This system has been described in some detail in order to show that changes in functional organization might be necessary to reconcile the conflicting demands of economies of stockholding and distribution transport scale and to show that the potential economies may be very substantial.

Chapter 16

Existing wholesale distribution trend

It has been argued that the proposed functional reorganization of wholesale distribution would be necessary to reconcile the conflicting demands of economies of stockholding and wholesaling distribution transport scale. By way of contrast it is proposed to examine some of the established trends in wholesale distribution in order to discover how far these trends are likely to enable the economies of scale described to be obtained, and how, and why, they may fall short.

Many manufacturing companies distribute their own products. Delivery size and density are limited by the manufacturer's turnover and the service given to customers. Manufacturers with a large turnover of goods on which the margin is slight, or with control of outlets, may be able to impose, for example, weekly delivery cycles with delivery density as high as the number of customers allows; other manufacturers may be compelled by competitive pressures to deliver to any recognized outlet on demand.

Beer distribution to tied public houses is an example of wholesale distribution in which, by control of the outlet, delivery size is usually increased by restricting the number of deliveries, and delivery density is often increased by imposing delivery cycles which ensure that delivery density is as high as it can be with the given pattern of tied outlets. Unloading and handling problems are often significant in deliveries to tied outlets, only partly because of the relatively high delivery density and size, aggravated by the awkward stocking arrangements at many public houses. However, the potential density is dependent upon the number of outlets tied to one brewery, and is obtained, in some areas, at the expense of local monopolies and a significant reduction in the drinker's choice (e.g. 16.1). The position is totally different as far as deliveries to free, or untied, outlets are concerned, when, because of the competitive situation with marginal sales at stake, deliveries are usually small and scattered; the proportion of driving time in the delivery journeys is much higher, and the physical problems of unloading are relatively less significant.

However, most manufacturers are not well placed to obtain transport economies resulting from delivery size and density, except by increasing their range of products, or their market domination in each, e.g. by take-over. The few companies which are already achieving a significant degree of delivery size and concentration have a smaller financial incentive to share facilities with others than the many companies with products which are consumed in smaller quantities. It is the companies with relatively low turnover which should stand to benefit most from sharing facilities, whether in terms of reduction of distribution cost, or in terms of provision of much better service for the same cost. The consumer would presumably stand to gain from the greater choice made possible by increased availability of these products, and from any associated reduction of distribution costs. (This is a naive interpretation of the likely course of events; it would be possible to utilize more sophisticated arguments to justify the anticipation of different outcomes.)

Some companies have introduced, on a regular or experimental basis, transhipment from trunk haulage to delivery transport at 'no stock' depots. With careful packing or arrangement of trunk loads, mechanical handling methods at these transhipment depots need not be complicated, and from this point of view there is little need for the transhipment operation to be on a large scale. This practice appears to be confined at present to one or two commodities consumed in considerable quantities. Although vehicle transhipment and physical sorting problems are simple, because the technique is confined to products shipped from the one factory or central warehouse, nevertheless, this simplicity is only achieved at the expense of an implied limitation of the potential delivery size and density to that associated with this single source.

Many multiple retail chains have established their own distribution systems which handle a substantial proportion of the goods sold. At many of these warehouses comparatively little stock is maintained relative to turnover, the goods mostly being unloaded, sorted and stacked, then selected and dispatched again very rapidly. One recent forecast (16.2) of the way in which multiple retailers' distribution systems will develop, which bears on the discussions in this, and the last chapter, follows:—
A position may be foreseen in which the multiple retailer would have no inventory (outside the retail stores) except that on his own production lines or in transit to a store.
Inventory making, production ordering and delivery scheduling would be instantaneous, while intermodal containers — whose forerunners are already in use — would make obsolete any storage other than a covered meeting point for transhipment from the suppliers' containers to those for delivery of made-up orders to stores.

The reasons given for the establishment of their own distribution systems by multiple retailers fall into three basic categories.

The first reason is that by concentrating the buying function it becomes easier for commercial pressure commensurate with the potential level of purchases to be exerted on the supplier; and this is true even if the only real change is that, as buyers are no longer concerned with the details of ordering and scheduling deliveries for each shop, they become more able to concentrate on negotiation, supervision and bargaining. Manufacturers are showing alarm at the concentration of purchasing power into the hands of a very small number of accounts (e.g. **16.3**).

The second reason for concentrating purchases through a distribution system run by the retail chain is that it becomes possible to attain a much greater degree of control of stocks in the retail shops. Deliveries are made to the retail shops under the company's control, thus enabling the lead time to be determined, usually according to an established delivery cycle. As much of the stockholding may therefore be transferred to the company controlled warehouses, it is possible to obtain some of the economies of scale of stockholding already described.

The third reason often given is that, by concentrating deliveries of purchases from each supplier into distribution warehouses, rather than to individual shops, it becomes possible to take advantage of the discounts offered for bulk deliveries by many suppliers in return for extra transport efficiency made possible by increased consignment size. Since the goods are sold through shops, whether delivered directly by manufacturers, or sent via distribution warehouses, and since the distinctive feature of deliveries to the warehouses, and of deliveries from the warehouses to the shops, is the large delivery size, then, at its face value, this is powerful observational evidence for the economies of increased consignment or delivery size.

However, the discounts offered for bulk deliveries may not be evidence of increased transport efficiency associated with the larger deliveries. Undoubtedly one of the major reasons for the success of retail chains is associated with the greater bargaining power which can be exerted on manufacturers and distributors by larger customers. If the total discount obtainable by large customers depends primarily on their commercial bargaining power, and if suppliers are concerned to obtain as much compensation as possible for the discounts they are forced to concede, then suppliers should attribute as much of the concessions as possible to distribution economies, and offer concessions in the form of quantity discounts. Alternatively, the manufacturing company may offer a discount for large deliveries which is the difference between the estimated cost of the deliveries replaced, based on current observed average cost, and the directly estimated cost of large deliveries; if the marginal costs of extra deliveries are less than average costs, as is probably the case with intermediate journeys, then the average cost of the deliveries remaining after some have been concentrated into large warehouse deliveries may be increased; thus, the reduction in transport cost could be less than is estimated and conceded as a discount. While both these circumstances may occur on occasions, it seems unlikely that there is not, as a general rule, some increase in transport efficiency associated with the increase in delivery size.

While establishment of warehouses and distribution systems by retail chains enables some advantages of delivery size to be obtained by enabling consignments of many different items to be combined into each delivery, and by enabling retail stocks to be reduced, nevertheless, the potential benefits appear to be limited by some of the essential characteristics of the system. Some extra handling may be involved in the delivery, stowage and selection of items at the retail company's warehouse. The density of deliveries which is obtainable by an individual retail company is determined by the density of its shops; if the retail company is relatively specialized in its types of trade, and does not hold a virtual local monopoly in one or more trades, the delivery density will be relatively low.

It is worth noting that many retail companies which have installed their own distribution systems nevertheless allow a large proportion of goods to be delivered directly to their shops. Consequently, the effective concentration of delivery size is confined to a proportion of those items which are handled by the retail chain. Finally, some retail chains, including some renowned for their prowess, have, up to the present, not established their own distribution systems.

Wholesalers and independent retailers have been banding themselves together in voluntary chains to gain advantages parallel to those obtained by the retail chains operating their own distribution system. In 1968, in Britain, (16.4), 31,000 food shops run by independent retailers were connected with voluntary chains, which had 297 depots, and these shops were responsible for 21% of grocery turnover. There were 100,000 unaligned independent food retailers, which were responsible for 20% of grocery turnover. It is the larger independents which are members of voluntary chains.

The main advantages are the same as those obtained by multiple retail companies: increased bargaining power *vis-a-vis* the supplier, enabling better terms to be obtained; some concentration of the size of deliveries both to the retailer and wholesaler, enabling transport costs to be reduced; and, because of the availability of wholesale stocks, some concentration and control of retail stocks. But again, the potential delivery density is limited by the number of adherents to the chain, while, partly because wholesaler tend to think primarily in terms of keeping stocks, the scope for concentrating stocks is limited.

Manufacturers, multiple retail companies and voluntary chains establishing their own distribution systems all suffer one disadvantage in common. Economies of scale in warehousing, whether to reduce stocks by reducing the number of warehouses, to concentrate mechanical handling and transhipment facilities, to mechanize item selection procedures, or to apply more sophisticated machinery and systems to the administrative procedures, are obtained at the expense of an increase in the distribution area and associated transport costs. Individual firms, when distributing the own goods, could reduce this effect by acquiring a degree of local commercial dominance that would almost certainly prove unacceptable.

Public warehouses have traditionally hired out warehouse space. In recent years, however, they have been developing, in addition, delivery services; it is now common practice for public warehouses to offer a comprehensive local distribution service, as well as services confined to any specified part. While this may be regarded as a trend towards the sharing of warehousing and distribution services, nevertheless, it may not lead to construction of the type of local distribution system which has bee described. Warehouse-keepers are oriented towards maintaining stocks; the premises, whether modernized or not, are oriented towards stockholding; furthermore, many of their premises are in fully built-up areas in or near the centres of cities, and are usually too small to justify significant installations of mechanical transhipment and sorting equipment, or of communications facilities. It is probable that the proposed transhipment and communication centres would require both scale and space to the extent that most public warehouse-keepers would be unable to provide unless they were to move to new premises and to increase capital investment in facilities relative to that in buildings.

Showing similar characteristics, there are some other companies which specialize in the provision of local distribution services, having started from a transport, rather than warehousing, background. Only a few of these are active on a national scale. Many of these specialist companies have developed relatively recently. National Carriers Limited, with 9,000 vehicles, have announced the introduction of similar services (16.6). Less committed historically to stockholding and to traditional warehouses and their environment than the public warehouse keepers, these companies may be better placed to exploit economies of transport and distribution handling scale simultaneously. Attempts are also being made to develop very large warehousing estates with the potential to become distribution centres (e.g. **16.7**). Thus, the projected development of large distribution centres with shared transhipment and transport services has some forerunners.

Another wholesale distribution trend which has developed over recent years is that of cash-and-carry. Retailers go to the wholesale warehouse, select their goods, pay cash, and carry their purchases away. There is little possibility of delivery density concentration, and delivery size is restricted to the immediate needs of the one customer which can be satisfied on one journey. Very little of the available vehicle time is used for this purpose, while the vehicles used are, almost invariably, small. Clearly, any trend towards cash-and-carry wholesaling is the antithesis of the development of economies of scale through concentration of the stockholding and transport services. The existence of such a trend is of considerable theoretical, quite apart from practical, importance, and the cash-and-carry movement therefore warrants a detailed examination.

Most customers of cash-and-carry wholesalers are small independent retailers. The time they spend away from their shops, providing their wife, or some other dependent relative, is available to serve, particularly during slack periods, is virtually costless. Furthermore, a vehicle is usually considered necessary to the business, whether for the provision of service, as an expression of independence, or for family convenience (for many small independent shopkeepers the words 'family' and 'business' are virtually synonymous). Consequently, a retailer's assessment of the cost of fetching goods from a cash-and-carry warehouse may be restricted to the variable cost of running the vehicle, calculated in terms of the usage of petrol, lubricants, and tyres.

Most cash-and-carry wholesalers have added cash-and-carry operations to a business which is primarily devoted to other purposes (**16.5**). Where cash-and-carry wholesaling facilities are added to existing wholesaling facilities, the marginal cost of the cash-and-carry facilities may be very slight; stockholding requirements increase but slightly with increased throughput, while the extra work, space, and other facilities required are very cheap so long as the basic facilities provided are not over-extended by the main business. Customers select their own purchases, relieving wholesalers of order selection and assembly; customers also pay cash and carry their purchases away, so that accountancy and transport facilities do not have to be provided. As a result, cash-and-carry wholesale margins, in the grocery and provisions trade, of as little as 3% or 4% are said to be profitable, as against more normal margins of 7% for conventional wholesaling.

It could be suggested, therefore, that cash-and-carry is a proper, but specialized, result of the application of marginal costing principles by both wholesaler and retailer, and that, since this view of retailers' marginal costs is essentially confined to small independent retailers, who belong to a declining breed, any trend towards cash-and-carry is essentially transient. After all, the number of independent grocery shops declined by 24,000 between the 1961 and 1966 censuses of distribution and it is widely believed that the decline will have accelerated since 1966 due to the impact of selective employment tax and the abolition of resale price maintenance.

But the record of cash-and-carry hardly encourages acceptance of the suggestion that it is an essentially transient phenomenon. In seven or eight years up to 1967, the movement grew from nothing to 573 wholesale establishments, with a total turnover of £250M. annually. It has been forecast that the movement will double in size by 1972 (16.5). By March 1970, it was reported that annual turnover was 'around £500M.' (16.8). Some major companies are entering cash-and-carry wholesaling as part of diversification moves, e.g. in 1969 it was reported that Gallaher's intended to invest £10M. over three years in establishing new cash-and-carry wholesale outlets, thus renewing competition with Imperial Tobacco, who had already opened some outlets, in a new sphere (16.9). Furthermore, while most of the customers are small independent retailers situated within a radius of ten miles of the cash-and-carry warehouse, making an average weekly purchase of between £30 and £60, nevertheless, a significant proportion of customers are outside this category, seeking fill-in supplies between regular deliveries (16.5). And, while independent retailers are under economic pressure, and many are closing down, nevertheless, there is probably a limit to the extent to which this will proceed:

It is questionable, however, whether stiffer economic pressures will threaten the small shop which barely ekes out a living for its owner who is not wholly dependent upon it for a livelihood . . . . . . In 1961 there were 178,000 with turnover of £5,000 or less, accounting for only 5% of retail trade. (16.5).

Thus, the evidence available about cash-and-carry wholesalers and their customers hardly encourages any suggestion that they are a completely transient phenomenon.

This review of wholesale trends suggests that there are some developments which are entirely compatible with the organization of the wholesale distribution function outlined in the last chapter. The major established trends, however, in which manufacturers and retailers, some by participation in voluntary chains, are dividing up the wholesale function between themselves, appear to be limited in the extent to which they can exploit the full range of wholesale distribution economies described, except by reducing competition and consumer choice to an extent which would almost certainly be unacceptable. There is also one vigorous trend, cash-and-carry, that appears to contradict the assumptions and conclusions of most of the discussion so far.

Chapter 17

Retail trends and functional organization

In Britain, between the 1961 and 1966 Censuses of Distribution, there was a drop of 8% in the total number of shops, but an increase of 7% in the volume of sales; there was a decline of 19% in the number of grocery shops The expanding portion of retail trade is associated with self-service stores, and supermarkets.

In the United States the 'most rapidly growing segment of entire retail trade' (17.1) is the discount store. Between 1960 and 1967, the number of discount stores more than doubled, the average area per store nearly doubl while the turnover per store nearly tripled to 4.3 million dollars per store i 1967. In contrast, the number of grocery stores declined from 285,000 in 1958, to 226,000 in 1967.

Although discount stores started in, and are still predominently confine to, general goods retailing, nevertheless, they have recently been devoting increasing attention to food retailing. In this context, typical discount stores specializing in food offer goods in case lots, have no special promotions, are open for limited hours, and offer no subsidiary services (17.2). Cash-and-carry wholesaling is being offered to retail shoppers (17.3)

Intriguingly, however, there are other growth points in the retailing of goods in the USA. Thus, the number of convenience or 'bantam' stores has increased from 500 in 1957, to 8,000 in 1968; typically, these are open twenty hours a day, and confine their sales lines to dairy products, bread, beverages, snacks, and a few staples (17.2). The growth of 'bantam' stores is attributed to the reluctance of customers to travel to the large stores for only one or two items, a reason which is very similar to that given for the fill-in purchases from cash-and-carry wholesalers.

Another feature of the retail scene in the United States is the growth of out-of-town 'shopping centres', which have been described as 'islands of stores in a sea of parking space'. In 1955 there were approximately 1,000, mostly serving their local neighbourhoods. By 1968 there were 10,000, and those being added were showing a tendency to grow bigger all the time Some of the shopping centres being planned in 1968 had sales areas of up to 2,000,000 square feet (17.4); in Britain a shop is defined to be a supermarket if it has a sales area in excess of 2,000 square feet.

Although with some hesitancy, the shopping centre concept is being introduced into Britain. The Woolco (subsidiary of Woolworths) store at Oadby, near Leicester, has been reported as drawing customers, travelling by car, from places as far as fifty miles away. Woolco are planning to establish several more such stores each year; in 1969 they were reported to have four under development with average selling space approximately 100,000 square feet (**17.5**). In the same report it was stated that Fine Fare had six sites under negotiation at the start of 1969, and Tesco had 120 sites under development in 1969. The implications were spelt out a little more clearly by the report that three such centres were to be opened by Asdaqueen in 1969; in Castleton with 55,000 square feet of selling space and parking space for 1,200 cars, in Pudsey with 60,000 square feet of selling space and parking for 850 cars, and in Morley with 50,000 square feet of selling space and comparable parking facilities.

The same trend can be observed everywhere in Western Europe. For example, in October 1968 there were 333 'hypermarkets' (sales area greater than 1,000 square metres) in West Germany, with total sales area 1.25 million square metres, annual turnover equivalent to approximately £600M., and parking space for 95,000 cars. Sixty 'hypermarkets' were reported to be under construction or planned, with an average sales area of 6,000 square metres each; it was estimated that 450,000 square metres of hypermarket sales area would be completed during 1969 (**17.6**).

There are two new patterns of retailing which are general for Britain, Europe, and USA (**17.7**).
a   A declining number of establishments is dealing with an increasing trade.
b   The development of in-store boutiques and sub-contracting of various operations within a department or variety type of store. Both these patterns are attributed to the need for an increase of retailing scale to obtain benefits from own brands, expensive packing, handling, and check-out equipment, computers and other mechanical aids to stock control and stock handling, and mass advertising associated with brand consciousness.

Cash-and-carry is not just a fringe development in wholesaling, but is also a major factor underlying the main trends of retail distribution. Retail organizations are enabled, by the development of methods analogous to those of cash-and-carry wholesaling, to exploit economies of scale in retailing. These economies of scale in retailing are, when passed on to customers in the right context, sufficient to attract them from considerable distances. To some extent these developments are blurring the traditional lines of demarcation between wholesale and retail activities. As far as customers are concerned, the choice between local and distant shopping may not be based solely on financial considerations, but it is clearly not divorced from them.

Shopping is already one of the main reasons for journeys. In London, in 1962, 8.2% of person journeys on a typical weekday, excluding foot journey started or finished at shops (**17.8**). This was equivalent to nearly 0.11 per inhabitant per day. In Northampton, in the same year, the average daily number of home-based shopping journeys (i.e. starting or finishing at home) on a typical weekday was 0.28 per person, while in Reading it was 0.46 (**17.9**). As many as 30% of home-based shopping journeys in Northampton were on foot, 55% were by public transport, and only 12% were by car (**17.10**). The small number of shopping journeys using vehicles, reported in the London Traffic Survey, was probably because a significant proportion of shopping journeys were on foot and were not included in the survey.

If shops become larger and more remote, then it is to be expected that walking to and from shops will decrease, and that wheeled transport will be used increasingly for shopping journeys. Furthermore, if shops move out of the town centres, which are usually well served by public transport, to more remote areas, an increasing proportion of shopping journeys will take place by car as opposed to public transport. This may explain why in American transportation surveys the number of shopping journeys made in vehicles is much higher, both relatively and absolutely, than found in Europe (**17.11**). Almost inevitably, some of the purpose-built, out-of-town shopping centres in the United States are reported to be encouraging the development of bus services to reduce the congestion resulting from their own success (**17.4**). The failure to incorporate allowances for the effects of these retailing developments into forecasts of traffic in London may prove to be a significant weakness in these and the traffic plans based on them.

The concentration of retailing into fewer, larger, establishments and centres must result in an increase in the amount of travelling to and from shops. Whereas at one time most retail customers only carried goods from the corner shop to their homes, and one of the criteria of the 'high-class' retail establishments was that they delivered goods to the home (usually free of charge) it is now becoming general practice for the retail customer to carry goods over substantial distances. The amount to be carried is not insubstantial, and may exceed one ton per person per year. Inevitably, more cars are used for shopping, and roads and parking facilities become congested. The position is admirably summed up by the following quotation from a Yorkshire schoolboy's essay (**17.12**):—

When we go to town we always leave our car at the back of the Co-op. They've got a big car park at the back. Then we go round the supermarkets. Now we've gotta buy at the Co-op. They've blocked up the way out on to the street. You have to drive in by the back way and the only quick way out on to the main street is through the Co-op shop. So, if you use the car park you've gotta buy something there. Dad says it's a twist, but now he buys a lot of stuff at the Co-op to use the car park. Dad says it's worth it because the town's so full, there's nowhere else to put a car on a Saturday.

Another commentary is provided by a report in *The Times,* April 27, 1970, that planning permission has been granted for a 'park and shop centre' at Brent Cross on the North Circular Road in London, which it is intended to upgrade to become the northern section of Ringway 2. The new centre will provide 800,000 sq. ft. of shopping space, including two large department stores, four other major stores, and the equivalent of 80 shops. Besides this there will be restaurants, cafes and other entertainment facilities.

'But the *real virtue* of the scheme is that the 30 acre site will provide parking at first for 3,000 cars at ground level, which may be increased later to 4,000 cars or more by the addition of a deck.' If that parking space is utilized then that centre could result in sufficient traffic to saturate a motorway lane for several miles, in which case the construction cost of the centre, £10M. could be exceeded by the associated motorway costs. In addition, local car traffic will inevitably increase, as will the decline of neighbourhood shopping centres.

When the retail customer, or small independent retailer, uses his own vehicle for cash-and-carry shopping, it is normal practice for transport costs, insofar as they are calculated at all, to be calculated on the basis of the marginal operating cost, assessed primarily as the fuel cost. However, assessments of the marginal operating costs of vehicles based upon the cost of fuel consumption do not represent the total marginal costs of operating an extra vehicle in congested areas; the cost is under-estimated at least to the extent either of the congestion costs inflicted on other road users, or of the appropriate contribution to the capital costs of new roads to relieve that congestion. In congested areas, at least, the extension of cash-and-carry is based upon customer choices between costs and services which do not reflect the cost to the community. Application of an appropriate apportionment of the costs inflicted on the community by car and van shoppers would inevitably have some effect on the readiness to use cars or vans for shopping, whether at the wholesale or retail level. This suggests that there is some degree of economic distortion involved in the development of cash-and-carry in areas subject to congestion; equally, cash-and-carry, and its associated developments, has considerable drawing power under existing conditions.

There is little doubt that the trends towards concentration in retailing have been associated with increases in retailing productivity, and that these trends are welcomed by retail customers. But the congestion costs arising from cash-and-carry traffic may well be greater than the benefits arising from the increases in retail productivity.

Congestion generated by the shopping centre or hypermarket is similar to the increase in transport demands generated by warehouse concentration, and already noted. In the case of warehouse concentration it was shown that an increase in traffic demands could be avoided if the organization of distribution were to be changed, and it is appropriate to examine whether the advantages of more concentrated retail facilities need necessarily be associated with the generation of traffic.

While cash-and-carry shopping at both wholesale and retail levels of distribution might survive the spread and increasing severity of chronic congestion, since the implied valuation of time spent on the task appears to be low, other means of controlling congestion might reverse the current trends towards cash-and-carry. In particular, congestion taxation, or price co-ordination, might so change the perceived marginal cost of shopping journeys by car as to reduce sharply the potential catchment areas of shops in areas subject to congestion, and thus nullify attempts to achieve economies of scale in retailing.

If road use charges were to deter the widespread use of private cars for shopping, then it is to be hoped that the service offered by public transport could and would improve; but it might be difficult for public transport to offer a convenient, attractive, or even acceptable, means of carriage of large amounts of retail shopping. Even without increased charges for congested roads, many people will be unable to shop by car, especially the old, the poor, and the handicapped. For these, the gradual disappearance of local shopping facilities is already, and will continue to be, a serious social loss.

It might be possible to facilitate concentration of retail outlets without adding significantly to road congestion, or forgoing the recreational and social aspects of shopping, if a larger proportion of the main bulk of purchases were to be delivered to the home. Yet for many trades, for example, groceries and greengroceries, home deliveries are virtually non-existent.

There are already regular home deliveries. In most areas there are two deliveries of letters, at least one, and sometimes two, deliveries of papers, and a milk delivery daily. In addition, parcels may be delivered by the G.P.O., or by other parcels and 'smalls' delivery services; there are periodical deliveries of laundries and dry-cleaning; while purchases of furniture, domestic appliances, and even bulk purchases of wines and l spirits, may be delivered to the home when required. It is interesting to note that one of the reasons given for home deliveries of newspapers and magazines, which may be carried easily, and of milk and dairy products, which are heavy, is sales promotion.

There should be economies of scale in delivery density and delivery size in home deliveries just as in wholesale deliveries; there may also be organizational difficulties in achieving these. This can be illustrated by a comparison of the methods of distributing dairy products observed recently in London and Rotterdam.

In London, most milk floats carry butter, margarine, eggs, bread and similar basic items as well as the different varieties of milk. But most deliveries are of milk only, to a regular order. Many residents are not at home when the milk delivery takes place, and alterations of regular orders are communicated by notes. Attempts have been made to supply customers with order sheets, presumably with a view to stimulating orders for the other products carried, but these attempts do not appear to have met with much success. Deliveries are made on credit; in general, money is collected weekly. In some areas, because of the absence of all members of many households during the week, most calls for collecting money have to be made on a Saturday. Partly because deliveries are on a credit basis, minor variations to the regular order may be a considerable nuisance to milkmen; they may have to make two visits to the house, the second time to bring any extra goods ordered, while the order variation has to be recorded in the accounts. All such variations increase the difficulty of calculating the amount owing when the time comes for payment. Disagreements about the payments due, and goods received, are common. In the circumstances, it is not surprising that many milkmen show little enthusiasm for obtaining credit sales which break up the regular order pattern. Housewives appear to have reservations about buying items other than milk products from the milkman, because the items carried may be the more expensive and offer little choice, goods may have to be left outside if no-one is home to receive them, and any disagreement over amounts owing may give rise to long term distaste and distrust.

In a contrasting pattern of milk delivery observed in Rotterdam, the goods carried extended to various types of bottled milk blancmanges and puddings, beer, minerals, and fruit drinks in addition to milk, butter, eggs, etc. Good were purchased from the milkman in person each day and paid for on the spot. Someone had to be home when the milkman called, but if they were it was easier to buy a much wider range of goods. The attendance calls too much longer than the doorstep deliveries in London, but were associated with much larger purchases (that is, the average purchases appeared to be much larger and of a much wider variety of items; whether the increased size of the typical purchase was sufficient to offset the extra cost of attendance calls is not known); however, payment was made on the spot, and there was no problem of keeping accounts.

Perhaps because of the relatively low number of customers dealt with, neither milkman uses mechanical aids to help calculate the charges. However, milkmen whose basic job is delivering regular orders often use ready reckoners, which become less useful as the orders vary from day to day. Items are selected from stock by the milkman, or supplier, rather than by the customer. (In general, it is difficult to establish self-service methods in travelling shops because the comparatively small amount of space available demands careful packing, and results in poor display). Thus, both techniques of using milkmen for household sales and deliveries described are contrary to such prevalent retailing trends as those towards self-service and mechanical cash registration. Nevertheless, the widespread existence of home delivery for milk establishes that home delivery can be inexpensive; it is estimated that the average delivery cost of milk in urban areas was of the order of 2d. per pint in 1967 (17.13), representing between 3d. and 4d per delivery.

Mail revenues were approximately £11 per household in 1967-8 (17.14), or approximately 9d. per household per day for the conveyance and delivery of just over two items; the operation includes far more than delivery, but again this figure tends to suggest that, given sufficient delivery density, the costs of home deliveries need not be excessive.

Among the problems associated with home deliveries are:
a   the need either for someone to accept the delivery or for temporary safe storage, if the delivery is attractive;
b   accounting and collecting the money for goods delivered, when no one is at home to receive the goods;
c   selection of the goods required.

One way of reducing the problems would be for the customer to select and pay for goods at the shop of his or her choice, as at present, but to deposit them within a reserved section of the store according to the area of delivery; the goods would then be delivered later. Customers need only leave for delivery those items which are bulky, heavy, and capable of being left for, say, 24 hours before delivery without any risk of deterioration. If individual shops were carrying out the service, different areas could be nominated for deliveries on different days of the week, and goods would be delivered for those who had bought them the previous day. Alternatively, a delivery service could serve many shops, obtaining delivery density at the expense of a sorting procedure which would mainly be directed at merging the deliveries for a given area from different shops. This service could be provided by one of the organizations already providing household deliveries, for example, a parcels, or even the milk, delivery service, at comparatively small unit cost. The cost per delivery of this type of system would almost certainly be less than the true marginal costs associated with the use of private transport in congested areas.

More radical methods of reconciling efficient home delivery services and retailing are conceivable. A not insubstantial part of the cost of running retail shops is the cost of receiving goods, taking them to the stockroom for storage, selecting from the stockroom and transporting them to the sales floor to add to the display stock; to which may be added other stock-holding costs. If, instead of selecting their goods at a store, customers merely identified the items required and paid for them at the store, high turnover items could be made up into orders by automatic selection and handling procedures at a depot at which this business was concentrated, thus reducing much of the handling and stockholding of high turnover goods in the store. Indeed, orders for many of the basic bulky, heavy, high turnover goods, which are of established quality, e.g. either branded or own-label goods, and known or declared, price, could be placed over the phone or by post, providing methods of credit control and cash collection were established. It is doubtful whether the problems offered by credit control and cash collection would be difficult to solve in a society which, it is forecast, is moving towards being 'cashless'; but in any case prepayment systems which avoid these problems are possible.

Automatic selection of high turnover items and home delivery recalls mail order business, which has been growing very rapidly and accounts, in Britain, for some 7% of non-food retail sales, i.e. in the markets in which it competes. The extension of mail order methods to non-perishable, high turnover, goods, would be a natural step if consignments were of sufficient size and density, and operations were on sufficient scale to justify local selection and delivery, rather than centralized selection and despatch of parcels over long distances and through several stages of transport and sorting. Despite the relatively high consignment costs of parcel mail, the other characteristics of mail order distribution make it very competitive with orthodox distribution methods. There appears to be scope for extension of the basic techniques into other areas.

Given sufficient demand, which presumably depends upon the benefits anticipated, there would be little difficulty in designing relatively safe, cheap, boxes in which deliveries could be deposited. Selection of goods could depend upon self-service, or upon automatic methods which might be cheaper than handling goods through shops, as at present. The transport cost of home deliveries would depend upon the delivery density generated, whether through retail deliveries on their own, or in conjunction with other household deliveries; given sufficient density, costs of less than 12d. per delivery should be achievable.

Thus, without necessarily reducing the number of shopping trips, or the exposure of customers to the goods on offer, it is possible to propose the basis of household delivery systems which would enable the main bulk and weight of goods, particularly non-perishable goods, to be delivered to the house at very little cost, leaving only the highly perishable goods, and those wanted for immediate consumption, to be carried by customers. However, the organizational problems to be solved are by no means insignificant.

Recent developments in home selling, such as the sales methods of Tupperware and Avon Cosmetics, have shown there may be room for major changes in retailing methods. To quote one survey,

It is tempting to see the future pattern of consumer purchasing habits revolving around, on the one hand, bulk shopping visits to out-of-town hypermarkets or in-town department stores and supermarkets and, on the other, the ordering of more personal articles and services, together with certain other suitable products from home-calling demonstrators and agents. (**17.15**)

That survey then suggested that home selling might be limited to certain products and certain types of consumers. In contrast, it has been shown in this chapter that bulk shopping by car may have its limitations. It is possible that retailing is on the verge of yet another point of departure as radical in impact as the introduction of self-service.

Although the main trends of retail distribution will lead, in the absence of functional changes, to increased traffic, and increased expenditure on goods transport if this were to be defined to include transport to the point of consumption, nevertheless, it is possible to envisage circumstances in which retail productivity can be reconciled with transport economy. The key, as in other goods transport activities, is that the methods and organization of transport may need to be changed when the activities to which the transport service is being given are changed. It appears possible to reverse this conclusion, at least in more densely populated regions. The activities served by transport may need to be adapted to transport developments. In particular, the transport price distortion associated with road congestion appears to be responsible for the development of large retail stores beyond the size which might be economically viable in the absence of both distortion and home delivery services, unless public transport proves to be flexible enough, both in routes and carrying capacity, to cope with bulk shopping from new centres.

Part 6

An introduction to journey planning

Chapter 18

The significance of journey planning

It is possible to view road goods transport as a craft, or cottage, industry. So far consumers have not been offered an attractive range of good quality, mass-produced, standardized road goods transport services at a price which is low relative to that of the craft product. This is another aspect of the apparent lack of economies of scale, and of the dominance of private, or own-account, vehicle fleets, to which attention has already been drawn.

That mass production methods can be applied in activities analogous to goods transport is shown by the history of letter postal services, however fashionable it may be to criticize them. Letter post offers services at prices which have generated, and satisfy, a very large demand. None of the parcels or 'smalls' services has achieved a penetration of their market, or an influence over the carriage of goods, comparable with that exercized by the letter post over communications between individuals; although manufacturers send 65% of their consignments less than 22 lbs. in weight by the G.P.O.'s parcel services (18.1).

Letters and parcels are handled, as far as possible, in batches. Individual items are treated in standardized ways, e.g. at each stage of sorting only a part of the address is examined. But this type of treatment is less satisfactory, or even impossible, for larger goods consignments. These larger consignments may require specialized equipment or careful handling; for example, compare the shunting of railway wagons with parcel sorting, and the use of special cranes to tranship containers with the manhandling of mailbags. Further, the larger the consignment the less possible it is to ignore the problems of batch sizes; a single consignment may comprise one or more complete loads, and such consignments cannot be incorporated in batches but must be given individual attention.

Individual attention may also be necessary to achieve satisfactory standards of service. Batches of letters are treated as individual consignments which are timetabled and scheduled separately in advance in order to maintain the prescribed standards of service. Wholesale and retail systems are based upon assumed transfer times; these need to be both short and reliable for stocks to be kept down while customer service is maintained at a high standard. Individual consignments may b so valuable in themselves that security and speed may be desirable, e.g. whisky, cigarettes or a machine tool; alternatively the consignments ma although of little intrinsic value, have high imputed value because other activities are dependent upon them, e.g. batches of orders or receipted delivery notes, or replacement parts for failed machine components. Service requirements may go beyond speed and security; thus, most deliveries to shops are required to take place when that shop is open, b alsc when trade is relatively slack, e.g. not on Fridays or Saturdays. Speed, security, and attention to requirements peculiar to the consignment, consignor or consignee, all require that consignments be given individual attention.

The quality of public goods transport services is under constant criticism (e.g. **18.2**). On the basis of at least some of these criticisms British Railways might be thought to offer the worst service, with British Road Services next; the non-nationalized public hauliers are usually considered to be better, but still inferior to private transport (some objective evidence for this ranking exists, e.g. **18.3**). This type of observation has been used as an argument against nationalization. It should be noted, however, that this ranking of service quality is the same as the ranking of the organizations by size.

Communicating information about a large number of consignments has already been described as a complex technical and financial problem in chapter 14; the problem is made more difficult if each consignment may require specialized services and these requirements have to be communicated. But if they are not communicated, and the special services have to be noticed while the consignment is in transit, it would normally be expected that the larger the flow of consignments the greater the difficulty of avoiding lapses in service. Similarly the difficulty of preparing operational plans for dealing with a larger flow of consignments each of which has to be recognized separately, is likely to increase unless, as is often the practice, the task is segmented; but segmentation increases the problems of communication and the possibility of inefficiency. To some extent it becomes relatively more costly to give individual attention to consignments in larger flows, and the risk of failure increases.

Journey planning is the operational task of allocating jobs to the crew of each vehicle. If the service requirements associated with each consignment are to be satisfied, then plans must be prepared in such a way as to permit this. The only certain way of matching transport supply to deman is by preparing feasible journey plans which assign particular crews, together with their vehicles, to perform particular sets of demands. This is the factor which underlies the discussions in chapters 3 and 4, in which the inadequacy of simple measures of transport demand, supply and expenditure is shown. Indeed, although it emerged, in chapter 4, that the number of vehicles required was an approximate guide to the level of expenditure, the problem of estimating the number of vehicles required, which is a journey planning problem, was ignored. The discussions in part 5 of the problems of organizing flows of consignments in such a way as to obtain economies of scale in road goods transport without jeopardizing economies in other functions, or standards of service, showed that a crucial role would be played by communications and journey planning systems and procedures.

But journey plans must not only be feasible, so that the demands allocated to each planned journey may be performed, but they must also be efficient. If, as is the intention, the plans are performed, then any inefficiency incorporated in the plan, e.g. a long empty run between two jobs, is performed. An efficient road transport operation cannot exist without efficient journey planning, and, in general, efficient journey planning depends upon planned, full, productive utilization of the available time.

The problems of efficient journey planning are one of the major pre-occupations of the remainder of this book. Part 7 is devoted to estimation of the duration of planned journeys, which is necessary if full utilization is to be made of the available time. Methods of calculating journey plans are explored in part 8, while in part 9 financial and administrative aspects, including the design of computer and communications systems around the journey planning task, are discussed.

The next chapter is devoted to the problems of measuring efficiency. It links with chapters 3 and 4 through the lack of simple measures of demand, supply and expenditure. It also links with later chapters in that it is suggested that efficient journey plans are the best measures of efficiency. The remaining chapters of part 6 are devoted to a more detailed exposition of the range and detail of factors which have to be considered, and adequate allowances made, when journey plans are prepared in practice. As such it is inevitable that any reader who has been involved in transport operations may find much that is already extremely familiar. The purpose is not to teach transport managers about lorries; it is hoped, rather, to establish, for those who have not been involved in transport operations, a frame of reference for the subsequent parts.

In chapter 20 an attempt will be made to describe, at an operational l
the heterogeneity of road goods transport, and the great variety of
activities, conditions, objectives and restrictions which are to be met in
practice. One purpose of this is to stress that there are many radically
different journey planning problems to which it would be unreasonable
to expect one common method of solution; another purpose is to try to
help those who may wish to define a particular problem by providing a
tentative outline and checklist of possible features.

A closer examination is made of the problems of planning wholesale
delivery journeys from a typical depot in chapter 21. A purpose of this
examination is to stress the importance of the links with other activities,
and the extent to which these may dictate many of the detailed features
of any particular journey planning problem.

Chapter 22 is devoted to a description of one particular, probably
unique, journey planning problem. This problem is not so important in
itself, but the description shows how quite minor details of operational
behaviour may complicate the problem, and re-emphasizes some of the
other points emerging from chapters 20 and 21 in a different and
specialized context.

Chapter 19

Measurement of efficiency

Theoretically, a general statement of the financial objective of any commercial activity might be the maximization of either the owners' equity or the present value of (net) cash flows. Practically, this type of statement of objectives is rarely useful. One reason for the failure to use this type of objective as a constant target and measure of efficiency, i.e. measure of how well the target is being achieved, is that the calculations and estimates required are usually far too complex for everyday use. Further, existing assets reduce flexibility, at least until it is possible to change the assets; and when attention is concentrated upon existing assets it is usually both easier and simpler to utilize more elementary and short term objectives. It is also simpler and easier to use elementary objectives, even when the assets can be changed, if the changes are restricted to changes of quantity rather than nature. Consequently, it is usually only when considering investments which are different that a financial analysis is undertaken which is intended to examine at a basic level how the owners' equity or the present value of cash flows is affected.

As far as road goods transport operations are concerned the general statement of financial objectives is particularly difficult to use operationally because of the lack of obvious simple methods of measuring transport demand or supply, and of converting these into expenditure, as shown in chapters 3 and 4. But problems of measuring efficiency are not confined to road transport, and the general problem will be examined in a general context.

Before proceeding with this examination, however, it should be noted that it may be possible to exaggerate the extent to which owners and managements are, or should be, concerned with the measurement of road transport efficiency. Many vehicles belong to small fleets (detailed are given in chapter 13) and the owner-manager is in such close contact with the drivers and work done that he may not be interested in a formal measure of efficiency. Furthermore, because so many vehicles belong to such small fleets, and because the major factor affecting the level of operating expenditure is the number of vehicles and drivers available for work, there may be no purpose in pursuing transport efficiency unless there is a real prospect of changing the number of vehicles utilized. Additionally, as mentioned in chapter 3, many vehicles are not primarily used for the transport of goods.

In general, the function of measures of efficiency is to provide management with measures, which are as objective as possible, to judge performance, to provide those being managed with a measure or target by which they can gauge their performance, and to provide some sort of objective criteria, mutually acceptable, as a basis for their transactions. In a very small organization, the relationship and degree of contact between the managed and their manager may be such as to render these functions largely unnecessary; on the other hand, in transport operations drivers spend most of their time away from base and outside management immediate view or supervision; consequently, even in small transport organizations, some measures of performance or efficiency may be desirable.

To replace more elaborate financial measures, results are often expressed in terms of costs per unit of some relevant parameter. This approach is typical of accountants, and serves as a very simple means of recording observed performance. In a transport organization a measure of this type might be that of the cost per ton-mile performed; and, in a transport organization concerned with providing a public haulage service the cost per ton-mile performed might be very meaningfully compared with the revenue per ton-mile performed, if the method of charging adopted is closely related to the performance of ton-miles.

The major advantage of measures of performance of this type is that such unit costs are often meaningful with regard to financial and competitive performance. But there are objections to unit costs as a measure of transport efficiency. Most road goods transport vehicles are owned by the organizations utilizing them; the work performed is on own-account. The types and standards of service required and performed are rarely fully defined, and the market prices for obtaining each of the variety of ill-defined services elsewhere may be but imperfectly establish Bayliss and Edwards found that manufacturers only knew the cost of alternative modes for 22% of consignments dispatched by their own vehicles (19.1). Consequently, these figures may not be available to serv as a basis of comparing internal with external costs. Further, figures which utilize recorded costs as a means of comparing performance over time are always difficult to interpret whenever there is any degree of movement in price levels, while interpretation is also dependent upon transport service requirements remaining constant, or the effects of any changes in requirements being estimated. If comparison with market prices, or with historical costs, is difficult or impossible, then the information conveyed by the observed unit cost loses much of its apparent precision. While unit costs may be of considerable importance financially, and of interest commercially, they may not be very relevant to the problem of assessing efficiency, since they often do not measure organizational performance in a way which enables it to be evaluated objectively and separately from environmental effects outside the control of the organization.

Another set of indices frequently used for measuring performance are the ratios of values of selected factors; current ratios may be compared with those obtained previously, or with results obtained elsewhere. Typical examples of measures of this type are the number of ton-miles performed per employee, the miles driven per delivery in distribution operations, the ratio of driving to non-driving time, and percentage return on capital employed. Again, ratios such as these are often meaningful and important, but, equally, they may be poor and confusing guides to efficiency.

Many unquantified, and possibly unquantifiable, factors may have a significant bearing on the actual figures utilized in the various ratios. Consequently, changes in these factors, when the comparison is historical, or differences, when the comparison is geographical or organizational, may be responsible to an unknown extent for differences between observed values of the ratios. Interpretation of any ratio and its values is therefore liable to be difficult.

An unlimited increase in the value of some of the ratios may not always be regarded as desirable, and may even be regarded as undesirable in some circumstances. Thus, for example, there are those who would assume that achieving a return on capital employed above some limit would be undesirable because it would be inviting either competition, or retaliation by customers, or questioning on the grounds of the possible abuse of public interest. In these circumstances the ideal may be a matter of opinion.

It is not uncommon, when ratios are being utilized as measures of performance, to utilize several ratios to illuminate different aspects of performance, but the reconciliation of these different ratios may be difficult; the ratios may even be mutually contradictory.

Many ratios may be very meaningful when utilized in restricted circumstances, but deeply misleading if extended to other situations;

for example, ton-miles per employee is a figure that is deeply influenced by the size of vehicles and the size, density, and distance of consignments.

Finally, measurement of performance by a set of ratios focuses attention, as it is intended to, upon the improvement of those ratios; but it may easily be that these ratios do not reflect all the factors which are important, or do not reflect the proper balance between such factors. Thus, ton-miles per employee may encourage concentration upon the long distance bulk haulage market, and result in neglect, not only of potential markets, but also of service to existing customers for small consignments to be carried short distances, even though these may be highly profitable and offer scope for major expansion. Similarly, a ratio like maintenance man-hours per ton-mile may not only offer encouragement to skimp maintenance in the short term at the expense of long term maintenance or depreciation costs, but also encourage the reduction of maintenance effort during a period of slack vehicle utilization to maintain the ratio; whereas the best policy, especially if the slack period is likely to be short, may be to increase maintenance effort while the vehicles are readily accessible.

A third major set of indices consists of measures of the utilization, the actual productive use in comparison with some norm. A typical example is the vehicle utilization, defined as the percentage load capacity utilized on any journey.

Implicit in the use of percentage load utilization as a measure of efficiency is the assumption that 100% load capacity utilization is both achievable and desirable. Yet, on the one hand, it is not general practice, and would sometimes be very difficult, to determine whether it is possible to achieve 100% utilization of load capacity of a particular vehicle fleet when employed to satisfy a parficular set of work demands on the other hand, if 100% load capacity utilization is achieved, there is some basis for suspecting that vehicle load capacity is acting as a limitation on the amount of work performed. It has been shown that, in general, an increase in vehicle size is only accompanied by a very small increase in vehicle operating cost; it follows that an increase in vehicle load capacity which enabled greater loads to be carried would probably be associated with a reduction in unit cost. A reduction in unit cost would normally be regarded as an improvement of performance whateve the change in the load capacity utilization.

If it is not possible to change the composition of the vehicle fleet, at least in the short term, it is true that a higher degree of load capacity utilization is preferable to a lower degree. However, lower utilization may be the result of lack of demand, or of the particular patterns of demand, and in neither case is the low value of the load utilization an indication of transport operating, as opposed to marketing or management, inefficiency.

A similar index which is sometimes used is the percentage utilization of the capacity ton-mileage; this is calculated by dividing the actual ton-mileage performed by the capacity in tons multiplied by the distance driven. This ratio has an additional disadvantage as a measure of efficiency; it could be increased by minor adjustments to the operating methods, which would actually decrease efficiency and increase costs. This can be illustrated by consideration of a return journey involving the delivery of a vehicle load at one destination; ordinarily this return journey would involve 50% utilization of the capacity ton-mileage; but, by using a circuitous route on the outward journey, and a direct route on the return, the utilization could appear to be increased, despite an unproductive increase in cost.

A fourth type of performance measurement depends upon measurements of technical efficiency; these are used primarily in activities with a technological bias, e.g. the fuel burning and chemical industries. Technical efficiency is often measured by comparing actual performance with some measure of ideal, or theoretically achievable, performance. Examples of this type of index of efficiency include measures of thermal efficiency (conversion of heat into other forms of energy) and the yield of a chemical reaction, or of a steel conversion process.

The distinction between the third and fourth types of index of performance is not always sharp. Typically, however, in the third type of index the ultimate level of performance is not known, and may not even be meaningful; for example, in industrial, commercial, or administrative contexts, the maximum amount of work which can be done by a man is not a very precise concept; while, even when it is a precise concept, it is not always possible to measure it, and it only has practical relevance for very specialized and restricted situations (19.2). In cases where the measurement of performance falls into the fourth type, the ultimate performance which could be achieved is a precise concept, and a relevant value is capable of being measured or estimated. It follows, almost as a matter of definition, that, if the ultimate achievable is a precise concept which can be estimated precisely, the effects of variables on the ultimate achievable are known, and can be taken into account. It is the degree of knowledge associated with this fourth type of measure of performance that makes it both distinctive and important.

Efficiency is a concept which, by definition, is associated with a knowledge of the causes or effects, and hence measures of efficiency should, ideally, be objective measures of performance, as in the fourth category of measures described. But many measures of performance used in practice are poor measures of efficiency because the state of knowledge about cause and effect, or the interrelationships between variables, is extensive only in relatively simple, easily isolated and manipulated, situations, such as those which are common in the physical sciences; in most other situations, such as those which are typical of industry and commerce, knowledge is often extremely limited, usually being restricted to qualitative knowledge of some relationships. Measures of performance which are subject to influences which are beyond control, whether because that is part of the definition of the function or because means of control are not available, and whose effect cannot be estimated with a precision of at least the same order of accuracy as that of the performance measurement, are poor indicators of efficiency.

Estimation of the performance that might be ultimately achievable with a particular vehicle in terms of a particular goods transport situation is usually extremely difficult. The maximum safe cruising speed may be known, but may only rarely be achievable under normal road and traffic conditions. The maximum load capacity may be known, but the characteristics of the goods to be carried, whether due to density, shape, or delicacy, may prevent full loading. The maximum number of hours that it is possible to utilize a vehicle, together with either a driver, or a team of drivers, may be known, but the number of hours that can be productively utilized may depend upon the times at which loading and unloading effort, which may be under separate control, is available, together with the time taken to perform the loading and unloading.

In the very short term, actual demands for transport have to be translated into journey plans, or operational instructions; to carry out this conversion process some standards must be utilized for converting driving, loading and unloading tasks into estimates of journey duration. Thus, the ideal journey plans, the best journey plans possible utilizing the present assets and proper working standards, form a basis for assessing performance.

If the working standards used for converting the components of the task into time utilization were the maximum that either could, or would, be attainable in practice, whether due to external conditions or to restrictions imposed by drivers or management, then this assessment of performance would be a measure of efficiency. Such a measure of efficiency, if practicable, would reflect varying patterns of transport demand, and enable inefficiency due to transport operation or management to be distinguished from that due to other factors.

Furthermore, notionally at least, it should be possible to assess the cost of the ideal set of journey plans, and compare it with the cost of actual performance based on the same set of cost conversions. In this way it should be possible to ensure that this measure of efficiency reflected the cost factors involved. Alternative ways of expressing the measure of efficiency, though not so relevant in terms of cost, could be devised on a similar basis by comparing the number of vehicles, or the mileage, or the vehicle hours, required notionally, as compared with those required in practice.

The measurement of short term efficiency is concerned with measuring the utilization of current assets. The measurement of longer term efficiency is concerned with measuring what could be achieved if circumstances, such as the restrictions or working standards governing the operation, demands to be satisfied, or assets to be utilized, were changed. But this longer term aspect of efficiency measurement is identical with the general problem of evaluating plans for the future; thus, it is suggested that the journey planning function is as important for the planning of future operations as it is for current operations.

Journey planning appears to offer, in theory, the best way of measuring both short and long term efficiency. The main objection is the potential cost and nuisance associated with such a complex method of measurement and the calculations required to use it in practice.

Chapter 20

The variety of journey planning problems

In this chapter an attempt is made to outline the range and type of road goods transport operating situations from the point of view of the associated journey planning considerations. Any attempt to describe all the different situations individually is out of the question; there are far too many. It is, however, the intention to mention as many of the individual factors as possible; actual operating situations incorporate combinations of these factors.

Journey planning objectives.
Journey planning is concerned with the preparation of sets of operating plans to satisfy specific transport demands. Journey plans should be efficient, if not the most efficient possible. It may be assumed that the definition of 'most efficient' is identical with that of 'least cost'; but, if so, it may be necessary to consider some rather obscure forms of cost.

In the examination of vehicle operating costs conducted in chapter 4 it was suggested that most of the costs, those of vehicles and drivers, are fixed at least in the short term, and that the variable costs associated with mileage are only a small proportion of the total operating cost. If the planning organization bears the total operating cost directly, e.g. it owns the vehicle fleet, the main objective of the journey planning procedure should be efficiency in the long term, e.g. utilization of the minimum number of vehicles and drivers in the long term, with immediate reduction of the variable costs being only a secondary objective. When fleet capacity is more than adequate to meet current transport demands there may be other secondary objectives to be balanced against reductions of the variable driving cost; for example, the cost of increased mileage associated with sharing out work evenly between the drivers of vehicles may be more than offset by the benefits, whether arising from driver contentment or from the convenience of having the yard cleared for other work during the day. The allocation of work in such a way that maximum possible use is made of vehicles and drivers may only become the main objective of journey planning when transport demand is close to the maximum capacity of the fleet.

However, the balance between fixed and variable cost may be changed if marginal vehicle requirements are met by short term hire; depending upon the contract and methods of charging, and the periods for which the vehicles are hired, costs may appear to become completely variable. In these circumstances, the main objective of journey planning may be the lowest immediately recognizable cost all the time; this objective, if the methods of charging reflect the incidence of costs, may be interpreted as the utilization of the minimum number of vehicles to perform the given transport tasks. Within this main objective, the different cost structures of different vehicles, including patterns of charging for hired vehicles, may change the ideal allocation of tasks to the different vehicles; for example, relatively high mileage charges for hired vehicles may justify the allocation of journeys with a high proportion of stationary time, whether waiting, loading or unloading, to them.

There are other factors, as well as the methods adopted for charging, which may make subtle variations in the objectives of the journey planning procedure desirable; for example, hired vehicles may only be available for minimum periods which are longer than the immediate requirements, or hiring arrangements may have to be made before the demands are known in detail, with the result that there will be an inevitable over-supply of vehicles on some occasions.

Thus, even when patterns of transport demands are identical, the objectives of the journey planning operation may depend upon superficially minor aspects of vehicle supply.

Journey planning time cycle.

Journeys are rarely planned for a vehicle more frequently than it completes journeys; alteration of journey plans in the middle of journeys depends upon communication between the driver and journey planner, and would usually be expensive if it involved any alteration in, or diversion of, the load being carried. Journey durations tend to impose a time cycle on the planning procedures. The most common basic planning cycle is that of one day. However, when journeys of less than one day's duration are common, there may be subsidiary planning cycles within the day; equally, when journeys frequently exceed a day in duration, the basic cycle may be two or three days or even a week, with shorter subsidiary cycles.

Some transport demands recur, or are made to recur, in a fixed time cycle; sometimes the recurrence is not complete in all details, e.g. the location of the demands may be identical on different occasions, but there may be a variation in the size of the consignments. In some other situations the pattern of transport demand may be, or appear to be, random, and the problems of collecting information about transport demands may be so great, that any attempt to plan the journeys on the basis of actual demand may be, or appear to be, impossible, impracticable, or simply unattractive financially. In other circumstances, one of the features of the transport demand may be not only that it recurs regularly, but also that it requires the same personnel to perform that particular service, e.g. there is a premium on personal recognition in transactions involving transfers of cash by security organizations. Alternatively, the transport organization may gain by using the same personnel on regular journeys; for example, extremely detailed local knowledge of roads, or of access or parking points, may reduce considerably the time required to perform a particular journey, while drivers may obtain business or collect cash, or their special knowledge of the foibles and needs of particular clients or customers may be of mutual advantage in many other ways.

When regular journeys are the main feature of a transport operation, the functions of journey planning may occur at two levels. The first is the very occasional major modification of the regular journeys to take into account such factors as changes in the pattern of demand; but full scale revision of a set of regular journey plans tends to be rare, partly because staff practised and skilled in the revision of journey plans is not available, and partly because the adoption of a new set of journey plans in an organization whose operation is geared to a regular set tends to be a traumatic experience. The second level of journey planning for regular journeys is detailed and continuous; if regular journeys are used to satisfy demands which vary from time to time, and the variations are known in advance, the journey plans may be subjected to continuous adaptation.

When journeys are planned for each cycle (usually daily), the order time cycle may emerge as a factor of importance. The longer the period which can be tolerated between the time when the transport demand becomes known, and the time by which it must be performed, the greater the possibility that it can be planned to coincide with other transport demands in such a way as to reduce the overall cost. On the other hand, the time between the order being placed and its performance is usually one of the factors which is fundamental to customer assessment of the service being provided.

Some planning time cycles may have been adopted for reasons of

economic choice which are more or less susceptible to change as the methods
of meeting the transport demands are changed. The nature of the cycle
adopted may change the level of effort or expense that can be tolerated
for the journey planning procedure, or change the desired level of precision
of the planning output. If the methods and techniques utilized in journey
planning are under examination, then it is worth while examining critically
the associated planning time cycles. Inter-action between the basic and
subsidiary planning time cycles, and between these and the order time
cycle, can alter the journey planning procedures.

End-to-end and intermediate journeys.
Two basic journey types have been distinguished in surveys of road goods
transport: end-to-end journeys involve the carriage of a single load to a single
destination; intermediate journeys are those in which goods are picked up
or set down at several points. In 1962, of the 866,000 vehicles of more than
one ton unladen weight, 47% were employed exclusively on intermediate
journeys, while only 31% were employed exclusively on end-to-end
journeys (**20.1**). The difference between the utilization of vehicles engaged
on intermediate journeys and those engaged on end-to-end journeys is
shown by the observation that vehicles engaged on intermediate journeys
carried 30% of the total tonnage, performed 26% of the total ton-mileage,
and drove 47% of the total mileage (**20.2**). Thus, while the vehicles engaged
on intermediate journeys drove somewhere near their share of the mileage,
they carried, and performed, much less than their share of the tonnage and
ton-mileage respectively. (The distinction would have been even clearer if
it had been possible to include the 548,000 'C' licensed vehicles of less than
one ton unladen weight in the comparison; but it was assumed in the 1962
Survey that all of these were engaged on intermediate journeys, and, because
of this assumption, vehicles of less than one ton unladen weight have been
omitted from this comparison.)

The differences between end-to-end and intermediate journeys reflect
not only differences in transport operating characteristics, as shown by the
statistics of mileages, tons and ton-mileages, but also, because intermediate
journeys are inevitably associated with relatively small consignments, reflect
a difference in the demands for service associated with the demands for the
transport of goods. This distinction, therefore, will be regarded as fundamental.

End-to-end journeys: trunking.
Trunking services involve the scheduled movement of vehicles between
specified places. When operated over long distances, most of these

scheduled movements take place at night. The number of public haulage
vehicles engaged in trunking in the U.K. is probably very small, the bulk
of these being operated by British Road Services. In Holland there has been
a road transport licensing policy which is intended to discriminate in
favour of trunking services in order to create a national network of regular
services carrying out line haulage. Hauliers carrying out scheduled services
are partially protected from competition by other hauliers. Nevertheless,
in terms of ton-kilometres, unscheduled services carry out 93% of the
total ton-kilometres performed by public road hauliers (**20.3**).

It is possible to envisage a number of factors which would hinder the
establishment of scheduled trunk services. Full utilization of trunking
services requires a regular, or large, demand for the transport of goods betwe
the terminal points. If demand is small and irregular then the scheduled
service must operate at a low average level of utilization; for operation at a
low level of utilization to be profitable it may be necessary to charge
premium rates, as is common with scheduled services in other types of
transport; yet the road goods transport market is so fluid that it is usually
possible to obtain ordinary rates for the occasional consignment. Further,
the attractions of scheduled services, their regularity and reliability, may
only become appreciated by the user as a result of the establishment of the
scheduled services, and, if so, supply may stimulate the demand but be
initially unprofitable. The haulier, however, has no certainty in advance
that any such service will ever become profitable. Finally, in the U.K.,
48% of public haulage vehicles are in fleets of 10 vehicles or less (**20.4**);
and firms may have little scope for risk investment, or for the
concentration on marketing and the absorption of its associated overheads,
which is probably necessary to establish scheduled trunk services.

Since the scheduled journeys for trunk services are performed repeatedly
there is little difficulty in establishing time schedules. If there were large
networks of trunking services, there might be considerable difficulties
involved in constructing time-tables which ensured maximum vehicle
utilization; these problems would be analogous to those met in the
construction of time-tables for air services, and of the corresponding
aircraft operating schedules. However, in the absence of such networks,
and of attempts to run a network of scheduled services as an integrated
operation, planning journeys for trunking services is unlikely to be difficul

Private trunking operations are a much more common feature; many
firms organize the conveyance of semi-manufactured goods between
factories, the conveyance of finished goods to markets, or the collection
of raw materials, in this way. The journeys involved in private trunking

operations are often very short, and each vehicle carries out several such journeys in a day; when this is the basic pattern, journey planning may be primarily concerned with the scheduling or sequencing of journeys, and will be dealt with later under this heading. Less than 3% of loaded end-to-end journeys carried out by 'C' licensed vehicles are more than 100 miles in length, while more than 80% are shorter than 25 miles (20.5).

Where scheduled journeys are solely concerned with the carriage of a uniform stream of material between two places some distance apart, journey planning is relatively trivial; furthermore, the problems of longer term planning under these circumstances may also be relatively trivial, because there may be a much better relationship between the tons moved, mileages run, ton-mileage performed, and cost. (Many fixed costs, because of the form of charges for the road infrastructure, virtually disappear for bulk haulage operations; significant variations in load require changes in the number of vehicles, and all vehicle costs in these circumstances are variable). However, the situation is often complicated by attempts to reduce the cost of empty return journeys; it is comparatively rare for an organization to have balancing flows of material in opposite directions. Typical stratagems for reducing the cost of empty return journeys have included utilizing return journeys for the distribution of finished goods, and performing public haulage work under 'B' licences. (One of the reasons given by the Geddes Committee (20.6) for suggesting changes in goods vehicle licensing was that additional flexibility might make it easier to utilize return journeys). In circumstances such as these, the patterns of journeys performed become more akin to those associated with tramping, which are described in the next section.

End-to-end journeys: tramping.
Tramp vehicles perform unscheduled services, and have no set routes. Just as tramp freight ships, or taxi-cabs, tramp goods vehicles proceed from place to place, the drivers finding work, or having work found for them, *en route*. The organizational constraints are usually minimal, being confined, in general, to periodic returns to base, e.g. at weekends, and observance, at least in the maintenance of drivers' official log-books if not in practice, of statutory requirements, e.g. with regard to drivers' hours. In planning the next journey, important factors are the supply or demand in the region around the destination of the present journey, the range of destinations which might result from the next journey, and their likelihood of offering further work, or convenience for base. In these circumstances, the journey planning decision depends upon the evaluation, usually implicit, of the

probability of various events, including the outcomes possible at the next destination, together with the rewards or penalties of standing idle, travelling empty between loads, conveying part loads, and quoting higher or lower prices. In essence, the decision is very complex; in practice, it is often delegated, to a greater or lesser extent, to the driver, who may develop his own contacts and use brokers or clearing houses to find work.

If it is assumed that little trunking work is carried out by public haulage vehicles, then it seems probable that most of the 'A' licensed vehicles engaged solely on end-to-end journeys are involved in tramping; this would amount to some 36,000 vehicles. Much of the work carried out by the 73,000 vehicles with 'B' licences, when acting as public haulage vehicles, which seems to be for about two-thirds of the time, may also fall within the category of tramping (**20.7**).

End-to-end journeys: scheduling or sequencing.
80% of all end-to-end journeys performed by road goods transport are shorter than 25 miles long. 70% of the tonnage carried on end-to-end journeys is carried for less than 25 miles, the average distance of journeys in this category being approximately 8 miles (**20.8**). The typical work pattern involves the bulk collection or delivery of minerals, chemicals, fuel, building materials and iron and steel products. However, the range of task which may be included in this category is very wide.

When vehicles are operating short end-to-end journeys it is usually necessary for them to perform several journeys within a day to obtain full vehicle utilization. Journey planning may therefore be primarily concerned with allocating a set of journeys to each vehicle in such a way as to utilize fully the time available. Furthermore, there may be restrictions on the times of starting or finishing at least some of the journeys, and statutory restrictions on the total duration of the working day, and the period between rests; with the appearance of this type of restriction, the task of journey planning involves the preparation of a time-table, or schedule, of journeys for each vehicle; the purpose may be to obtain maximum utilization within the pre-determined time units.

Fulfilment of the general requirements may be subject to a number of specific and detailed constraints; examples follow:
1 constraints may be applied to the pattern of work of the vehicle crew, the duty or shift patterns, the places of starting and finishing work, the places at which rests, or meals, can be taken, and the corresponding time periods when they should be taken; the time periods may be measured from the beginning of the duty, or the last rest, or within certain clock

times, or a combination of all three;

2 constraints may be associated with the journey, e.g. specified start and/ or finish times;

3 constraints may be associated with the places visited, e.g. size and/or type of vehicle which can be accepted, times of opening or closing;

4 constraints may be associated with the products carried on successive journeys, or the mix of products carried on a single journey.

Intermediate journeys.

According to the results of the 1962 Survey of Road Goods Transport, 957,000 vehicles, or more than 67% of the total, were employed exclusively on intermediate journeys (comprising 409,000 vehicles of more than one ton unladen weight, which were found by a sample survey to be concerned exclusively with intermediate journeys, and 548,000 'C' licensed vehicles of less than one ton unladen weight which were assumed to be devoted to intermediate journeys, but questions were not asked about the use of small 'C' licensed vehicles because it was feared that the response rate would deteriorate if the questions were too detailed). A further 190,000 vehicles, or 13% of the total, were employed on a mixture of intermediate and end-to-end journeys (**20.1**). Less than 2% of intermediate journeys were found to be more than 100 miles in length (**20.9**); it therefore seems comparatively safe to assume that nearly all intermediate journeys finish within the day at the depot. This assumption is reinforced by the observation that 555,000 'C' licensed vehicles, or more than 50% of those working, were mainly engaged on retail and wholesale delivery (**20.10**), and deliveries to shops are usually only possible during opening hours.

It seems natural to distinguish from the mass of vehicles engaged on intermediate journeys those engaged in deliveries of small consignments. In addition to the 'C' licensed vehicles engaged on wholesale and retail distribution, most, but not all, of which are concerned with the distribution of small consignments, there are many 'A', 'Contract A' and 'B' licensed vehicles engaged on the same sort of work; furthermore, many of the 58,000 vans and lorries operated by the General Post Office under the Crown Vehicle scheme, and not included in the statistics for road goods transport, because exempt from goods vehicle licensing, are employed in the collection and delivery of small consignments. In addition, there are other vehicles engaged in the collection of small consignments, e.g. the collection of milk from farms, and the assembly of loads for public haulage trunking and tramping, which is sometimes known as shunting. A large proportion of the vehicles engaged in intermediate journeys perform journeys which are primarily concerned with either collection or delivery of small consignments.

Intermediate collection or delivery journeys.
The allocation of a set of collection or delivery tasks to journeys which must not exceed a time limit is fairly complex; for the journeys to be efficient, the time available must be fully utilized, but not exceeded. Consequently, efficient journey planning includes estimation of the duration of the journeys; but the distance to be driven during a journey, or the time spent driving, usually depends to a significant extent upon the sequence in which the collections or deliveries are performed. Even in the simplest of circumstances, the planning of intermediate collection or delivery journeys may involve the manipulation of a large number of variables in many combinations.

But intermediate collection or delivery journeys must usually conform to a number of special restrictions or limitations, and the number of combinations of the restrictions which occur in practice is extremely high.
1 A variety of restrictions may be placed on the drivers' working day in addition, or as alternatives, to statutory limitations; for example, British Road Services limited the drivers' day to ten hours when the statutory limitation was eleven hours.
2 Vehicles may be subject to duration or use limitations. Some vehicles are tuned, and their tyre pressure adjusted, for high speed driving on motorways, and others for much slower conditions; some managements forbid delivery drivers to use motorways. Some vehicles are utilized for shift working, which may impose an additional limitation on journey durations.
3 Drivers may have restrictions on their working shift types, e.g. night or day work, as on other conditions of service, e.g. meal times, or be limited by their local knowledge, or their physical abilities, e.g. to handle weights.
4 The load capacity of vehicles may impose limitations, which may be effective in more than one dimension, e.g. the limitations may simply be those of weight, or of both weight and volume.
5 The goods to be carried may impose restrictions, either because different types may not be carried on the same vehicle, or because they may mix, e.g. unpackaged liquids or powders, or because they may be of awkward shapes to load together on the same vehicle, or because they may be delicate and difficult to disentangle when unloading.
6 All the vehicles in a fleet may have the same characteristics, or the fleet

may be heterogeneous, for example, the load capacities may be different; amongst other special characteristics, which may vary and be important, are the turning circle, the type of unloading facilities attached to the vehicle, or the occurrence of tractors and trailers.

7 Particular restrictions may be associated with particular collections or deliveries; examples of these include particular times or time periods in which collections or deliveries may or may not be made, restrictions on the characteristics of the vehicle which may make the collection or delivery, or restrictions on particular drivers who should or should not make the collection or delivery, e.g. because of compatibility, or incompatibility, of temperament, or of special knowledge, such as where a key is kept or of the methods of stacking to be adopted.

8 There may be overall restrictions imposed by the depot, or its mode of operation; ultimate limits may be placed on journey start and finish times by the depot opening and closing times, while loading facilities may determine the rate of dispatch or turn-round, or may, for example, inhibit reloading during specified periods.

This list of restrictions is not exhaustive. Some other requirements or considerations have been noted in practical applications which may alter fundamentally the logical character of specific journey planning problems. These, again, are probably only a sample of those that could be found.

1 The transport and goods depots may not coincide; the basic journey pattern may involve leaving one depot, carrying out collections or deliveries, and returning to the other.

2 The sequence in which goods are loaded may determine the sequence of delivery, either absolutely, or allowing only slight changes in sequence. For example, when frozen foods are delivered in refrigerated vans, orders are usually assembled and loaded as such to reduce exposure of drivers to freezing temperatures, and of frozen foods to ambient temperatures; if, in addition, the volume capacity is fully utilized, access to the orders may be determined by the loading sequence.

3 When the time cycle for satisfying orders is greater than the journey time cycle, which is rarely more than a day, then orders may be given different priorities for fulfilment. Among the considerations which may be taken into account in the allocation of priorities are:— the time since the order was placed; a valuation of the customer, or of this particular order; the relationship to a longer term order cycle associated with representatives' calls or to a longer term delivery cycle established to achieve distribution economies; or an assessment of the customer's need based, for example, on a knowledge of the size of his stock.

4 There are usually prescribed standards for the period between order and delivery which can be tolerated; this time may be determined by marketing policies, or by historical precedents, but it may also depend in particular circumstances upon the expected time of stock-out or stock overflow; in any case it is usually considered desirable to fulfil delivery promises.

Within the class of intermediate delivery or collection journeys, there are a number of categories that may be distinguished when the form of the appropriate journey plans is considered. Three such categories may be distinguished by whether schedules, sequences or routes are required. The effects of time restrictions of various kinds may be such as to require a journey plan to be akin to a time-table or a schedule. Where the time restrictions are not of such importance it may only be necessary to specify the sequence of visits. Journey plans for some purposes involve a more detailed consideration of the routes, in terms of the actual sequence of streets to be followed, and even, on occasion, of the detailed performance of tasks within each street. Practical examples of activities which require plans of routes include the retail delivery of bread, milk and newspapers, the delivery of mail, and the collection of refuse (while some of these activities do not concern road goods transport, nevertheless some do, and the journey planning problems associated with them are similar). In some cases two categories of plan may be required under the same industrial description, e.g. plans for the delivery and collection of domestic laundry may require the specification of routes, but plans for the delivery and collection of industrial and institutional laundry may only need to specify the sequence.

Intermediate journeys involving mixed deliveries and collections.
Collections and deliveries are not always aimed at the concentration or dispersal of goods, nor are goods always transferred in bulk. Some vehicles that are utilized for the carriage of small consignments may carry a number of the consignments simultaneously; the collections and deliveries may be performed in any sequence. Journeys of this type, and the associated collections and deliveries, may be subject to any of the restrictions already described in the previous section. Fleets carrying out this type of transfer work may be specialized, a typical example being the carriage of cash and other valuables by security vans. An example of a similar type of work outside goods transport is the carriage of people by buses.

Chapter 21

Planning wholesale delivery journeys

Most wholesale deliveries are made by vehicles performing intermediate, multiple-delivery, journeys, distributing goods from a warehouse which is also the depot for several vehicles. Wholesale distribution may be carried out by manufacturers, as is common in the food, drink and tobacco manufacturing industries, by distribution agents, as is common with fuels, as well as by merchants or wholesalers. Manufacturers, and their agents, tend to deal with a range of goods determined by the manufacturers' activities; wholesalers proper tend to handle a wider range of goods which is nearer to the whole range of their customers' requirements. The depot envisaged as the basis of the description that follows is that of a food or drink manufacturing company which carries out most of its own wholesale distribution.

Because of the competitive atmosphere which surrounds the distribution of many consumer goods, there is a constant conflict between service to the customer and distribution economy. If a customer demands immediate delivery, and a competitor may be willing to meet that demand, then the pressure to satisfy the demand is strong. The conflict between service, in terms of the time taken to respond to an order, and economy has been resolved in most distributing companies by a policy directive; for example, companies may promise delivery on the day following receipt of order.

Even when the conflicts between service and economy have been resolved at the company level by a policy directive, conflict continues at the depot or warehouse level. The most convenient time to carry out warehousing operations is during the day. Even if vehicles are not available for loading until the late afternoon or evening, after the day's journeys have been completed, nevertheless, assembly of loads, which is often the major task, need not await the return of vehicles; the sooner it is started the better. On the other hand, customers still press for orders to be accepted for delivery on the following day as late as is physically possible, especially when competition is strong, whatever company policy directives may say. Ideally, to get the best allocation, loads should not be planned until all orders are available. In practice, because of the time taken to plan loads and to summarize the requirements of each item for each load, and because of the pressure to start load assembly as soon as possible, it is common practice to start planning journeys well before the last orders have been received.

The interaction between service and economy at the depot is not confined to pressure to accept orders as late as possible, but also to start making up loads as early as possible. It is quite as important to ensure that deliveries planned are, as far as possible, carried out. Should it prove impossible to carry out the journey plan, some deliveries will not be made. This is a failure of service that may annoy customers: it may also be a considerable inconvenience within the depot, if it occurs on any scale, since the failed deliveries are not apparent until vehicles return, and the need to deliver the failed deliveries may upset the plans for the following day's journeys at a stage when all, or nearly all, of the following day's loads will have been assembled, and some probably loaded. Consequently, returns, at anything more than a very low level, are unacceptable. In this case, the requirements for service and economy act in the same direction; planned journeys must be completed, and therefore journey plans must be capable of completion.

The number of outlets, primarily retail shops, on the books of a large wholesale distribution depot may be more than 10,000; of these, a substantial proportion may require deliveries very rarely. Most outlets do not accept deliveries outside their normal opening hours. Within the depot delivery area, most outlets close for a half day either on Wednesdays or Thursdays, but a substantial minority may close on Mondays, either completely, or as an early closing day. Furthermore, many outlets do not accept deliveries during busy periods; Fridays and Saturdays are often regarded as busy.

The number of deliveries dispatched on any one day from the larger depots may be as many as a thousand; for any one depot, it is common for delivery requirements on different days of the same week to vary widely, the range often exceeding the ratio of two to one.

The number of vehicles utilized for deliveries from larger depots may exceed fifty. It is common for nearly all vehicles to be either company owne or hired under a long term contract. If the goods to be delivered can be carried on platform vehicles or in vans, it may be possible to supplement the regular fleets at times of peak requirements by vehicles hired by the day or week. However, it is usually necessary for hiring arrangements to be made in advance, often before delivery requirements are fully known. The manning of hired vehicles may present difficulties when there are considerable advantages to be obtained from drivers having either-very detailed local knowledge of the delivery area, or knowledge of the customers to whom they are making deliveries. Where drivers are accompanied by ma⁺es to assist with unloading, as is common in the distribution of drin!:s, these teams may be split, when vehicles are hired, to ensure that there is a company employee on every vehicle.

Orders are often taken at the depot. When there is a short order and delivery cycle, half of the orders to be included in the journey planning process on any one day may be received on previous days; the remainder may be received by post or by telephone. It is common practice for a time limit to be placed upon the acceptance of orders which are to be included in the journey plans prepared on that day. The time limit commonly varies between noon and 5.00 p.m.; the main operational factor which may influence the time limit which is set on the acceptance of orders is the amount of work required to process the orders, both in the office and in the warehouse or depot. However, in practice, some orders are almost invariably accepted after the limit, either because of the commercial pressure for service (when this is high, some customers may expect a depot manager to be prepared to make an urgent delivery immediately, if necessary in his own car), or because of good relations between the customer and the depot, which may be to their mutual convenience. Thus, in some trades, e.g. petrol distribution, some customers may allow their stock to be topped up at the distributor's convenience; planned stocking-up for periods of peak retail demand is common, and distributors may have more control than usual over the timing and size of deliveries for this purpose.

The number of items stocked in depots varies greatly according to the nature of the business; but even a manufacturing company distributing its own products often maintains stocks of more than 100 items in distribution depots, when all the different packs and containers, including sizes, for the different products are taken into account; furthermore, both the number and identity of items is liable to change continuously. If 100 items are stocked, it may be typical for between 5 and 20 of these items to occur on most orders with an average of 10 items per order.

Orders, when received, are entered on a delivery note, of which several copies are required. An address plate system is often used for printing customers' names and addresses onto delivery notes. Typically, there are address plates for all known customers within the depot area; in addition to a name and address, each plate incorporates the appropriate account identification number, and any known special delivery instructions. Credit checking may also be carried out as the address plates are used on the basis of special instructions received from the accounts department concerning customers whose credit-worthiness is suspect; the absence of special instructions for a known customer is taken to indicate credit-worthiness. If vehicle load capacity is a significant restriction on planned journeys, order requirements are converted into load units and entered onto the delivery note; this conversion normally takes place when the order is received, except during the peak periods for receiving telephoned orders. The delivery notes, when completed, or partially completed, are set aside for the journey planning process.

The method of planning journeys which is probably most widely used is one which may be called pigeon holing. The depot area is divided into a number of districts which are easily identifiable, e.g. postal districts. Each district is assigned a compartment, or pigeon hole, in a frame which may contain 40 or 50 compartments. Delivery notes, when received, are placed in the pigeon hole appropriate to their district. The first journeys are planned, if possible, by selecting batches of delivery notes from single compartments which are considered to represent either full vehicle loads or full days' work. When no single compartment contains sufficient delivery notes to make a full load or day's work, delivery notes are gathered together from pigeon holes representing adjacent districts to make up journeys which are each as near to a full load or day's work as possible. Estimates of what constitutes a full load, when only the weight capacity of the vehicle is likely to be infringed, are based upon the sum of the weights of the orders as entered upon the delivery notes. However, estimation of what constitutes a full vehicle load may be more complex. Sometimes it may depend upon some rather arbitrary judgement, based on the experience of the journey planner, of the possible methods of loading and unloading.

The methods of estimating a full day's work for a delivery vehicle usually depend on journey planners' subjective judgements of what is reasonable, based, since many of them have themselves been drivers, on their impressions and past experience. These subjective judgements are often supported by some general rule of thumb, for example, that the number of deliveries allocated to a journey plan should not exceed an accepted limit, or that performance of all the deliveries in specified areas, although the number of deliveries may vary, represents a reasonable day's work. When the delivery work itself is a serious factor, as in the delivery of drinks when mates are often carried to assist with unloading and storage on customers' premises, a maximum day's work may be defined as being represented by the delivery of a specified weight.

These judgements and rules of thumb are often very poor measures of the work requirements. They rarely represent good estimates of the amount of delivery work, and, since there is frequently no attempt to assess the driving time except, perhaps, on the basis of an impression of the distance to the furthermost delivery, the implied estimates of the journey duration are poor. Quantitative methods of estimating all the elements of work in terms of the time requirements are rare.

The most advanced quantitative method of estimating the work content of journeys in use, known to the author, is as follows. Delivery work was measured by normal time study methods and the results expressed at standard, i.e. non-incentive, rates. The delivery task was divided into a number of elements, e.g. 'open cab door', and 'select and deliver goods'. Elements such as 'open cab door' were regarded as fixed, and constant, for any type of delivery. Elements such as 'select and deliver' were assumed to vary according to the type of goods and number of items being delivered. Delays at customers' premises are not incorporated into plans, so that habits of planning for, and accepting, delays at customers' premises should not develop. If, and when, a driver is delayed more than ten minutes at a customer's premises, he is allowed to claim credit for the delay. However, the management reserves the right to confirm such claims for delays with the customer. By this system, drivers are encouraged to report delays, and depot managers to attempt to eliminate them.

Driving times are estimated on the basis of dividing the estimated journey distance by an estimated average speed. The basis for estimating the journey distance is a knowledge of the return journey distance from the depot to the town, or village, which represents the furthermost part of the journey; to this basic return journey distance a kilometre is added for each National Grid square through which a deviation from the basic journey passes, and an additional half-mile for each delivery. Information about driving speeds was, and continues to be, gathered by work study officers, who accompanied drivers on many journeys. The observed journey times were increased to allow for any parts of the journeys where the observed speed was in excess of 30 m.p.h., since the average speeds are based on a speed limit, agreed with the drivers' union, of 30 m.p.h. When the information collected about journey speeds was analysed, it was found that the observed speeds tended to fall into three groups according to the 'character' of the roads travelled. The road characteristics were identified with, and described as, 'town', 'residential' and 'country', and the average speed associated with each was 10.3 m.p.h., 15.1 m.p.h., and 24.4 m.p.h., respectively. When planned journeys were analysed according to their road characteristics, it was found that they could be broken down into proportions of 'town', 'residential', and 'country' roads which tended to follow a pattern depending upon the total planned distance involved. Journeys of 30 miles planned distance were found to include 29% of the distance on town, 60% on residential, and 11% on country roads. Planned journeys of 90 miles included only 6% of the distance on town, 26% on residential, and 68% on country roads. It is from these observed standard proportions of distance on different types of road, combined with the appropriate average speeds, that the journey average speeds for different planned distances are derived. The major exception recognized is where more than 80% of a journey is on residential or town roads; this may occur, for example, in the major conurbations of London, Manchester, Glasgow and Birmingham. Such a high proportion of residential or town roads is easily recognized either by prior knowledge or by simple inspection of the journey plotted on a map; for these journeys special allowances apply.

In the organization where this method of estimating the work content of a journey plan is utilized, it is a fundamental part of an agreement with the trade union which extends to wages and hours of work. Broadly, weekly wages are fixed, except that overtime is paid for Saturday work if required by the company; maximum planned working hours are specified, the planned hours being measured by the method outlined, and the actual hours worked, providing the statutory limit is not exceeded, are ignored; a 'job and finish' system is worked under which drivers are free when they have completed the planned tasks they have been assigned.

The time required to prepare a journey plan for wholesale delivery journeys depends upon factors such as the techniques utilized for estimating the work content or journey duration, and the complication of the restrictions associated with the journey and its deliveries. However, even when relatively simple methods are used, between 15 and 30 minutes may be required to plan a journey. When a batch of delivery notes which represents a journey has been collected together, instructions are passed to the warehouse for the load to be assembled. Under certain circumstances it may be desirable for all the items for each order to be assembled separately and for load assembly to consist of collecting together the assembled orders. More commonly, however, selection of items for an order is carried out by drivers at the point of delivery, and loads are assembled by assembling the total quantity of each item required by the orders in the planned journey. Consequently, before loads can be assembled, it is usually necessary to summarize the total requirements of each item appearing in the orders; the time required for this process depends upon the average number of orders in the loads, and the average number of items in each order, but may easily be 15 to 30 minutes per load. At least one company, with a rather more complex task than most, has thought it worth while to install a central computer system, with telex communications links to depots, for the purpose of summarizing loads.

It is common practice for vehicles engaged on wholesale delivery journeys to leave the depot, fully loaded, in the morning between 6.30 and 8.00 a.m., depending upon the distance to be driven to, and the earliest acceptable time for, the first delivery. Few outlets accept deliveries much before they open, unless parking and unloading restrictions are such as to force them to accept deliveries outside peak hours for traffic. Deliveries normally have to be completed before outlets close at the end of the day; additionally, many outlets close for lunch, and most close for half days during the basic working week, i.e. excluding Saturday, and will not accept deliveries during these periods. Furthermore, deliveries which coincide with periods of peak business are rarely accepted willingly, if at all. There may be other special conditions attached to many deliveries. There may also be special arrangements which may enable what appear to be difficult situations to be circumvented, e.g. deliveries to sporting and other clubs, which are only open intermittently during normal working hours, may be facilitated by an arrangement whereby drivers collect the keys, which may even be kept at the depot, and make deliveries without supervision or immediate checking. Between 50% and 60% of the working day may be spent making deliveries, the remainder being driving time; but it is not difficult to find situations in which the day is divided in different proportions.

Vehicles must be loaded between return from one day's deliveries and departure for the next. Some vehicles are loaded overnight; but overnight working is generally more expensive and less popular with warehousemen. Consequently, many vehicles are loaded in the afternoon or evening. Furthermore, many warehousemen do not like working late into the evening, primarily because of its effect on social life. Consequently, a common aim is to complete load assembly before vehicles return, so that loading can be finished as soon as possible after return. Thus, to facilitate warehouse working, load summaries may be required early enough to enable assembly to take place before the vehicles return. This requirement may determine the time at which the process of journey planning and load summarizing is commenced. The organization of load summarizing and assembly is complicated by factors such as the time until which orders will be accepted, which may have been determined by marketing policies, the peak periods of order taking, and the time required to plan journeys and summarize loads; furthermore the arrangements may be complicated by coincidence of a period of peak working with the period during which most people prefer to eat a mid-day meal.

Drivers usually take two copies of each delivery note, one for retention by the customer, the other, after adjustment for errors and omissions, breakage, goods refused, and empties returned, serves as the receipt. Receipted delivery notes are usually used as the basis for the sales invoicing and accounting procedures. If, as is becoming more common, the sales invoicing and accounting procedures are based upon a computer system, receipts will be collected and dispatched to a computer centre for conversion into media suitable for computer input, such as punched cards or paper tape. As well as performing the sales accounting functions, the computer system may include maintenance of the depot stock record and preparation of sales statistics, since these can be prepared as by-products, on the basis of information concerning the totals of goods delivered. Replenishment of depot stock is often based upon computer stock figures which are a number of days out of date.

Thus, planning journeys for wholesale deliveries is a small, but integral, part of a complex administrative system. The system interacts with the marketing, or sales, functions in respect of order taking, order fulfilment, and provision of information in the form of sales statistics. It interacts with the accounting function, not only because of its own operating expenditures, but also because it is the essential source of information for sales invoicing and accounting, which deals with the main stream of revenue into the organization, and, finally, because it accepts and executes instructions from the accountancy function with regard to customer credit-worthiness. It interacts with the manufacturing function in that it is the channel through which products are distributed, and it provides the information on which factory production and distribution schedules are based.

Associated with many wholesale distribution depots there is a substantial number of employees, in a number of different functions, whose work has to be co-ordinated, scheduled and controlled. A depot, its stocks, and the associated vehicle fleet, may represent considerable capital investment, and the associated operating expenditure for a large depot may exceed £250,000 per annum.

As an essential link in the overall distribution function, journey planning should be regarded as part of the function, subject to the pressures inherent in the function, and not as an isolated procedure, solely concerned with the minimization of transport expenditure.

Chapter 22

Scheduling bulk transfers of mail

To contrast with the description in the last chapter of wholesale distribution of food and drink by manufacturers, which is typical of many journey planning problems associated with intermediate collection or delivery journeys, the next example is concerned with the preparation of duty schedules for a specific fleet which transfers mail in bulk by short, end-to-end, journeys.

Within the General Post Office there are fleets of vans and lorries under the control of district postmasters which perform such services as collection of mail from post-boxes and post-offices, delivery of parcel mail, and transfer of mail between various collection, distribution, and sorting offices. In the major conurbations there are additional fleets which provide many of the basic services and support for the local fleets.

In London this fleet is known as the Centrally Controlled Service (C.C.S.) which is under the control of the Director of the London Postal Region. The C.C.S. fleet comprised 689 vehicles in 1966 (**22.1**), including reserves and special purpose vehicles; vehicles were stationed at five garages, and driven, on a three shift rota, by 1,230 men. The fleet performed about 30,000 services (i.e. individual loaded trips) each week, covering some 250,000 miles, mainly within a circle of five miles radius with King's Cross as the centre. Of the 30,000 services, about 88% were scheduled against known requirements, while the remainder were performed on *ad hoc* demand; all *ad hoc* services were controlled from a central operations room. Most scheduled services involved bulk conveyance of mails between rail termini and district offices concerned with collection, distribution and sorting of mail. Some services, however, were concerned with bulk collections from, and deliveries to, large organizations. The number of terminal points of the services, e.g. district offices and rail termini, was 360.

Since nearly all tasks, e.g. collections, deliveries, and train movements, associated with mail transferred in bulk, were scheduled, bulk transfers were also subject to strict time requirements. Thus, a typical service consisted of attendance at a rail terminus to pick up specified mail consignments arriving by specified trains, and conveyance of these to a specified sorting office; to facilitate scheduling of sorting work, and ensure mail was ready for forwarding after sorting, the arrival time at the sorting office was also specified.

Requirements for services arose as by-products of the planning of mail circulation, in which all processes affecting mail between its collection and delivery were planned, in an attempt to ensure that desired standards of service, especially speed of transit, were achieved without undue cost. The costs of bulk conveyance of mail by vehicles were small relative to the costs of the labour intensive processes associated with sorting and delivery, and so, in general, requirements for individual bulk conveyances of mail by the C.C.S. fleet were formulated without consideration of the cost, or efficiency, of that fleet. Indeed, such was the complexity of the task of planning mail circulation on the one hand, and, as will be seen, the complexity of planning the utilization of the C.C.S. fleet on the other, that it was difficult to envisage, in practical terms, how consideration of transport economy at this level could have been incorporated into the planning of mail circulation.

There was a weekly pattern of scheduled services. The services scheduled for one Monday only differed from services scheduled for the previous Monday as a result of indicated revisions in requirements. Furthermore, many services required on Tuesday were identical to those required on Monday. There were differences, however, arising primarily from differences between the railway time-tables on different days of the week. A specified service could be repeated on any combination of any number of days.

Changes to scheduled service requirements occurred continuously, owing, for example, to alterations in railway time-tables, or in mail circulation arrangements. The number of changes to scheduled services was about 50 in most weeks. However, sometimes there were as many as 1,300 changes in a single week. The occurrence of large numbers of changes was often associated with the occasional major revision of railway time-tables, but also with changes in mail circulation arrangements due, for example, to changes in function or location of sorting offices, or alterations in arrangements for handling mail at stations.

The unscheduled, or *ad hoc,* services operated to special order; the daily number of *ad hoc* services was usually between 350 and 1,000. Most *ad hoc* services were the result of special requirements, e.g. consignments of mail to docks or airports to connect with irregular departures, or special collections from organizations with occasional peak postal requirements.

Some *ad hoc* services were arranged to provide emergency support when
other mail circulation arrangements failed; amongst these emergency
requirements were those arising from failure of C.C.S. vans to perform
scheduled services because of breakdowns, or lateness due to traffic
congestion. Some vehicles were scheduled to be available full-time for
ad hoc duties; other vehicles were scheduled to report to the central
operations room to be available for *ad hoc* work when a gap of more
than an hour occurred between successive scheduled services.

Journey planning, in this context, was concerned with the preparation
of duty schedules for carrying out scheduled services as cheaply as possible.
Service requirements were strictly timed, and plans for their fulfilment
took the form of time-tables which specified the work to be performed by
individual drivers on their tours of duty. Detailed contents of the time-
tables were subject to statutory limitations imposed by the Road Traffic
Acts, e.g. on the duration of each tour of duty, and on the duration of
periods of continuous working between rests or meals; the time-tables
also had to conform to agreements about conditions of employment which
had been negotiated between the Post Office and the Post Office Workers'
Union, representing the drivers, concerning such matters as attendance
times and places, duty rotas, meals, overtime, etc.

At one time this task of bulk conveyance had been performed by a publ
haulage company under contract to the Post Office. However, the company
was purchased by the Post Office when public road haulage companies wer
being nationalized as a result of the 1947 Transport Act. Since that time
the work and size of the fleet had increased substantially.

Preparation of duty schedules was a manual operation carried out by
clerks in the transport branch of the London Postal Region. Because of the
size and complexity of the task, alterations in scheduled service requiremei
were incorporated in existing duty schedules by piecemeal amendments.
While it was appreciated that piecemeal amendment might produce
inefficient schedules, nevertheless, it was considered that the task of
preparing a completely new set of duty schedules manually would take so
long that it would be out of date, in respect of amendments due to further
changes in service requirements, before it could be implemented.

Furthermore, when plans were made for changing the location or
function of sorting offices, garages, or canteens, it was found impossible to
predict the associated changes in transport costs. It was believed that the
only way changes in cost could be assessed with confidence was by
preparing a new set of duty schedules for the changed circumstances;
however, this was a major task which could not be undertaken except

when it was intended to carry through the change. Even if it had been possible to prepare hypothetical revised schedules, it was always possible that any apparent difference in cost, as measured by the relative costs of schedules prepared for the different conditions, might only reflect differences in the efficiency of schedule preparation for the two conditions. Potential major changes in mail circulation requirements, e.g. separation of conveyance of letter and parcel mail, had not been implemented because of the difficulties of preparing such a radical revision of schedules and assessing the resulting increase in cost.

Additionally, because of the difficulty of revising schedules, there had been few real changes in staff operating conditions of service for many years; for example, reductions of the working week had been nominal; the duty schedules had remained the same, except that scheduled overtime had increased as normal working hours had decreased. Operational control also suffered; because of the constant state of change, a major effort would have been needed to establish and maintain a record of the scheduled idle time, and the times and places at which it occurred; consequently, not only was it difficult to investigate the occurrence of scheduled idle time, it was also impossible to give the central operations room advance notice of drivers who had been ordered to report to assist with the performance of *ad hoc* services during idle periods between scheduled services.

The complexity of these tasks was not due to the number of scheduled services alone, although this was a significant factor. To schedule the services for a single day, it would have been necessary to prepare a list of the 5,000, approximately, scheduled service requirements for that day. To enable these to be incorporated into schedules without much difficulty, for example, to avoid having to look through all the service requirements every time a service was allocated to a schedule to check that there were no better alternatives, it would have been convenient to impose some order on the list of service requirements. Probably the most convenient system would have been to arrange them in the sequence of their scheduled starting times.

Before allocating services, which were intended to be consecutive, to the same duty schedule, it was necessary to ensure that there was sufficient time, between the finish of the first and the start of the second, to allow for unloading and loading and for any empty running necessary between the unloading and loading points. While this condition might appear obvious, it was not always obvious in practice; for example, there was at least one railway station in the London area where several minutes were required to drive between the unloading and loading bays, although they were only 100 yards apart as the crow flies.

When allocating consecutive services to a duty schedule, it was necessary to ensure that, in addition to the proposed sequence being physically possible, it did not infringe the many restrictions arising from the Road Traffic Acts or from the agreements between the Post Office and the Union Typical examples of these restrictions were those concerning rest periods and meals. A meal, and, under most conditions, a main meal, had to be taken within 5½ hours of starting work, but, if the duty covered the whole period between noon and 2.00 p.m., a main meal had to be taken within this period. A second meal had to follow within the next 3½ hours, unless the duty had finished by then. All meals were scheduled to be taken in canteens; there were 18 canteens available for this purpose which were attached to Post Office premises; each canteen could open for different periods for each meal category. There were four meal categories, mid-day main meals, other main meals, secondary meals, and secondary meals at night. Furthermore, because of parking difficulties at some canteens at some periods of the day, it was the custom to extend the times allowed for meals at these canteens during these difficult periods. Thus, the problem of incorporating meals into duty schedules was complex

Additionally, schedules were required to conform to regulations which applied to the duty as a whole, not just to parts. For example, a duty had to start and finish at the same garage; furthermore, if any overtime was scheduled it had to be more than a minimum amount. The duty had to conform to one of four different duty types: early, day, late or night dutie Each duty type had its own rules for starting and finishing times; but one the most significant was that no duty could be scheduled to start between 10 p.m. and 6 a.m. Additionally, individual duty schedules were fitted int a rota for each driver; rotas had to consist of the same type of duties, but were themselves of three further types, five, five and a half, and six day rotas; the pattern of rota requirements resulted largely from the relatively small number of conveyances required on Saturdays.

Many restrictions and agreements of this type exist, at least in an implicit form, in most other working situations; the distinguishing feature of the operation of this fleet was the extent to which they had become formalized.

Although many detailed problems have been ignored, sufficient have been described to explain why adjusting duty schedules as a result of changes in service requirements was a difficult task to perform manually, and why the preparation of a completely new set of duty schedules, starting with the service requirements, would have been virtually impossib by manual methods. The complexity of the task, and its significance, had been recognised by the management; hence their attempt to utilize computers for the purpose; the computer solution was neither easy nor obvious (described in chapter 39).

Furthermore, although some simplification of the scheduling task might have resulted if some modifications could have been negotiated to the agreements with the Union, it should be noted that the drivers concerned were comparatively poorly paid, by London standards, and that, although there were 1,230 drivers, they were only a small group in comparison to the total number of Post Office employees, and the adjustment of differentials is always difficult.

Preparation of the duty schedules has now been transferred to a computer system. The computational problems of preparing duty schedules under these circumstances are formidable, so that, although good schedules are prepared by the system, i.e. schedules which are better (use less resources, cheaper, more efficient) than those which were produced by manual methods, no way was seen of even attempting to prepare the 'best' schedules. Nevertheless, a large part of the work devoted to the design and implementation of the computer system was concerned with data handling rather than with computation. The problem of preparing a file of service requirements converted into a form suitable for computer input (e.g. punched cards or paper tape) only when it was required for immediate scheduling purposes was seen to be so expensive, time consuming, and fraught with the probability of errors, that it was found preferable to maintain a file of service requirements permanently within the computer system, amending it as service requirements were amended. The computer system only required a minimum amount of coded information to calculate the duty schedules. The schedules to be used by drivers, however, cannot be in code. Manual de-coding was seen to be too expensive and too time-consuming. Consequently, this function also was transferred to the computer system, requiring the storage of much additional information. Operational duty schedules are prepared by the computer system directly.

Thus, in this journey planning process associated with a very different transport operation, many common features of journey planning re-appear. The journey planning, or duty scheduling, procedure largely determines the current operating efficiency, but it is also needed for assessing the costs and benefits arising from changes, and therefore for effective longer-term planning. The procedure is so complex itself that within the time period available only limited attempts to prepare efficient schedules are possible. Furthermore, the journey planning or duty scheduling procedure is embedded in a system from which it cannot be isolated. If attempts are to be made to improve the efficiency of journey planning, then these attempts must be directed at the system as a whole, and not restricted to the journey planning function.

Part 7

Estimation of journey duration and the planned idle time

Chapter 23

Service, variable duration, and planned idle time,

Most road goods transport requirements include a very strong element of service, particularly with respect to time, as has already been emphasized and illustrated in part 6; additional time constraints are often imposed by other factors, e.g. legislation. Normally, when a vehicle is dispatched on a journey, the driver has been given a task to complete within a given time. Consequently, the preparation and allocation of tasks to drivers, or journey planning, must result in plans for journeys which can and will be completed under all but exceptional circumstances, nevertheless utilizing the available time as completely as is practicable. Hence the need to estimate or predict journey duration.

Journey planning involves compromise between service fulfilment, on the one hand, and efficiency, maximum utilization of available time, on the other. But the circumstances of the driving tasks are such as to introduce a bias in the nature of this compromise. Service failure results in complaints, and often in the need for expensive or troublesome remedial or pacifying actions. In contrast, there is considerable difficulty both in supervising drivers while they are outside the depot, and in measuring efficiency in the performance of driving tasks. Furthermore, numerous factors act so as to obscure the occurrence of inefficiency; two examples will be given:

a   while the average wages of drivers (£22.35 in 1968) are of the same order of those of other workers, basic wages (£12.67 in 1968) are very low, and average wages are only made up by very extensive amounts of overtime working (23.1); the practice of working substantial amounts of overtime to compensate for the low basic wage is widely condoned, with the result that it is very difficult to detect how much of the time worked was necessary to perform the task in hand, and how much of it was merely undertaken to increase overtime payments;

b   many components of the driving task are essentially very erratic in their demands for effort or time; subject to variable effects of traffic congestion and road conditions, the driving component of the duration of journeys is essentially variable, while the time spent on loading and unloading, associated administrative procedures and waiting for attention may also be very variable.

The effect of these two factors together is to conceal the presence and extent of inefficiency. Consequently, the demand for service is always likely to be given priority, since service failures and their consequences are so much more easily recognized.

The variable duration of specified tasks, when completion is required to obtain service, introduces a new type of problem to the estimation of duration. It is not sufficient to estimate the average or expected duration (23.2); it is also necessary to estimate the maximum reasonable duration for that particular task. Conversely, even the maximum task which should be allocated to a given period of time should only be expected to extend beyond the given period under exceptional circumstances. The expected duration of this task may be very much less than the given period, for under most conditions the expected, or average, journey duration will be exceeded on 50% of the occasions, and a 50% rate of failure to complete the planned task would often be completely unacceptable.

Under certain assumptions it is possible to calculate the allowance that should be made for errors of prediction due to variable conditions and durations. Thus, if a 2½% rate of failure were tolerable, allowing for failure to complete the planned task within the maximum time available on one occasion in forty, and if the variations in duration were normally distributed (23.3), then the difference between the expected duration and the maximum time available would need to be at least twice the standard error (23.3). If journey durations are variable, there is a permitted maximum duration, and planned journeys must be completed, then the expected duration will be less than the maximum duration.

If an allowance of extra time to counter the inevitable adverse variations in journey duration is not made, then, if maximum utilization of the time available at average work rates has been planned, satisfactory performance of service requirements depends upon the drivers compensating for adverse variations by extra effort, if this be possible. In urban districts, it is not clear how far greater effort exerted by drivers serves to reduce the duration of journeys without increasing the risk of accidents; while in rural areas, where the effect of traffic congestion is less, the relationship between effort, road configuration, including width, bends, cross-roads and turnings, journey duration, and safety, is equally unknown. It is possible that extra effort will not always lead to an adequate reduction in the duration of a given journey, nor to an adequate reduction of terminal administration, loading, or unloading time requirements.

While it is necessary for journey plans to make provision for the natural variability of journey durations by allowing for durations to be more than the expected durations, nevertheless, the average journey duration observed will only be equal to the average duration expected, providing that the basis for estimating the expected journey durations is accurate. The difference between the actual and corresponding planned durations will be very variable; and, since the occurrence and extent of these differences cannot easily be anticipated, it is difficult to utilize the time they represent. Consequently, the period allowed in excess of the average expected duration will be called the planned idle time. (Although he did not use this term, Smeed recognised this phenomenon in a passage which is quoted in chapter 25 (**23.4**).)

A number of factors affect the relative size of the planned idle time:
1 Different road goods transport tasks differ in the degree of variability that is inevitable, e.g. the speed of urban journeys is more subject to the variable effects of traffic congestion than is the speed of most rural journeys, and the duration of terminal tasks will vary more or less according to the type of task to be performed, and the attitude of those at the terminals.
2 In general, because variations in different components of tasks tend to offset each other to some extent, the greater the planned duration of a task, the less the relative size of planned idle time. Thus, one of the costs of accepting inflexible time restrictions on intermediate sections of journeys, as, for example, when retailers demand that deliveries take place at fixed times, may be that the size of the planned idle time is increased relative to the planned journey duration.
3 The planned idle time increases as the journey duration estimation procedure decreases in precision. Whatever method of estimation is used, it is necessary to make an allowance, whether explicit or implicit, for the difference between the estimated and the possible journey duration; this difference increases as the estimation accuracy decreases.

As has already been mentioned, it may be possible for drivers to vary their efforts to reduce, to some extent, the effect of variations due to external factors; this reduction could be reflected in a reduction of the planned idle time. However, if increased effort is exerted only occasionally to offset increased requirements, when that increased effort could, under other circumstances or suitable arrangements, be available regularly, then planned idle time is not being reduced, but only hidden, by the variable efforts. Variable effort only contributes to an effective reduction of planned idle time if it actually serves to utilize a degree of effort which would, whether by capacity or inclination, only be exerted occasionally, when necessary, and not on a regular basis. But, when this condition is met, if the occasional extra effort makes possible a regular reduction in the planned idle time it is highly productive.

The planned idle time may be concealed even when performance standards are applied, if these are too low, since it is always possible to expand work or rest to utilize the time available.

However, to attempt to obtain increased productivity by putting pressure on the drivers to produce enhanced performance without being fully aware of the implications is a dubious practice. To base driving schedules on observed average speeds, as has often been recommended, implies a completely untested assumption that drivers can offset, by extra effort, any variability in the driving conditions which may occur, without also incurring danger. This assumption may once have been reasonable when, for example, the maximum driving speed permitted during the observations of the average speed was 20 m.p.h.; the situation becomes very different when the permitted maximum driving speed is raised to 40 m.p.h., because there is far less scope, in practice, for the performance of speeds above the maximum permitted for scheduling purposes.

While comments are often made about the extent to which drivers waste time, whether in transport cafes or elsewhere, nevertheless, some under-utilization of working time is an essential feature of work which has to be arranged in such a way that the plans are performed and which consists of tasks with variable work content but fixed duration. Furthermore, one basic component of the time wasted, the planned idle time, could be reduced by the development of better journey duration estimation or prediction procedures; most of the procedures currently in use are extremely inaccurate, and must be responsible for a significant amount of unnecessary idling. The procedures used to estimate journey duration are the responsibility of management.

Another basic component of the time which drivers appear to waste may result from co-operation rather than time-wasting. The natural variability of journey durations increases relative to the average journey durations as these decrease; from their behaviour, this appears to be recognized, perhaps implicitly, by drivers, e.g. most wholesale deliveries were found, in the London Traffic Survey, to take place in the morning (23.5). Whether it is recognized or not, many drivers say that they try to get ahead of schedule early in their journeys, so that some time is in reserve in case it should be needed later. When this reserve time is not required to offset adverse variations, it is not unreasonable for drivers to spend it in transport cafes or elsewhere. However, the situation may be more complex; for example, the reserve time accumulated may be the realization of the planned idle time.

There is, therefore, a strong *a priori* case for a re-examination of some of the common attitudes and methods of road goods transport management; insufficient attention to the estimation of work content increases the planned idle time by an unnecessary element; encouragement, or acceptance, of conditions in which more than 37% of drivers' average wages are obtained by chronic overtime working inevitably results in the concealment of inefficiency; increasing scheduled work rates without appreciation, comprehension or examination of the factors involved, and of the effects which may follow, is a cavalier way of pushing the problems of road goods transport efficiency or inefficiency on to drivers. A preferable alternative method of increasing efficiency might be to pay fixed, acceptable, wages for the performance of planned tasks (incentive payments could be associated with increased working rates used in the preparation of the journey plans if this were worth while) associated with 'job-and-finish' conditions; if drivers finish work when their planned tasks are completed, there is an incentive to reveal, rather than conceal, inefficiency, and also to adopt improved methods of estimating journey durations. (In some organizations drivers' conditions of employment already include 'job-and-finish' provisions). However the key condition is the use of good methods of estimating journey duration, for without that condition there is no way of ensuring that the journey plans are exploiting, as far as is reasonable and practicable, the available working time.

The estimation procedure should, therefore, not only enable the average time requirements of the tasks to be estimated, but also enable the planned idle time to be estimated and reduced to the economic minimum that is compatible with the natural variability of the task. It is, in general, neither necessary nor financially beneficial to make the estimates as precise as is ultimately possible, since the way in which the various errors interact, providing they are independent, e.g. neither directly, nor indirectly, causally related, is such that little benefit is derived from increasing the predictability of one factor much beyond the predictability of another. For example, there is little point in expending effort to estimate the journey distance more precisely if the objective is to estimate the journey duration and if the journey speed is already less predictable then the distance, due to the variable effects of traffic congestion. Under a simple set of assumptions concerning the way in which errors interact (which, to statisticians, involves the combination of independent normal distributions) the combination of two factors with errors of the same size will produce a result with an error only 40% greater than the error of either separately; the combination of two factors, one with error which is half as great as that of the other, only leads to an overall error 12% more than the larger; when the error of one factor is one-fifth that of the other, the combined error is only 2% greater than that of the larger.

Chapter 24

Different methods of estimating journey duration

There are many different driving tasks; associated with the different tasks it is natural that there are very many different conditions which affect the choice of methods for estimating journey duration.

Thus, for example, some journeys are repeated many times; when this is so, it is possible to measure the duration of each journey repeatedly. and to estimate the duration of future journeys on the basis of these direct observations.

In contrast, wholesale delivery journeys performed by some organizations are repeated rarely, if ever. Customers may expect to receive deliveries within 24 or 48 hours of placing orders, and orders may be placed irregularly, with the result that, not only may complete journeys never be repeated, but also there may be a very large number of possible elements of journeys many of which may never be performed, and many of the remainder may rarely be repeated. In these circumstances, if the physical location of the customers can be identified simply, e.g. by the retrieval of stored information for known customers, then the most accurate and practicable method of estimating journey duration may be on the basis of the separate estimates of journey distance and journey speed.

In a further contrast to these two types of journey, is the type of intermediate journey where the number or location of the calling points, whether for administrative or information processing reasons, may not be known in advance; in these conditions it may be best to set up regular journeys whose distance and basic duration, excluding the provision of services, can be estimated from repeated observations, but where the time required for services is estimated as a function of the expected distribution of the number and type of calls; examples of this type of work include journeys for the collection and delivery of 'smalls', or 'sundries', and the delivery of mail.

It is not intended to attempt to examine all the possible ways of estimating the duration of planned journeys. Rather, the intention is to illustrate some of the problems by examining the elements of what is probably the most common procedure, separate estimation of distance and speed, and to draw some detailed conclusions about common methods of estimating distance and speed and their relative accuracy.

Chapter 25

Estimating the duration of a journey of known distance

The actual duration of a journey may differ from the expected duration for two distinctly different reasons. The natural variability would result in the actual duration being different from the average which would be found if the same journey were repeated many times and the durations observed. This variability, or unpredictability, can therefore be observed if the durations of repetitions of the same journey are recorded. In addition, unless the average duration is already known, there may be differences between the expected and average durations. This effect can be appreciated if the average speeds of a number of journeys over different routes, which would be regarded as similar for estimation purposes, are compared. In the discussion which follows an attempt is made to examine two components separately.

There is little published information about the variability of traffic speeds or journey durations on repetitions of the same journey. Smeed (**25.1**) reported some data on traffic speeds, which was obtained by timing a number of test journeys on a sample of roads in London and Glasgow, over a period of two to three weeks. For journeys of about one mile in length, the different observations of the average journey speed were found to be approximately normally distributed. (A distribution is a statistical term for the relative frequency with which different values of a variable are observed. A normal distribution is often thought of as being typically due to random variations). The results are repeated in table 25.1.
Smeed found that the data suggested that the standard deviation (the standard deviation is a measure of the scatter of the observations) of the journey speed tended to decrease slightly as the average speed decreased, but that the coefficient of variation, or ratio of the standard deviation to the average, tended to increase. He also noted that the standard deviation of the speed, for a given average speed, tended to be about the same in London and Glasgow. Relating these figures to the expected range of durations for journeys of one mile in length, Smeed found that, where the average speed was 18 m.p.h., only 20% of the journey durations would lie outside the range of 2.9 to 4.1 minutes; at an average speed of 6 m.p.h., 20% of the journey durations would lie outside the range of 7.3 to 16.5 minutes.

Table 25.1 Mean and standard deviation of traffic speeds in test runs on a selection of roads

	mean speed (m.p.h.)	stand'd dev'n about mean (m.p.h.)	coefficient of variation	number of journeys on which based
selection of roads in London	5.7	1.8	0.32	30
	7.1	1.8	0.25	
	8.2	1.8	0.22	
	9.2	2.0	0.22	
	12.8	2.3	0.18	
	13.3	2.7	0.20	
	13.4	3.6	0.27	
	19.7	2.8	0.14	
	21.9	2.9	0.13	
selection of roads in Glasgow	7.5	1.7	0.23	40
	8.4	2.0	0.24	
	8.9	1.9	0.21	
	9.9	2.1	0.21	
	10.5	2.3	0.22	
	11.9	2.4	0.20	

Smeed concluded:

The fact that the variability of journey time is great when the mean speed is low must – in practice – mean that the effective time for making journeys must be greater than the actual time, because road users often make a journey to a place which they wish to reach by a given time, and must allow for the possibility of their journey taking longer than the average time even when it actually may take less.

This is the first reference found to the phenomenon which is called here the planned idle time.

Unfortunately, there are grounds for a number of reservations about these reported results. One problem is to clarify what is meant by the average speed of a journey under different circumstances. On good roads, with little traffic, the major factor affecting the average journey speed may be the performance characteristics of the vehicle, together with its degree of loading. On poor roads, but still with little traffic, the road configuration and conditions will be added to the vehicle performance characteristics and degree of loading as factors determining the average speed of the journey. On any type of road which is subject to heavy traffic relative to its configuration, traffic congestion may be the major factor setting an upper limit to the possible average journey speed. Speed limits, whether applied to vehicles or roads set a limit to the maximum speed utilized during each journey. Legal speed limits vary somewhat with the type of vehicle; it is not uncommon to find speed limits imposed by managements, in order to protect vehicles from being over-driven, or by drivers, with the support of their unions, in order to protect drivers from being over-extended. The data for the reports of average speed variations quoted refers to urban areas, in which traffic congestion was the dominant factor determining the observed average journey speeds. In these circumstances, 'speed' may have an implied special definition due to the methods of measurement (**25.2**).

Thomson (**25.3**) also referred to the predictability of the duration of journeys over the same route. He utilized data collected in two Central London Traffic Surveys, in which the time taken to repeat segments of eight different routes twenty times each was recorded. His results are repeated in table 25.2.

Table 25.2 Predictability of journey times, and journey times as percentage of average (for journeys in central London between 2½ and 3 miles long)

journey durations as proportion (%) of average	proportion of journeys in 1960 (%)	proportion of journeys in 1966 (%)
30-40	–	0.2
40-50	–	0.3
50-60	0.5	0.6
60-70	3.6	4.8
70-80	9.5	13.0
80-90	20.6	19.0
90-100	23.1	20.9
100-110	16.7	14.7
110-120	11.0	9.0
120-130	5.5	7.8
130-140	4.5	3.5
140-150	2.5	2.4
150-160	1.0	1.4
160-170	0.6	0.8
170-180	0.5	0.5
180-190	0.2	0.3
190-200	0.2	0.3
200-210	–	0.3
210-220	–	0.2

There seems to be no reported observations of the variability or unpredictability of the duration or speed of rural journeys.

For many journeys, the repetition which is of interest is of movement from the origin to the destination, or from the origin to the destination calling at a number of intermediate points; in both sets of data reported it was the precise route which was repeated, and there was no scope for driver discretion in the route followed. Again, there seems to be no information available about the effect of minor route variations, especially when these are chosen at the driver's discretion to reduce the variable effects of traffic congestion on the journey duration.

Even within the restricted context of the variability of duration or average speed associated with the repetition of journeys in urban areas, these two sets of observations are subject to a further major limitation. The data reported by Smeed referred to journeys of the order of 1 mile in length, and that reported by Thomson referred to journeys of the order of 2½ to 3 miles in length. Neither set of observations gives any guidance as to the variability of duration or average speed to be expected for journeys of other lengths.

One incidental question associated with processing this type of data is whether to express results in terms of the speed or duration. One reason for expressing results in terms of the average speed is that this concept is more immediately and intuitively meaningful. There are also, however, sound reasons against this practice. It is usually the duration of a journey which is observed directly; the average speed is usually derived from known values of the distance and duration; similarly, it is usually the duration of a journey which needs to be estimated, whether directly, as for repetitions of the same journey, or indirectly, from estimates of the distance of journeys which are not repeated. In the discussion which follows immediately, attention will be directed primarily at the variability of the duration, and at estimates of the duration derived either from direct observation or from distance estimates.

The averages of twenty observations of the duration of journeys over each of eight different routes, the standard deviations and ranges of the observations, are presented in table 25.3; these results are based upon the 1966 Central London Traffic Survey data (25.4) which were utilized to obtain the results repeated earlier in table 25.2.

The only information found about studies of the way in which the magnitude of the variation, or standard deviation, of journey duration is related to the average journey duration, was reported in an internal Road Research Laboratory communication (25.5). It was based on data collected during a traffic survey in Central London in September 1947. Some of the findings are repeated in figure 25.4.

Table 25.3 Variability of journey duration (observations on 8 journeys each repeated 20 times)

journey distance (miles)	average duration (seconds)	standard deviation of duration (seconds)	minimum duration (seconds)	maximum duration (seconds)
11.01	3558	548	2750	4448
11.03	3669	807	2611	5833
9.42	3014	424	2408	3729
10.31	3650	387	2930	4422
10.87	3359	536	2673	4525
11.40	4361	791	3535	5676
10.96	4217	852	2860	6548
13.80	3457	521	2509	4460

For reasons explained in the appendix to this chapter, it was suspected that the relationship between the standard deviation and average duration might have changed since 1947; consequently, the relationship between the standard deviation and average duration was found for the data collected in the 1966 Central London Traffic Survey (25.6); detailed results are presented in figure 25.5. It will be seen that the standard deviation of journey duration increased more rapidly with an increase in the average journey duration in 1966 than in 1947 and, as shown in the appendix, the data are not inconsistent with the hypothesis that the standard deviation, or variability, was proportional to the average duration.

Thus the results of the enquiry into the way in which the duration of successive journeys over the same route varies may be summarized as follows:

1 the standard deviation of the duration of journeys in those urban areas where the average speed is of the order of 11 m.p.h. is approximately 20% of the average duration, and this relationship appears not to be affected very much by the length of the journey;

2 in even more congested areas the standard deviation of the duration is probably an even higher proportion of the average duration, and, again, the relationship is probably independent of the length of the journey;

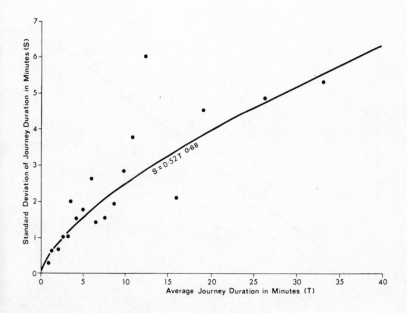

Fig. 25.4 Average duration and its standard deviation. Observations, London 1947.

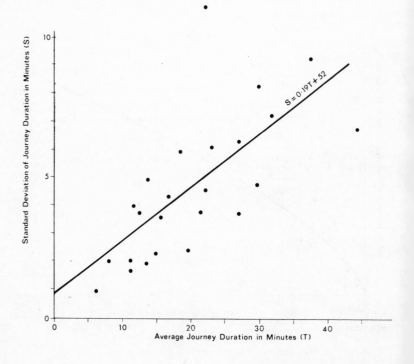

Fig. 25.5 Average duration and its standard deviation. Observations, London 1966.

3 in less congested areas the standard deviation of the duration may be less, and, at some level of decreasing congestion, it would be expected that the standard deviation of the duration would represent a decreasing proportion of the duration as the length of the journey increases;

4 there appears to be no published information about the variability of journey durations for journeys in rural areas, or on the main inter-city routes; extrapolation from observations of relatively short journeys in congested urban conditions would not be justifiable.

The objective of the last section was to estimate the pattern of actual durations for a given journey when the average duration is known. In many circumstances, however, the average duration of the specific journey under consideration may not be known. Consequently, it may be necessary to estimate the expected journey duration on the basis of some general relationship, usually between journey distance and duration. (In this section the average will be taken to refer to past observations, the expected to anticipations of future observations). Thus, there will be a contribution to the standard error of the estimated duration for that particular journey, due, for example, to errors or uncertainties in the relationship utilized to convert distance into duration, to add to the standard error resulting from deviations of the duration from the average.

There is little published information concerning the variation of average speeds of different journeys, or the variation of the relationship between duration and distance (**25.7**). The data reported by Smeed (**25.1**), and repeated in table 25.1, contain some observations of average speeds over different routes of the order of one mile in length in London and Glasgow. In the same paper, Smeed gave figures for average journey speeds, in normal working hours, in Central Glasgow, Central Newcastle and Slough, of between 8 m.p.h. and 10 m.p.h. He also gave overall average speeds for Central London of 10 m.p.h., and Central Edinburgh of 13.1 m.p.h. These figures appear to have been measured in the years between 1958 and 1960. In the 1966 Central London Traffic Survey, the overall average of the average speeds observed on the eight different routes was 11 m.p.h. To infer from this observation that the average speed of traffic in Central London was 11 m.p.h. appears to imply a definition of 'average speed'; otherwise the detailed meaning is not very clear. Considering the eight routes separately, the standard deviation of their individual average speeds from the average of the individual average speeds was 1.6 m.p.h.

Intuitively, the average speed of a journey is expected to depend upon the nature, or environment, of the journey. Average speeds of journeys in towns are expected to be different from the average speeds of journeys in the country. Furthermore, the average speeds of journeys in the centres of the big cities are expected to be different from those of journeys in the suburbs of the same cities. This is well illustrated in work done to estimate journey durations by the work study department of a company concerned with wholesale distribution, and already mentioned in chapter 21. In this work, roads were divided into three categories according to their environments, which were called 'town', 'residential', and 'country', and it was found that assigning average speeds for each of these of 10.3 m.p.h., 15.1 m.p.h., and 24.4 m.p.h. (the maximum instantaneous speed permitted was limited by agreement with the appropriate union to 30 m.p.h.), gave good agreement with observed times for journeys.

Clearly, the concept and nature of the average speed, or relationship between distance and duration, that is utilized in the estimation of journey duration, depends on the nature of the journey and its environment, and the overall effort put into the estimation of journey duration. No study has been found in which the errors of practical methods of estimating the expected duration or speed have been determined statistically.

It has been established (e.g. **25.8**) that the speed of traffic flow decreases as the volume increases within a limited range of conditions which includes, however, those most commonly observed. It follows that to obtain accurate estimates of expected journey durations it might be necessary to take into account variations in traffic flow, or congestion.

As far as urban area journey estimation procedures are concerned, it seems that the 1966 Central London Traffic Survey results for the eight different routes may reasonably be considered to provide an under-estimate of the standard deviation of the average speeds of different journeys. It seems highly unlikely that any journey duration estimation procedure will be made so precise as to discriminate between journeys so similar as the eight routes included in the survey, and to ascribe to them, or estimate their duration with the use of, different average speeds. On the contrary, journey plans are usually prepared for routes which involve a much greater range of environmental and traffic conditions than shown by these eight routes. Consequently, it is assumed that the standard error of estimates of the expected duration for journeys of approximately one hour's duration in urban areas, when the estimates are based upon a relationship between distance and duration, is at least 14% of the expected duration.

There appears to be no evidence available about the way in which this standard error varies with the duration of the journey, or with changes in any other factors. But it is intuitively reasonable to assume that, for journeys of approximately the same duration, the standard errors of estimates of the expected duration will be much higher if the journey traverses a less uniform area, in terms of town, residential or rural characteristics, or road configurations, particularly if no effort is made to compensate for this lack of uniformity. It also seems intuitively reasonable to assume that the longer the journey the less uniform its circumstances. From the known relationships between traffic speed and flow and road configurations (e.g. **25.**9) it is clear that changes in these factors which are not taken into account, when the expected speed is estimated, however difficult that might be, could result in the error in estimating the expected speed becoming larger than the errors resulting from the variable duration of repetitions of the same journey.

When an estimate of the duration is prepared for a journey of known distance, the error of that estimate will usually depend upon the contribution of two factors, the error of the estimate of the expected duration, and differences between actual durations and their average. As far as urban journeys are concerned what little evidence there is suggests that the combined standard error to be anticipated, as a result of these two component errors, is unlikely to be less than 25% of the expected duration for journeys of one hour or less (the combined effects of independent standard errors of 20% and 15% respectively is a standard error of approximately 25%) unless the expected duration has been estimated from repeated observations, in which case the standard error is likely to be about 20% of the observed average; it also seems unlikely that the standard error will decline much below 25% of the expected duration even for much longer journeys since, even if the deviations from the average become proportionally less, and the available evidence hardly supports this, it appears likely that the accuracy of estimates of the expected duration will decline in compensation.

Other factors may sometimes have an appreciable influence. For example, many journeys of extended duration in urban areas involve repeated stops, e.g. for collection or delivery. It may be assumed that, if the same traffic flows affect a vehicle over a significant part of the journey, resulting in correlation between the times taken to traverse successive segments, then stops, by removing the vehicle from the associated traffic flow, tend to decrease this correlation effect. Furthermore, it seems intuitively likely that the longer the stops the greater their effect in reducing correlation between the duration of successive segments of the journey. However, while this is a plausible assumption, there appears to be no evidence available to support or refute it.

There appear to be no observations on rural journeys from which the characteristics of estimates of journey speeds and durations may be deduced. However, it is possible to offer some tentative hypotheses. For most rural journeys the variability of the duration of the same journey when repeated is likely to be less marked than for urban journeys; there are, however, some rural roads which are as liable to congestion effects as most urban roads. If the average journey duration is not known, but must be estimated, then it is likely that the standard error of the estimates will be larger than those quoted for the eight routes in Central London, since road configurations and congestion effects are likely to vary considerably over different routes. The effects of towns and cities which have to be negotiated or bypassed may be relatively very important.

While, again, no direct evidence is available, it is probable that marked differences would be observed in both the averages and standard errors for urban and rural journeys if separate examinations were made for day and night journeys. (The data quoted was restricted to daytime observations). Speeds are probably faster and less variable at night; but if it were not known when a journey was to be performed, inclusion of the possibility of night journeys would probably increase the standard error of estimates of the speed.

Chapter 25

Appendix

Relationship between the average, and standard deviation of, journey duration.

Let the average duration of two successive segments of a journey be denoted by t_1 and t_2, and let the corresponding standard deviations be s_1 and s_2.

If the durations found on repeated journeys were normally distributed (this is only approximately true) and independent, then the average, and standard deviation of, duration of the two segments taken together, if denoted by t_{1+2} and s_{1+2} would be:—

$$t_{1+2} = t_1 + t_2$$

$$s_{1+2} = \sqrt{(s_1{}^2 + s_2{}^2)}$$

Furthermore, if the segments were, for practical purposes, indistinguishable and of the same length, then it might be assumed that,

$$t_{1+2} = 2t_1$$

and

$$s_{1+2} = s_1 \sqrt{2}$$

Generalising to n identical segments the average T, and the standard deviation S, are given by

$$T = nt_1 \tag{1}$$

$$S = s_1 \sqrt{n} \tag{2}$$

If $\qquad s_1 = at_1$,

then, substituting for s_1 in (2)

$$S = at_1 \sqrt{n} \qquad\qquad (3)$$

whence, comparing (1) and (3) to eliminate n

$$S = a\sqrt{(t_1 T)}$$

If $\qquad\qquad a\sqrt{t_1} = K$, a constant,

then $\qquad\qquad S = k\sqrt{T},$

$\qquad$ or $\quad S = KT^{0.5}$

Thus, if journey durations were normally distributed, and the durations for successive segments of the journey were not correlated, it would be anticipated that the standard deviation would be proportional to the square root of the average duration.

In fact, Turner and Wardrop (**25.6**), using data collected in 1947, found the relationship to be,

$$S = 0.52T^{0.68} \; ;$$

their results are plotted in figure 25.4.

For the 1966 survey data (table 25.3) the average duration of an 11 mile journey is approximately 1 hour, with a standard deviation of 10 minutes. From this, and on the basis of the theoretical relationship between the average duration and standard deviation, it would be expected that the standard deviation of the duration of a journey of 1 mile would be approximately 3 minutes, compared with an average duration of approximately 5½ minutes. These figures do not correspond with those given by Smeed (**25.1**), and shown in table 25.1, for mean speeds and standard deviations of the speeds for journeys of 1 mile in length.

Thus, the relationship between the average duration and its standard deviation derived theoretically is not consistent with these two sets of observations. The assumptions made in deriving the relationship must therefore be examined.

If traffic congestion is a major factor controlling traffic speeds, then the assumption of the independence of journey durations over successive segments becomes highly questionable, since the level of congestion does not usually change very markedly between successive segments, and hence would have similar effects on the durations of successive segments of the same journey. In the extreme, if the durations of successive segments of journeys were perfectly correlated, then equation (2) would be replaced by

$$S = ns_1 \qquad\qquad (4)$$

and the relationship between S and T in this case would be

$$S = K'T \qquad\qquad (5)$$

where K' is a constant.

In general, correlation between the durations of successive segments would be expected to result in the relationship between the standard deviation and average duration of the form

$$S = KT^{\alpha}$$

where $\qquad\qquad \alpha = 1$ for perfect correlation,

$\qquad\qquad 0.5 < \alpha < 1$ for partial positive correlation,

$\qquad\qquad \alpha = 0.5$ for complete independence,

and $\qquad\qquad \alpha < 0.5$ for negative correlation.

Judged on this basis, the results of Turner and Wardrop would be consistent with partial positive correlation, presumably as a result of the enduring effects of traffic congestion from one segment of road to the next.

Traffic flow in London has increased since 1947, as measured by flow indices; if 1947 is taken as base year, with index of 100, then in 1966 the off-peak index was 147, and the on-peak index was 176 **(25.10)**. There has probably been some increase in congestion effects associated with the measured flows. If traffic congestion results in correlation between speeds on successive segments of journeys, then it would be expected that the correlation would have increased, if traffic congestion has increased, since 1947. Correlation of speeds over successive segments might also be increased by successful traffic management schemes. If correlation has increased it would be reflected in higher values for d in a relationship between the standard deviation and average duration.

For the data collected in 1966 the relationship between the standard deviation and the average duration was found to be

$$S = 0.22T^{0.999}$$

The correlation coefficient between the logarithms of S and T was found to be 0.80; the index of T was significant at the 0.1% level. On the other hand the difference between the index of T and 1 was not significant, and consequently a linear relationship was calculated and is shown in figure 25.5. The best linear fit to the data was given by

$$S = 0.19T + 0.88 \text{ (the units are minutes).}$$

The correlation coefficient was 0.70, and the coefficient of T was significant at the 0.1% level.

These results on the 1966 data support the hypothesis that traffic congestion leads to the speeds over successive segments of the journey being correlated. However, the results imply that, in 1966, the correlation was very high, almost too high to be entirely credible.

Chapter 26

Some types of error in the estimation of journey distance

In some circumstances it may be possible to measure, store, and utilize directly the distances of all the different journeys which are likely to be undertaken by an organization, particularly when a restricted set of journeys is performed repeatedly. However, as the number of different journeys that may be performed increases, and as the frequency of repetition decreases, so the problems of measurement, storage, identification and retrieval of journey distance information become more complex, and their solution becomes more expensive.

One way of simplifying the use of measured distance information when there are large numbers of possible journeys is to divide the road network into a large number of segments. The distance of each segment is then measured and stored separately. Each segment will occur in many different journeys, and estimates of journey distance can be constructed by adding together the distances of the relevant segments. The journey distance estimates will not be very much more inaccurate in absolute terms, and will be more accurate in relative terms, than the measurements of the distances of the component segments. In general, if a is the standard error of measuring one segment, the standard error of estimating the length of a journey of N segments would be expected to be a $\sqrt{N}$.

When this method is used, however, while the measurement and storage problems are reduced, the data processing problems are increased. To estimate the length of any given journey, it is necessary to identify each segment contained in that journey before its distance can be retrieved and added to the sum which will become the overall journey distance estimate. If a journey is not specified in detail, but only, as is common, by a specification of the origin and destination, together with an assumption, often implicit, that the shortest or quickest route will be used, then identification of the segments which are included in the shortest journey may entail identification of all the segments of the many part-journeys between the origin and the destination, so that the distance of each may be calculated and the shortest entire journey found by comparing the alternatives.

This method of computing the distance of the shortest journey between given origins and destinations has been adapted for use by computer. It is easy either to select the best route, or at least to eliminate most of the possible alternatives from consideration, by visual inspection; computational tests have been developed to screen the alternatives, but do not yet appear to be so discriminating as visual inspection. Consequently, a significant part of the increase in computational power associated with the use of computer for this purpose is not realized in practice.

If the origin or destination of a required journey is not located on the main road network which has been measured and stored, then the method described so far is insufficient to estimate the journey distance. In these circumstances, it may be necessary to identify, in an initial step, the nearest points on the main road network to the required origin and destination, and to estimate the distance between these points on the main road network in a separate process from the estimation of the distances between these points and the required origin and destination.

A method similar to the one described is often used to plan journeys manually. Estimates of distance prepared in this way may be extremely accurate, since it is possible to measure the distance of each of the segments of the main road network repeatedly, by different methods. and, presumably, to a relatively high degree of accuracy. There is, however, a major objection to the use of methods of this type for estimating journey distances for most road goods transport operations. Even when the journeys are between cities which are far apart, so that the major part of most journeys is confined to a relatively simple network of trunk roads, nevertheless, if the journeys performed involve many terminal cities, estimating distances in this way manually is a cumbersome and time consuming operation.

If the operation is mainly concerned with short, urban journeys the number of possible routes, and the demand for computation, is liable to become so great that to apply this method manually is inconceivable. Even if a very large computer is used the road network may have to be simplifie: furthermore, it may become necessary to identify, and calculate the distance between, not the actual terminal points of required journeys, but the areas, or zones, containing them; finally, despite the simplification resulting from identification by zones, rather than terminal points, and despite simplification of the road network, the problem of measuring the distances of the various road segments may still be beyond the capacity of many organizations. Nevertheless, this method of estimating distances has become a standard part of traffic survey and road planning exercises in large urban areas (e.g. **26.1**).

Since the utilization of measured distances leads to considerable storage or processing difficulties for many types of transport planning application, alternative methods have been devised which are less demanding. Possibly the simplest of these is based upon the multiplication of the straight line distance between the origin and destination by a factor to compensate for deviations of the road from the straight line. Measurement of the straight line distance between two identified points on a map, and conversion by the appropriate scale to ground straight line distance, is a relatively simple procedure. Similarly, calculation of the straight line distance between two points which have been identified on a co-ordinate system such as the National Grid, utilizing Pythagorus' Theorem, is an extremely simple computational procedure.

However, it may be necessary to identify the position of the origin and destination on a map, if it is intended to measure the straight line distances or to read the appropriate co-ordinates or grid references. Locating points precisely on a map can be a very slow procedure; but it becomes very much simpler and faster if it is only necessary to locate points within predetermined areas or zones, such as those utilized with the road network method. Identification of the areas or zones within which points are located need not include reference to maps if the areas used are selected to coincide with, for example, postal districts included in the addresses.

It is the intention to compare the accuracy of three different methods of estimating road distances:
1 the road network method using the centres of containing zones to represent the origins and destinations;
2 the straight line method utilizing precisely identified locations of origins and destinations;
3 the straight line method using the centres of containing zones to represent the origins and destinations.
These three are neither the only methods of distance estimation that could be devised, nor the only ones in use; nevertheless, they are more common than some others, and serve to give some idea of the problems, especially those of accuracy, associated with estimating distances.

Unfortunately, it is not possible to compare these three methods directly with data that is freely available. The quantity of data required for direct comparison would be substantial, and its special collection would have been a considerable task; moreover, the special collection of this data, and the form which it would take, might not encourage conviction that the data and its collection was objective and independent of the method and purposes of the collection or collector, or that the results were capable of being repeated. In the event it was decided to try to use data which, although unpublished, was available; but use of this data necessitated the use of a tortuous and obscure method of treatment. Consequently, the next section is devoted to a further examination of the errors that may be associated with the different methods of distance estimation.

Road network method.
In this method, the main road junctions of the road network to be utilized are identified, and called nodes. The road network is described by specification of the connections, and corresponding distances, between adjacent nodes. The distance between any pair of nodes can then be found by adding the distances of connections between adjacent nodes until the shortest distance between the specified pair of nodes is found. Conceptually the method is essentially simple; computationally, the method is liable to be expensive because of the large number of possible routes between two nodes; computationally, the method is also fairly complex because of the necessity to devise methods, suitable for use on a computer, for finding the shortest route from amongst all those possible. The task may be shortened and simplified in many ways; for example, many of the road junctions, and connections between road junctions, in urban areas may be ignored so that the conceptual road network utilized only represents a simplified version of the actual road network. In the London Traffic Survey the road network used was 1,933 miles of 'main roads'; the total length of road in the inner two-thirds of the survey area was more than four times as great (26.2).

From this general description of the method it will be seen that the accuracy of the distance estimated between two specified nodes may be affected by two factors; the accuracy cannot be greater than is permitted by the accuracy of measurement of the distances between adjacent nodes; equally, even if the distance estimated for a given route between two specified nodes is highly accurate, the estimate of the shortest distance between the two nodes may not be very good if some connections, which form part of the shortest route between the two nodes, have been omitted from the specification of the road network. It is assumed here that the accuracy of measurement of the distance between adjacent nodes can be extremely accurate, at least relative to other sources of error, and it is therefore ignored in the discussions that follow.

The distance that is being estimated is that of the shortest journey between given points; these terminal points may not coincide with the centres of the zones in which they are situated. Consequently, there is a further potential source of error associated with the assumed correspondence between the centres of the zones containing the terminal points, and the terminal points themselves; this error is likely to depend upon the distances between the terminal points and the zone centres, and, since it is possible for this distance to be greater as the size of the zones increases, this error may be expected to increase as the size of zones increases.

It is intuitively reasonable to assume that the estimation errors will depend upon the distribution of terminal points within zones. To collect data representing the possible, likely, or representative distributions of terminal points within zones would be, at best, a mammoth task and, at worst, because of the difficulty of defining possible, likely, or representative distributions in this context, might be meaningless. However, the worst of this problem can be evaded, if, instead of attempting to find a representative distribution of terminal points of journeys within zones, an attempt is made to estimate the errors resulting from a random distribution of terminal points. While a systematic distribution could give worse errors than a random distribution, a systematic distribution is unlikely to be consciously chosen to give worse errors. It is possible that, where there is freedom to choose, the systematic distribution would give smaller errors than a random distribution if, for example, zone centres were chosen to be in the middle of the main business centre within each zone. However, if the overall area covered is large enough relative to the number of zones that is used it is unlikely that most zones will be small enough to contain only one centre of activity. In the London Traffic Survey an area of 941 square miles was divided into 933 zones (26.3). Furthermore, it is often necessary for zone centres to represent, in addition, junctions in the road network. In these circumstances a random distribution may be realistic and representative. An attempt has been made to estimate the errors resulting from a random distribution of terminal points within zones for different zone sizes in a way, and with results, to be described later.

The straight line method.
This method of estimating journey distance is based upon calculation or measurement of straight line distances between known terminal points, and multiplication of straight line distances by a factor which represents the deviation of the road system from straight lines. The estimation errors reflect the degree to which the deviations of particular roads from straight lines differ from the average deviation. Evaluation of this method therefore depends upon an assessment of the variability of these deviations for different journeys.

A casual inspection of any map indicates that the road system is irregular. There are far more roads in urban areas than there are in remote country districts; but the road density varies considerably even within urban areas. There are also discontinuities in the road system due to physical barriers formed by the coast line, estuaries, rivers and mountains. Ideally, to test this method of estimating distance, the sample of journeys utilized would need to represent, in frequency and type, the journeys which would be expected to occur in practice. Unfortunately, the patterns of journeys which occur in different transport situations are not identical, and selection of any pattern which is representative of one transport situation is likely to be biased with regard to other situations. Furthermore, existing data, which refers to journeys whose distance is already known and available, will tend to refer to journeys, or journey segments, which are regularly performed and which may therefore emphasize the effect of good road connections, and under-estimate the deviations, and variability of the deviations, met in some transport situations.

In remote rural areas, where mountains or rivers are typical physical barriers, towns and villages tend either to be directly connected by road or to be connected by lengthy detours around the physical barriers. The relative effect of direct connections, and of detours, on this method of journey distance estimation, which intuitively is likely to be considerable, depends upon the relative proportion of each type of connection. The selection of a sample of journeys which may be regarded as representative of anything but themselves presents some problems.

Method of the straight line between zone centres.
In this method, distances between terminal points are estimated on the basis of the straight line distances between the centres of zones containing the terminal points. The particular advantage offered by this method is that the terminal points need only be located within zones, and not more precisely; consequently, use may be made of existing location information especially addresses. The main anticipated disadvantage is that this method of estimating distances would combine the errors of the two previous methods; estimates of distances between centres of zones may be expected to suffer from all the inaccuracy of the straight line distance method of estimation, whilst use of the centres of zones to represent the terminal points of all journeys terminating within the corresponding zone areas may be expected to be liable to the same errors in this method as when it is used in the road network method.

Chapter 27

The accuracy of methods of distance estimation

Three types of error have been identified in the last chapter:
1 an error peculiar to the road network method which may occur when roads or cross-roads are omitted from the description of the road network in order to reduce and simplify the task of manipulating it;
2 an error due to the use of zone centres to represent terminal points of journeys ending within the defined zonal areas, an error which may be expected to increase as the size of the zones utilized increases;
3 an error peculiar to the straight line approximation method which is due to the irregular deviations of particular routes from the average proportion by which road distances normally exceed straight line distances; this error may be expected to be greater in areas where the road density is not uniform, where roads are scarce, or where there are physical barriers.

The first type of error, associated with omissions and simplification of the road network, will depend to a large extent on the skill with which the road network is specified, and the complexity with which the computer program utilized can cope; in urban areas, where simplification is likely to be most necessary, it seems intuitively unlikely that the degree of error introduced by the omission of a moderate proportion of roads or cross-roads will be very great. No evidence is offered here as to the degree of error that may occur in practice from simplification, whether forced by complexity and computer capability, or arising from choice.

The second type of error is associated with the use of zones. For a given zone size it seems likely that the size of the error will depend upon the distribution of terminal points within zones. An attempt has been made to estimate the size of errors arising as a result of a random distribution of terminal points within zones. Because of the difficulty of obtaining suitable data to isolate this source of error, the method used was to estimate the combined errors due to the straight line method and zoning, as represented by errors found with distance estimation by the straight line between zone centres; to extract from this combined error that portion of the error which can be identified as being due to the straight line method on its own; and to treat the remaining error as being that due to zoning.

Given a suitable sample of data it is possible to estimate the error due to the use of the straight line method of estimating road distances by a direct comparison between straight line and known road distances using regression methods.

The Route Planning Department of the Automobile Association has prepared, in order to plan members' journeys, a road network divided into elementary road segments whose lengths have been measured to a high degree of accuracy. The lengths and terminal points of all the road segments in two regions were made available and used as test data; the data for each region was processed separately. The Greater London region was assumed to represent dense urban districts, while the South Wales region, because it includes both industrial and rural districts, together with a variety of physical barriers in the shape of valleys, rivers, estuaries, coast line, and mountains, was treated as representative of less uniform areas. In addition, to represent longer journeys, the distances between the forty cities in England and Wales, which are recorded in the mileage chart in the Automobile Association's Handbook (27.1), were utilized as a third set of data. (The eight cities in Scotland were excluded partly because, with the most convenient computer and programs, only 1,000 distances could be handled, so that no more than forty-five cities could be used, partly because road journeys between all the cities in England and Wales and all the cities in Scotland are concentrated along the two coastal roads between England and Scotland, and partly because it was wished to omit a complete category of cities rather than appear to pick and choose.)

The errors associated with the straight line distance estimation method on its own may be summarized as follows (detailed results may be found in Appendix A to this chapter). In the Greater London region the road distances of the journey segments were found to be 21% greater than the corresponding straight line distances, and the standard error of estimates of individual road distances based on this straight line distance relationship was approximately 11% of the average road distance. In the South Wales region the road distances of the journey segments were 13% higher than the corresponding straight line distances, and the standard error of estimates of the individual road distances based on this relationship was approximately 17% of the average road distance. For journeys between the A.A. mileage chart towns, the road distances were 17% greater than the corresponding straight line distances, and the standard error of individual road distances estimated was approximately 10% of the average road distance. In statistical terms the relationships between the straight line and road distances in all three cases were very highly significant.

It may seem rather surprising that the results suggest that road connections are relatively more indirect in the Greater London region than in South Wales. However, in another study (carried out by the G.P.O. in connection with the development of the system for scheduling vans for the bulk conveyance of mail to which reference is made in chapters 22 and 39), which was confined to journeys within a five mile radius of the centre of London, and in which it was found that the road distance was 22% greater than the straight line distance, this high ratio was attributed to the effects of traffic schemes, especially those involving one-way streets and diversions, and to the need to find bridges to cross the River Thames.

Detailed examination and comparison, for journeys between the A.A. mileage chart cities, of actual road distances and the corresponding estimates based on the relationship found, revealed an interesting pattern. Although, taken overall, the standard error of estimates based on straight line distances was relatively small, and the statistical relationship between straight line estimates and road distances was very significant, nevertheless, a small proportion of the estimates were seriously in error. 19 out of the 780 estimates were more than 50 miles in error (if the distribution of errors was normal, which would be expected if they were occurring randomly, only 2 or 3 errors would be expected to be this large; 50 miles is nearly 2.9 times the standard error); 17 of these were estimates of distances between Penzance, Plymouth, Barnstaple, Exeter, and Taunton on one side of the Bristol Channel, and Aberystwyth, Carmarthen, Holyhead, and Cardiff on the other. This observation illustrates clearly the effect of physical barriers in general, and of this very large physical barrier in particular, on the accuracy of estimates of journey distance based on the straight line method.

To reduce the effects of significant physical barriers, however, it is possible to calculate the straight line distance between two points as the sum of two or more parts chosen to avoid the physical barriers. When straight line distances are measured, the distances can be measured in sections chosen to circumvent the physical barriers, e.g. distances can be measured over land, or a bridge, when the physical barrier is an expanse of water, or over low ground when the barrier is a mountain range. When straight line distances are calculated by computer, a similar effect can be achieved by identifying sectors on each side of the physical barriers, by specifying transfer or bridge points between the different sectors, and, when a journey starts and finishes in different sectors, by calculating straight line distances between the terminal points of the journey and the specified bridge points between the sectors; the overall straight line distance is the sum of the component straight line distances. When there is more than one straight line distance due, for example, to the possibility of using alternative bridge points, then the shorter or shortest may be taken as the one to be used.

When a bridge point modification to the method of calculating straight line distances was tried on the estimation of road distances between the A.A. mileage chart cities, restricting the number of sectors and bridge points so that no more than two bridge points were incorporated in any journey, it was found that road distances were 14% more than corresponding 'straight line' distances, while the standard error of estimates of road distance based on this relationship was reduced to approximately 6% of the average distance. More detailed results are given in appendix A. Detailed examination of the new estimates of the road distances which were most in error, when the unmodified straight line method was used, confirmed that the improvement in the estimation of these was significant. The 19 segments with errors in excess of 50 miles had an average error of 81 miles when the simple, unmodified, straight line distance method of estimation was utilized; with the modified method of calculation of the straight line distances, utilizing bridge points, the average error of these 19 segments was reduced to 22 miles. Thus, it is possible to obtain a considerable improvement in the accuracy of estimates of the road distances of journeys in which physical barriers must be negotiated by comparatively simple modifications. The modification used did not represent the ultimate that could be achieved; on the other hand, complicating the method of calculating straight line distances is likely to be associated with increasing complexity of computation and data collection.

The absolute size of the standard error of estimates of road distances based upon the calculation of straight line distances appears to be affected by the average length of the journeys; the standard errors found being 0.9 miles for journeys of 8.8 miles, 4.6 miles for journeys of 27.6 miles, and 17.6 miles for journeys of 168.9 miles. This is intuitively acceptable, since the longer the journey the greater the potential for error. If the errors of estimating the distance of successive segments of a journey are assumed to be independent, then it could be anticipated that the standard error would be proportional to the square root of the journey distance being estimated (The argument would be similar to that presented in the appendix to

chapter 25 for anticipating a similar relationship between the standard
error of the estimate of the duration, and the journey duration).

Considering the three sets of data which have been utilized to examine the
errors resulting from straight line distance estimation, the standard error of
estimates for the Greater London region is approximately 30% of the
square root of the average distance; the standard error of the estimates in
the South Wales region is approximately 90% of the square root of the
average distance; while the standard error of the estimates for the A.A.
mileage chart data is approximately 135% of the square root of the
average distance. The result found for the A.A. mileage chart distances
must be treated with a degree of reserve for the nature of this sample of
data is such that a single error may affect several journeys; a comparatively
simple modification to the method of calculation, to reduce the effect of
physical barriers such as the Bristol Channel, reduces the standard error to
approximately 70% of the square root of the average distance. While the
evidence is slender, because of the small number of observations, it does
not seem to contradict a tentative hypothesis that the standard error of
estimates of road distance, utilizing the straight line method, are
proportional to, and, when distances are expressed in miles, probably
rather less than, the square root of the road distance being estimated.

Additional support for this tentative hypothesis was found during a
check on the accuracy of journey distance estimates incorporated in two
sets of plans for wholesale delivery journeys, which had been prepared by
computer, using the straight line method. The journeys planned by
computer were plotted on maps and the road distances measured by
opisometer. These measurements of the road distances were then
compared with the estimated road distances. Both sets of journeys were
confined to London and the Home Counties. The average journey distance
for one set was 40 miles and the standard error of the estimates was almost
40% of the square root of the average distance. The average distance of the
second set of journeys was 79 miles; the standard error of the estimates was
approximately 27% of the square root of the average journey distance.
(This is not presented with all the detail that would be expected for formal
evidence, because it would be extremely tedious to repeat this work; if the
hypothesis is examined further it would be easier and more rewarding to
repeat or extend the work on journeys for which the road distance has
already been established).

The standard error of estimates by the straight line method have been
assumed to be proportional to the square root of the distance being
estimated, on the basis of an assumption that the estimation errors of

parts of the journey will be independent and will partially compensate for one another. If this assumption is correct, then the standard error of estimates of the distance of intermediate journeys, based on straight line estimates of the road distance of each of the segments, would also be expected to be proportional to the square root of the overall journey distance, and independent of the number, and distribution of lengths, of the segments.

Studies which were confined to finding the ratio between road and the corresponding straight line distances (called route factors) under different circumstances were carried out by Janice Timbers at the Road Research Laboratory (27.2) and show broad agreement with the results reported here, insofar as they overlap. For the distances between forty cities in England and Wales, the average ratio between road and straight line distances was found to be 1.25, which was reduced to 1.17 if straight lines were confined to overland routes via the bridge nearest the sea. The longer journeys were shown to exhibit less variable ratios than shorter journeys. The ratios measured along established trunk roads were much lower, ranging between 1.06 for one mile trips and 1.14 for fifty mile journeys. Between points in towns the ratio was found to be of the order of 1.25 for one mile trips, but this was reduced to 1.18 if one point was the town centre. Some frequency distributions of the ratios, or route factors, were given, and, although the standard deviations, broadly equivalent to the standard errors discussed, were not reported, the distributions appear to be consistent with the results given here.

To estimate the errors due to the assumption that journeys terminate at the nearest zone centre, and the extent to which these errors are influenced by the zone size, the co-ordinates of the terminal points of journeys were progressively rounded to a greater extent to represent their location within larger square zones. The error due to straight line distance estimation was extracted from the total error; the error remaining was assumed to be due to location of the journey terminal points within zones. The zone error appeared to be virtually independent of the distance being estimated, proportional to the side of the square zones used, and equal to 0.47 of the zone side. These conclusions were confirmed by direct calculation of distances between points chosen at random in two squares, and comparison of these distances with that between the centres. Details of both methods and the results obtained may be found in appendix B of this chapter.

The errors associated with the zoning method occur at the terminals, when these are assumed to be identical with the centres of the containing zones. Consequently, where each segment of an intermediate journey is estimated separately by the zoning method, there will be a zoning error contributed by each segment. If the zoning errors contributed by successive segments are assumed to be independent, then the total standard error is assumed to be proportional to the square root of the number of segments. (The justification for this chain of reasoning is similar to that presented in the appendix to chapter 25. But the errors contributed by successive segments are not notionally independent, since they share terminal points. The contribution of the identification of the common terminal point with the centre of the containing zone to the standard error of each segment depends upon the angle of approach and departure, relative to the deviation-of the terminal point from the zone centre. The resultant effect may be independence, in practice, of the errors contributed by successive segments).

Since the standard error of distance estimates by the straight line method increase as the distance increases, whereas that of the zoning method does not, the straight line method is likely to be at its best, comparatively, for short journeys, and the zoning method for long journeys. For short journeys the straight line method may be more accurate than the zoning method using real road distances for the network.

For intermediate journeys, since the errors associated with zoning probably increase as the number of segments increases, it is probable that the length of the journey, for which the straight line method is the more accurate, increases as the number of segments in the journey increases.

The relative accuracy of the straight line and zonal methods of estimation for different purposes is examined in appendix C. The results may be summarized, on the basis of assumptions detailed in appendix C, as follows:— if the journey distance, measured in miles, is approximately equal, numerically, to the zone area, expressed in square miles, multiplied by the number of segments, then the two methods are of a similar order of accuracy; but if the distance in miles is appreciably less than the zone area in square miles multiplied by the number of segments then the straight line method is likely to be the more accurate, while if the journey distance is appreciably greater, the zone method is likely to be the more accurate.

The estimated relative accuracy of the two methods when applied to different tasks may be illustrated by reference to examples drawn from the London Traffic Survey (27.3). The average zone area was almost exactly one square mile, 933 zones being used for an area of 941 square miles.

The average journey was approximately 2.8 miles long. The standard error of a straight line estimate of the length of a journey 2.8 miles long would be of the order of 0.9 miles, as against approximately 0.5 miles for a zone estimate. Goods vehicles of more than 1½ tons unladen weight averaged 35.9 miles per day in 16.1 journeys, or segments. An estimate of the overall distance performed by a heavy goods vehicle in an average day by the zone method would still be more accurate, with a standard error of approximately 2 miles, than by the straight line method, with a standard error of approximately 3 miles. Goods vehicles of less than 1½ tons unladen weight averaged 25.6 miles per day in 28.8 journeys, or segments; the corresponding standard errors of estimates of the complete distance would be approximately 2.7 miles by the zone method, and 2.5 miles by the straight line method.

Such is the uncertainty associated with the size of these estimates of the standard errors of the two methods that it would be unwise to assume, on the basis of these calculations, that either method is very much better than the other. The common prejudice for the use of estimates based on real road distances is probably mistaken, or at least exaggerated.

It has been assumed that the method of estimation based on straight line distances between zone centres is less accurate than either of the other methods, and this assumption has been incorporated into the method of calculation. However, according to these assumptions the standard error of estimates by this method cannot be more than approximately 40% greater than the larger standard error of the other two, for the same journey characteristics.

For many purposes, if the straight line method of estimation is being used, there need be no restriction on the number of zones; information about the accuracy of this method is more important, therefore, in respect of the guidance given as to how accurately it is necessary to locate the terminal points of journeys for the resultant errors of end point location to be reduced to any specified proportion of the composite standard error. Formulae expressing the relationship between location accuracy, contribution to overall standard error, the number of segments, and journey distance are developed in appendix D. From these it appears that, for many journeys and degrees of accuracy, location of the terminal points of journeys within National Grid square units (1 kilometre, or 0.625 mile, sides) will be adequate, and that greatest care is needed when estimating the lengths of short, intermediate journeys with many segments. In general, when preparing grid references for distance estimation purposes, it is unnecessary to go beyond identification of the appropriate kilometre square.

The arguments employed in the appendices can be applied to other special situations, e.g. there may be, for reasons of cost or computer capacity, a processing limit on the number of zones which can be utilized, which, together with the nature of the task being undertaken, may set an upper limit on the size of the area within which the zone method of estimation is the more accurate.

So far, the discussion of problems associated with distance estimation has been free from those philosophical intrusions which are so often necessary in examinations of empirical work. Unfortunately, the meaning of such expressions as journey distance, or road distance, in the context of estimating distances for journey planning is not as clear as it may appear. In a number of studies of computer methods of planning multiple-delivery journeys, it has been found that, when journeys, as performed, or as performed according to reports, are plotted on maps, and the road distance of the journey plotted is measured by opisometer, the measured road distance fails to correspond to the distance driven as recorded on the milometer. Furthermore, the discrepancies between the road distances measured from maps and on the milometer have usually been variable between different journeys, and sometimes substantial. An estimate of the milometer distance based upon the map distance would often be worse than, for example, estimates of the map distance based upon the straight line distance. This observation is based upon a limited number of studies that were each, of necessity, specialized. However, the variety of situations in which this phenomenon has appeared suggests that it may be a general, and not restricted, feature.

The errors detected have been much larger than could be explained by simple measurement inaccuracy. The only rational explanation of these errors, when they occur, is that the estimates and measurements are of different routes. The preceding sections refer to the accuracy of estimates of the shortest, or most direct, route between a given sequence of points by the straight line method. When there are significant discrepancies between milometer readings and map measured distances, the route followed by drivers may be different from that measured. If so, the shortest, or most direct, routes may not be the ones whose distance should be estimated.

In a few cases, some tentative attempts have been made to trace the source of the discrepancies between map measured road mileages, and the mileages recorded on milometers, for wholesale delivery journeys. However, one of the most attractive features of driving, to drivers, is their independence and lack of detailed supervision, and many drivers will go to considerable lengths to protect this independence whenever they believe it may be threatened. The strength of resistance to the installation of tachometers as 'spies in the cab' is an indication of this feeling. Consequently these enquiries were not pushed very far, and the relatively inconclusive results should not cause surprise.

Occasionally it has appeared after investigation that drivers extend service beyond that recorded; for example, when a driver arrives at a particular place in the sequence which he records, it may, for some reason or other, appear to him to be inconvenient for the client to transact the business immediately; consequently, he may proceed with the journey, and make an unrecorded return visit at what he may believe to be a more convenient time. It was suggested that some part of the discrepancies might arise because drivers were not too well acquainted with the 'best' route for their prescribed journeys; to test this suggestion, in another series of tests, drivers were shown their planned journey plotted on a map before they set out. In these tests the observed discrepancies appeared to be smaller than before, but the tests were not continued long enough to obtain a statistically significant result; the discrepancies were so variable that the number of observations required to establish a significant change would have been very large.

The discrepancies observed between the map and corresponding driving distance may, however, reflect a more general discrepancy between the objectives imputed to drivers and their behaviour. It has usually been assumed that drivers select, as far as they are able, either the shortest, or the quickest, routes. Some studies however have cast doubt upon this assumption. They

...... explain the choice made between alternative routes on the basis of drivers' attitudes, which indicated that neither time nor costs, the traditiona explanatory variables, were dominant. What seemed to be indicated was tha drivers chose routes on direct experience, and choices were made to reduce the total stress. The tension generated on a trip was a function of travel time, in that time controlled the frequency, though not the intensity, of stressing interferences. The main tension on a freeway was found to increase lineally to about 1,400 vehicles per lane per hour, after which it increased very rapidly. Although car drivers attempt to make a rational evaluation of transportation, their choice appeared to have very little in common with the economic criteria normally used in highway transportation. (27.4).

The intuitively reasonable hypotheses that 'stress' and route knowledge are major factors in the choice of route would be consistent with discrepancies between the shortest, or quickest, route and that actually followed.

If discrepancies of this type arise for reasons which are acceptable, i.e. not unreasonably wasteful or inefficient, then they may lead to further complications and errors in the estimation of journey duration. Conversion of an estimate of the minimum road distance into an estimated duration by the use of estimates of the speeds based upon observed speeds may lead to an under-estimate of the duration by an amount equivalent to the discrepancy. The planned idle time may also be under-estimated for the same reason. From this point of view, the distance estimated should be that recorded on the milometer, or that which should be recorded without the use of inefficient routes. The concept of journey distance is not entirely clear or precise; in practice the measurement of minimum distances may often be redundant and misleading, except insofar as it is desirable to ensure that routes followed are not unreasonably wasteful or inefficient.

There are other implications of substantial discrepancies between routes actually followed and the shortest routes. Firstly, any difference between the estimation accuracy of the zone and straight line methods may be insignificant in comparison with the route discrepancies. If so, the case for preferring the more convenient of these two methods of estimation, which is usually the straight line method, becomes overwhelming. Secondly, the contribution of the route discrepancy to the standard error of distance estimation may be larger than that of estimating the distance of a given route. If so, the contribution of distance estimation to the planned idle time may be almost entirely dependent upon the route discrepancy. Finally, the route discrepancy may well vary from fleet to fleet, task to task, or depot to depot; on this point more information is needed. If so, the amount of investigation required to establish the accuracy of distance estimation and its contribution to planned idle time in each case may be substantial.

In the absence of route discrepancies, it would appear that the accuracy of distance estimation may often be high relative to that of the procedure for converting distance estimates into estimates of duration. But route discrepancies may be large enough to compare with variations of speed.

Chapter 27

Appendix A

Errors of the straight line method of estimation.
a For road segments in Greater London region there were:
197 segments of average length 8.79 miles.
The linear relationship between the straight line (L) and road (R)
distances found was

$$R = 1.21L + 0.01$$

The standard error of estimates of R based on this relationship was 0.94,
giving a coefficient of variation of 0.11.
The correlation coefficient between R and L was 0.98.
b For road segments in the South Wales region there were:
110 segments of average length 27.64 miles.
The linear relationship found was

$$R = 1.13L + 2.65$$

The standard error of estimates of R based on this relationship was 4.62,
giving a coefficient of variation of 0.17.
The correlation coefficient between R and L was 0.93.
c For the distances between 40 cities in England and Wales there were:
780 distances of average length 168.9 miles.
The linear relationship found was

$$R = 1.17L + 2.9$$

The standard error of estimates of R based on this relationship was 17.63,
giving a coefficient of variation of 0.10.
The correlation coefficient between R and L was 0.98.
It should be noted that the distances between many of these cities are
based upon journeys which have sections in common; for example, the
distances between Penzance and at least half of the other cities will

include the distance for a common section between Penzance and Bristol. Consequently these observations are not properly independent. The main justification for ignoring this lack of independence is that the results are consistent with those obtained from processing the data from the two regions, which do not contain common sections.

d The distances between 40 cities in England and Wales using the bridge point modification: there were 780 distances of average length 168.9 miles. The area was divided into 10 sectors, with a total of 20 bridge points between them. The linear relationship found was

$$R = 1.14L + 1.2$$

The standard error of estimates of R using this relationship was 9.19, giving a coefficient of variation of 0.06.

The correlation coefficient between R and L was 0.99.

Chapter 27

Appendix B

Relationship between the standard error due to zoning, and the length of the zone side.

Co-ordinates of the ends of the A.A. route segments in Greater London, and of the cities in the A.A. mileage chart, were used to calculate straight line distances of the segments and of the journeys between the cities. Linear relationships were established between the straight line and corresponding road distances, and the linear relationships thus found were utilized to estimate the road distances. The standard errors of these road distance estimates were then calculated. The co-ordinates were rounded to different degrees of accuracy, to represent the identification of the terminals of journeys with the centres of square zones, of side equal to the rounding, containing the terminals, and the distance calculations were repeated. The co-ordinates were expressed in kilometres, being a simple conversion of the National Grid References which are themselves based on metric measurements. The distance calculations were carried out, and the results expressed, in miles. The results are given in table 27.1.

Table 27.1 Accuracy of road distance estimates using the straight line method between terminal points determined to varying degrees of accuracy

co-ordinates rounded to (in km)	standard error of estimates (in miles)	co-ordinates rounded to (in km)	standard error of estimates (in miles)
0.1	0.855	1	17.632
1.0	0.942	20	19.221
3.0	1.274	40	21.043
5.0	1.743	60	25.974
10.0	2.779	80	28.960
		100	34.683

A.A. route segments in Greater London, average length 8.788 miles.

A.A. mileage chart journeys, average length 168.9 miles.

It was then assumed that the standard error of the estimates with the most accurate co-ordinates in each set of data represented the contribution of the straight line method to the overall standard error. If a represents the combined standard error, b the standard error attributed to the straight line method, and c the standard error attributed to zoning, then it was assumed that

$$a^2 = b^2 + c^2$$

The contribution of zoning to the standard error was found on the basis of these assumptions for each degree of rounding, and is presented in table 27.2.

Table 27.2 Standard errors of zoning for zones of different size

source[1]	co-ordinates rounded to (side of square zone)		standard error due to zoning (in miles)
	in km	in miles	
G.L.	1	0.6	0.4
G.L.	3	1.9	0.9
G.L.	5	3.1	1.5
G.L.	10	6.3	2.6
M.C.	20	12.5	7.7
M.C.	40	25.0	11.5
M.C.	60	37.5	19.1
M.C.	80	50.0	23.0
M.C.	100	62.5	29.9

[1] G.L. indicates results from use of Greater London road segment data. M.C. indicates results from use of Mileage Chart distances.

The correlation coefficient between the zone side and the corresponding standard error was 0.997, which, even for such a small number of observations, is highly significant. The linear relationship between the zone side, Z, and the corresponding standard error, E, is
$$E = 0.0028 + 0.47 Z$$
(The standard error of the coefficient of Z is 0.018)

This is based upon the assumption that the terminal points are distributed at random within the zone.

It should be possible to derive such a relationship using integral calculus, but, so far, attempts have failed. This failure, combined with the remarkably high correlation found between the zone sides and corresponding standard errors, suggested that some form of independent verification was desirable. To supply an independent test, the distances between points chosen at random in two squares were compared with the distance between the centres of the squares.

It was envisaged that three factors might enter into the relationship, the side of the squares used, the distance apart, and their relative orientation. To ensure a variety of conditions, the co-ordinates of the centre of one square relative to that of the other were 10, 0: 10, 10; 50, 0; 50, 50. For each set of co-ordinates the size of the side of the square was increased by units; 10 observations of the standard error and zone side were obtained for each of the first two cases, and 50 for each of the second two; overlapping of squares was avoided. Each observation was of 100 distances between points chosen at random in each square; the same series of 400 pseudo-random numbers was used for each observation. A linear regression equation between the standard error and square side was fitted to the observations for each relative position of the squares separately. The results are given in table 27.3.

Table 27.3 Errors due to the use of zones: relationship between the standard error and square side.

x	y	A	B	R^2	N	F
10.0	0	0.21	0.388	1.0	10	2.2×10^5
10.0	10.0	-0.03	0.406	1.0	10	2.5×10^7
50.0	0	0.85	0.389	1.0	50	1.2×10^6
50.0	50.0	-0.14	0.406	1.0	50	9.5×10^7

x and y are the co-ordinates of one square relative to the other, A is the constant, and B is the co-efficient of a regression line of the form   Standard error = $A + B$ x square side
fitted to the observations.
R^2 is the coefficient of determination (to four significant figures at least).

N is the number of observations.
F is the value given by

$$F = \frac{\text{Mean square of regression equation}}{\text{Mean square residual error}}$$

These results confirm that the zone error is closely related to the size of zone. The coefficient found in the two studies, 0.47 and 0.40, are entirely consistent, since the first study relates to the standard errors of road distance estimates and the second to standard errors of unadjusted straight line distances, if a ratio of road to straight line distances of 1.17:1 is accepted.

Chapter 27

Appendix C

Comparison of the accuracy of the straight line and zoning methods of journey distance estimation as a function of the distance, size of zone, and number of journey segments.
The relationship between the standard error (e) of straight line estimates and the distance (d) may be of the form

$$e = a\sqrt{d}$$

where a is a constant. The case for this is discussed in the text.

The relationship between the standard error (E), of the zone distance estimates, and the zone side (Z), appears to be approximately

$$E = 0.47\,Z$$

This has been established for square zones, and a random distribution of terminal points within the zones.

It has also been suggested that the relationship between the standard error and the number of segments (N) may be of the form

$$E \propto \sqrt{N}$$

For zones of irregular shape, but area A, the relationship between the standard error, the zone area, and the number of segments, may therefore take the form

$$E = b\sqrt{(AN)}$$

And if

$$e = E$$

then

$$a\sqrt{d} = b\sqrt{(AN)}$$

and, since a and b may be of the same order of magnitude, when the distance is expressed in miles, and the area in square miles, (a appears to lie between 0.3 and 0.9, while b appears to be close to 0.5)

$$d \approx AN$$

for the two standard errors to be approximately equal.

If $\qquad\qquad d \ll AN$

then $\qquad\qquad e < E$

and the straight line method is probably the more accurate.

Chapter 27

Appendix D

The contribution of errors due to zoning to the total standard errors resulting from use of the straight line distance between the centres of zones as a method of distance estimation.

From appendix C,

$$e = a\sqrt{d}$$

and $$E = b\sqrt{(AN)}$$

For the contribution of the zoning error to be small relative to the straight line error

$$E \ll e$$

or $$b\sqrt{(AN)} \ll a\sqrt{d}$$

or, assuming $$a \approx b$$
$$A \ll d/N$$

(These relationships are numerical, and are intended to be confined to the use of units based upon miles).

To reduce the contribution of the approxmate location of the terminal points to less than x% of the resultant standard error (F)

$$F - e < xF/100$$
or $$F < 100e/(100 - x)$$
but $$F = \sqrt{(E^2 + e^2)}$$
$$100e/(100 - x) > \sqrt{(E^2 + e^2)}$$
or $$E^2 < [100e/(100 - x)]^2 - e^2$$
or $$E < e\sqrt{(100^2 - (100-x)^2)}/(100-x)$$
or $$E < e\sqrt{[x(200 - x)]}/(100 - x)$$

and if x is sufficiently small, this approximates to

$$E < 10e \sqrt{(2x)} / (100 - x)$$

or even $\qquad E < e \sqrt{(2x)} / 10$

Substituting, now, for E and e

$$bZ \sqrt{N} < a \sqrt{(2xd)} / 10$$

or, if $b \approx a$ $\qquad Z < \sqrt{[2 \times d / 100N]}$

or $\qquad d > 100NZ^2 / 2x$

or $\qquad d > 100AN / 2x$

(These are numerical relationships when the units are based on miles).

Chapter 28

Some implications of planned idle time

It is now possible to make a tentative estimate of the amount of planned idle time which may be associated with the planning of journeys in urban areas when the duration is unpredictable. The amount of time which should be allowed for an 11 mile car journey through London to catch a train depends upon the amount of information available. If the journey has been performed many times before, and it is known that the average duration of the journey is one hour, then the least time that should be allowed in order to ensure catching the train on 39 occasions out of 40 would be approximately 84 minutes; if the distance is known to be 11 miles, but the average duration is not known, then the least time allowed should be increased to approximately 89 minutes; finally, if the distance is not known, but has to be estimated from a map by the straight line method, then the least time allowed should be increased to approximately 92 minutes. The planned idle time, that is the expected time spent waiting for the train to depart, would be at least 24, 29, and 32 minutes in the three situations respectively; it represents a significant proportion of the total time devoted to the journey.

The planned idle time may not always be utterly wasted; in the example given, a better, or more comfortable, seat may be obtained on occasions of early arrival, while some time may also be utilized to buy magazines, or enjoy refreshments. But, if these actions were considered essential, the time allowed for the journey would have been increased to allow for them, instead of the journey duration being adjusted so as to just catch the train in the marginal case. However, the analogy does give some indication of ways in which planned idle time can be at least partially utilized. Tasks of secondary importance, i.e. tasks which may be neglected on occasions when sufficient time is not available without serious consequences ensuing, may be scheduled to be performed during the planned idle time in order to make some use of it. For example, drivers may be scheduled to clean their vehicles or to carry out elementary routine maintenance or greasing of the vehicles when journeys take less than the total time planned for their performance.

The example illustrates the extent to which the variability due to one factor can overshadow that due to others. On the basis of the figures derived in earlier chapters it would be very difficult to obtain much reduction in planned idle time by improving the accuracy of estimation of distance or average speed. In general, the overall effect of an increase in accuracy of estimation of a variable will be more noticeable the more that variable contributes to the overall standard error, and the larger is its standard error relative to those of the other variables.

But it is not always apparent how the accuracy of any estimate can be improved without going to technically impossible or financially unacceptable lengths. Thus, the variability of the duration of urban journeys is usually heavily dependent upon the variability of traffic conditions; it might only be possible to improve the accuracy of estimates of the duration of these journeys if traffic conditions were sampled soon enough before or during the journey. However, the sampling might not only be too expensive, but the improved estimates might become available too late for the improvement to be exploited.

In general, the sources of variability can be divided into two categories, those for which improved methods of estimation or prediction might, and might not, be practically realizable. Attention should be directed in turn at the least predictable elements in an attempt to improve their predictability until the variable being considered is one for which improvement is not practically realizable, or it is found that improvement, although possible, is likely to be too expensive. Once this point has been reached, further improvements in the accuracy of estimation of other elements will only lead to secondary improvements in the overall accuracy, and are not worth either much effort or much expense.

It is often possible to consider satisfying transport demands either by a regular service or by one which is subject to continuous re-scheduling to take into account the situation as it develops. If the least predictable factor in the working situation is one whose predictability could not be improved if a shorter time-cycle of scheduling were introduced, e.g. if the demands cannot be known in advance, then the potential advantage of re-scheduling is limited. One of the main advantages which may be derived from flexible scheduling systems is a reduction of the planned idle time which would have to be allowed under a less dynamic arrangement.

Because the planned idle time is a part of the total time allowance for the performance of a service, it follows that an improvement in the average time and a reduction in the planned idle time may be alternative ways of achieving the same thing; on the other hand, it is possible, under some circumstances, to reduce the average time requirement, for example, by using a technically more advanced mode of transport, but to lose much or all of the advantage by an increase in the unreliability or unpredictability; this may be experienced with air services, especially those over relatively short distances. On the other hand, it is to be hoped that British Railways manage to offer both greater transit speeds and greater regularity with the scheduled freight liner services.

Some suggestions for alterations to the system of milk delivery to homes (28.1), made in the supposed interests of efficiency of distribution, may serve as a further illustration of the problems introduced by the need to plan tasks of a variable work content. One suggestion was that it might be economically desirable to introduce price differences between milk bought in shops and delivered to the house to reflect the different costs, and also to adopt charging systems which would encourage customers to require larger and less frequent deliveries. Underlying these suggestions is the assumption that costs are significantly influenced by, and virtually proportional to, the number of deliveries.

Even if daily re-planning of milk rounds were to be attractive financially, it would almost certainly be impossible to obtain orders, other than regular ones, early enough to make daily re-planning an operational proposition. Consequently, milk rounds must be established for a significant period. The time required for a particular delivery is not, for most household deliveries, very substantial, involving primarily, for a regular order, the time for selecting the order and for a return journey to the delivery point from the public way, providing it is necessary for the milk float to pass. The reduction of some deliveries, especially if the length of street to be traversed is not reduced, would not result in a proportional reduction in the duration of the rounds. Furthermore, althoug there would be some reduction in the average duration of rounds due to the reduced number of deliveries, the variability would probably increase; because the rounds planned would have to make provision for peak deman much of the reduction in average duration would not be available for planned utilization, i.e. there would be an increase in planned idle time resulting from irregular deliveries which would counteract the decrease in average duration. Irregular deliveries would also make at least some increased demands for workings time due to the increased need for recordi deliveries and accounting, and, probably, due to disruption of established patterns upon which working methods appear to rely. It remains to be established, and is unlikely, that a reduction of delivery density and regularity in this way would lead to any significant reduction of cost.

On the other hand, the effective average round duration could be reduced without a counteracting increase in planned idle time if the frequency of regular deliveries were reduced. Delivery density need not be reduced if complete sections of rounds could be regularly omitted on certain days. An obvious delivery scheme along these lines would involve deliveries on alternate days, three days per week, with each milkman working two rounds on alternate days. (Whether such a reduction in service would be acceptable or desirable is outside the scope of the present discussion).

Providing for variability in services which have to be planned is expensive, and, as a general rule, proposals aimed at reducing costs which reduce average demands while increasing the variability or unpredictability should be treated with suspicion, unless supported with detailed estimates.

Some attempts have been made to experiment with wholesale deliveries to shops after shop closing hours (28.2). The avoidance of daytime congestion effects while driving and unloading, and increased customer satisfaction at not having to accept deliveries during their busy periods, were expected to be the main advantages. As far as the shops were concerned, some advantage was anticipated from receiving goods outside shopping hours. The number of participants, both from the point of view of delivery and reception, was limited, and it has been suggested that this was a major factor limiting the potential success of the experiments, and in practice largely responsible for a mild failure. But, regarded from the point of view of the variable duration of the tasks to be planned, other problems might have been anticipated and be responsible for some of the difficulties.

To receive goods after shop hours it is necessary for staff to work late. Keeping staff late is unlikely to be financially attractive unless they are kept fully occupied. There is a limit to the amount of background work in a shop, e.g. shelf-filling, and much of this may be utilized to ensure continuous employment for staff during slack periods while the shop is open. Thus, from the point of view of the shopkeeper, there should either be a queue of vehicles awaiting unloading, or vehicles should arrive to a schedule which avoids under-utilization of the staff working late. But for vehicles to wait in a queue to make deliveries removes much of the attraction of the scheme to delivery organizations; on the other hand, for vehicles to keep to a timetable over relatively short journeys implies a relatively larger planned idle time.

To complicate the situation further, drivers of most vehicles to be employed in the evening would be given afternoon work and, if this was finished early, would either have to sit out the afternoon planned idle time before starting the evening's work, or would start the evening's work before planned. In practice, vehicles often arrived in the late afternoon or early evening before they were expected, and either had to wait for the shop staff to be ready for them, or the shop staff had to dispense with both an ordinary closing routine and any break before the evening's work. As, for many shops on most days of the week, the period before closing time is the busiest of the day, early arrival is unlikely to be popular.

Traffic speeds are usually faster and more regular at night, which should enable average journey durations to be reduced, but the natural demand for delivery schedules must lead to a counteracting increase in planned idle time. Many of the evening deliveries took place, in practice, in the relatively early evening when increased speed and regularity is not necessarily available. The relative lack of financial advantage is, therefore, not surprising, especially as the density of after-hours deliveries was greatly reduced by the small number of shops participating.

However, the difficulties experienced with evening deliveries associated with the need to schedule deliveries are due to the need for deliveries to be received into the shop. If shops provided a secure delivery reception area, without direct access to the shop, at least one delivery (to avoid confusion between, and possible pilfering from, more than one delivery) could be made each night at a time chosen to suit the convenience of the delivery organization, without increasing the planned idle time, since the delivery could be checked the following day (28.3). Naturally, provision of a secure delivery reception area would often be inconvenient and would normally require some compensation, although a reduction in the disruption caused by unscheduled deliveries during busy hours (many shops will not accept deliveries on Friday or Saturday) would itself be some compensation. The benefits to be derived from the provision of a secure delivery reception area would be expected to be greater, and therefore offer more scope for compensation, the greater the concentration of delivery size, and the greater the reduction in delivery costs from the transfer of deliveries from day to night-time. A transfer of wholesale delivery traffic away from the congested hours would also benefit other road users, but this would hardly be taken into account by wholesale delivery organizations unless sufficiently sensitive congestion taxes, e.g. involving reductions at night, were imposed, when they could derive benefit from the reduction in these taxes.

The planned idle time may often be a very large proportion of total driving time; on the basis of the results presented the planned idle time associated with planned urban journeys may often be in excess of 50% of the average journey duration. As has been mentioned, there seems to be little or no evidence available about how much drivers can affect the journey duration by varying the effort applied, but it is most unlikely that increased effort applied on the occasions when it was most needed could reduce the exceptionally long journey durations by as much as a third. And, if it were possible to achieve such a reduction by effort in excess of normal, it would become of interest to enquire whether the normal level of effort was acceptable.

Most drivers, with their vehicles, are engaged on activities other than driving for a significant proportion of the working day. These activities are, mostly, part of the task which has to be planned and whose variability therefore contributes to the overall planned idle time. Deliveries, for example, are often dependent upon the presence of someone authorized to accept the delivery, and upon access to unloading facilities, and as it is often necessary to wait until these are available, the waiting time may be variable, unpredictable, and completely unaffected by the exertion of effort by the driver.

Turn round times at some outlets, and types of outlets, are notoriously longer than at others (e.g. **28.3**).

A primary objective of statutory restrictions on the hours which may be worked by drivers has been to prevent excessive fatigue, and reduce the potential danger from tired drivers. It is widely believed that most drivers work a very high proportion of the permitted hours, and the belief that these are excessive has resulted in the inclusion of clauses in the 1968 Transport Act which enable the permitted hours of driving to be reduced. The form of restriction, under the clauses which can be invoked, is different from that previously used, making a direct comparison difficult; with this reservation, the permitted drivers' hours can be reduced from 11 to 9 hours per day.

Where drivers are actually working in excess of 9 hours each day the new restrictions may reduce chronic fatigue, and any dangers associated with it. Where the hours worked are boosted artificially to compensate for the very low basic wages, the effect of the new restrictions may be small so long as employers recognize the almost inevitable outcome and increase basic wages (actually under the new restrictions drivers may work, but not drive, for more than nine hours, so even the change in basic wages might prove to be unnecessary). The implications of shorter permitted hours for planned journeys may be more complex.

If, as has been estimated tentatively for planned urban journeys, the planned idle time is as much as 50% of the average journey duration, then even under the 11 hour restriction the average journey duration would not be more than $7\frac{1}{3}$ hours unless either drivers were overcoming adverse conditions by extra effort or a relatively high risk of exceeding the 11 hour restriction were being accepted. Under the same assumptions a reduction in the restriction to 9 hours would reduce the average journey duration to 6 hours. Such a reduction in the average journey duration would not at present be thought necessary on the grounds of chronic fatigue. An incidental disadvantage of a rigid restriction is that, if taken seriously, tired drivers may try to increase speed when it becomes obvious that the restriction may be infringed, at the end of difficult journeys.

If an alternative form of the restriction were offered, based upon approved methods of estimation, which placed a restriction upon the planned average journey duration of, say, 8 hours, together with a planned probability of exceeding some specified maximum journey duration, e.g. 10 hours, which could be tolerated in isolation, both the cumulative and extreme causes of fatigue would be curbed. Estimation methods could be submitted for approval to a body devised for that purpose, but, preferably, since development of these methods is so complex they would be produced by a suitable organization; a suitable organization might be established as a joint venture, financed by operators and the government, as are many of the trade research associations. This alternative form of restriction would have the desired effect of limiting fatigue while offering the chance of increased productivity through an improvement of estimation techniques and working standards, and by directing attention at the factors acting to increase the planned idle time. More flexible restrictions on drivers' hours have been urged by the Economic Development Committee for the Distributive Trades (28.4).

It is often possible, therefore, for some restrictions, and agreements which have restrictive effects, to be expressed in ways which are more or less conducive to efficiency. A key to the potential effect on efficiency is the extent to which the restriction or agreement makes provision for sufficient flexibility of performance to match the variability of the working, or duration, demands which are likely to arise. If sufficient flexibility, equal to the planned idle time, is not provided, then the restriction, or agreement, will have adverse practical effects beyond the formally apparent conditions.

Without proper methods for the estimation of journey duration, efficient transport operation is unlikely, while attempts to achieve efficient operation are likely to put unreasonable stresses on drivers. Knowledge of the proper methods, without their application, may call attention to many sources of inefficiency, particularly with regard to variability, that might not otherwise be apparent. Application of such methods to estimate journeys already planned may not be particularly difficult, but to exploit the available time to the maximum financially possible, that is, to obtain an efficient operation, based upon efficient operational plans, it is necessary to construct journey plans and corresponding duration estimates together; for this, planning and estimation techniques based upon computers will almost invariably be necessary.

The present examination has drawn attention to many problems, but has provided only a few tentative answers. Much more information is needed, especially about the speeds of rural journeys, the variability of 'average speeds', especially in typical mixed urban-suburban-rural journeys, and the differences between routes driven and the most direct routes. There are no theoretical difficulties in the way of collecting this information.

Part 8

Calculation of journey plans

Chapter 29

Combinations, permutations and manual planning

The function of journey planning is to produce an efficient set of operational plans for the satisfaction of transport demands. Transport demands may have many different characteristics; consequently, to provide a simple basis for the examination of the nature of the computational methods required to plan journeys, discussion will initially be centred around one simplified typical situation, intermediate wholesale delivery journeys. The journey planning task in this case consists of allocating the deliveries required to journeys which should satisfy given restrictions, and which should make the most economical use of the available transport facilities.

One of the most common journey restrictions is that journeys shall not exceed a specified duration. If it is considered that the journey duration may be divided into two components, these being the time spent driving and at customers' premises respectively, then, while the time spent at each customer's premises may be independent of when the visit takes place, the driving time for visiting a number of customers and returning to base will not be independent of the sequence in which customers are visited; consequently, to determine whether a given set of deliveries may be allocated to a journey, it is necessary to pay sufficient attention to the sequence to ensure that the driving time can be reduced to a level which is compatible with any restrictions on the journey duration. (In practice the assumption that the time spent at customers' premises is independent of when the visit takes place may only be justifiable because little is known about the factors affecting it, and the cost of finding out more may not be worth while; nevertheless delivery times often depend upon such factors as the amount of help available for unloading and availability of someone authorized to accept delivery; both of these are likely to be affected by the immediate level of trade and the coincidence of other deliveries). When it is the duration restriction which determines how much work can be effectively performed by a driver and his vehicle, the ideal delivery sequence would be that requiring the least driving time.

Another common journey restriction is imposed by the load capacity of the vehicle and its relation to the delivery sizes. In simple circumstances, which are most common, the task of verifying whether a planned journey conforms to this restriction is limited to the addition of the corresponding quantities, e.g. weight or volume, associated with each delivery. Sometimes this task is more complex; it may be that the goods required for two different deliveries are incompatible, e.g. rat poison and biscuits, fish and flour, or paraffin and matches; alternatively, the restriction may be on several dimensions, each of which has to be checked, as in the delivery of different grades of petrol to garages, when the tankers have a number of compartments of varying sizes and combinations of sizes. Sometimes, ensuring satisfaction of the load restriction includes consideration of the sequence of delivery.

In most circumstances, it is impossible to ascertain whether all restrictions have been satisfied by addition only of data concerning the characteristics of each delivery included in the journey. In the particular case of duration restrictions when driving time is a significant component of planned journey time, the driving time is not a simple function of data about the deliveries, considered separately, but rather a complex function of all of them in combination. The extra driving time, which would result from the inclusion of another delivery in an established journey, is not determined simply by where that new delivery is, but by the location of that new delivery relative to the deliveries and delivery sequence already assigned to the journey; if the new delivery is on the established journey the driving time may not be increased, but if the established journey is confined to a diametrically opposite direction from the new delivery, the driving time is increased by that of a return journey to the new delivery location. The driving time depends upon the particular combination and sequence of deliveries.

A similar condition is met when it is necessary to ensure that any restrictions associated with the time of particular deliveries can be satisfied. The sequence of deliveries prior to the one with the specified delivery time must be determined in order to determine the associated driving time, and hence whether the specified delivery time restriction can be satisfied. There may be several deliveries with time restrictions allocated to a single journey, and these time restrictions may interact.

But journey planning is rarely concerned with a single journey. If there are several journeys, it is not only the sequence of each which has to be planned to determine the associated driving times, but the transfer of a delivery from one journey to another will have different effects according to the rearranged journey sequences which result from excluding and including it. There is a combination and permutation effect which is not confined to the determination of the sequence of a single journey, but extends to the determination of the sequences of all the journeys with the different possible combinations of deliveries that may be allocated to them. If the driving time is, or could become, a significant proportion of the total working time, then the ideal delivery sequence for each journey would be that requiring the least driving time. Within the journey planning situation, there are, effectively, two problems to which any computational method must offer solutions; it must allocate deliveries to journeys, and specify the sequence within journeys, the two problems being interrelated by the need for overall economy and for planned journeys to conform to restrictions.

It is easy to demonstrate theoretically that this type of problem may be exceedingly complex. If ten deliveries to specified outlets are to be made in a journey, it is possible to make a delivery to any one of the ten outlets first, to make the second delivery to any one of the remaining nine outlets, the third to any one of the remaining eight, and so on: the number of different sequences is 10 x 9 x 8 . . . . . . 3 x 2 x 1, or 3,628,800. If no distinction is made between the direction of travel, because, for example, there are no delivery time restrictions, then there are only 1,814,400 different sequences. For eleven deliveries, without distinguishing between the direction of travel, there are 19,958,400 different sequences, and for twelve deliveries there are 239,500,800 different sequences.

Clearly, when journey plans are prepared in depots, whether by clerks, foreman, or managers, under the type of time pressures that are usually experienced, there can rarely be any question of all the different sequences for a single journey being examined, let alone all the sequences for all the different journeys which may result from the combination and permutation of the deliveries between several journeys. Nevertheless, journeys planned are usually performed, and, while it is often possible to find fault with them by careful examination, given sufficient time, they do not, as a general rule, appear to be extremely inefficient. Since journey plans cannot be prepared manually by any method which involves enumeration of the possibilities, they must be prepared on the basis of some methods, or preconceived notions, which enable relatively good solutions to be found quickly and simply. Examination of methods used to prepare journey plans manually may serve to throw further light on the nature of the problems involved.

The most commonly used method of planning wholesale delivery journeys has already been described. Delivery notes are placed into pigeon-holes which represent easily identifiable areas such as postal districts. As far as possible, journeys are formed by selecting delivery notes from individual pigeon-holes. When this is no longer possible, journeys are constructed from delivery notes selected from the pigeon-holes representing adjacent areas. Finally, any remaining delivery notes are examined to see whether they can be inserted into any of the journeys already prepared, providing the processing of these has not already gone beyond the stage where recall and revision would become extremely inconvenient; if not,

Figure 29.1 Distances between 48 cities used in sample problems

Diagonal city labels (top-left to bottom-right): Aberdeen, Aberystwyth, Barnstaple, Berwick upon Tweed, Birmingham, Brighton, Bristol, Cambridge, Cardiff, Carlisle, Carmarthen, Colchester, Doncaster, Dorchester, Dover, Edinburgh, Exeter, Fort William, Glasgow, Gloucester, Guildford, Hereford …

```
'427
'573 '214
'172  306  441
'403  114  181  263
'540  244  198  388  160
'480 '121   93  348   88  136
'443  211  239  291  100  105  148
'484  107 '137  362  102 '177  '44  174
'208  219 '365   88  195  351 '272  256  276
'472   45 '201  351  129 '242 '108  225   68  263
'491  252  249  339  141 '101  169   48  209  304  260
'326  172  274  175   93  214  181  117  195  139  206  165
'540 '181   86  407  145  113   61  172 '104 '332 '169  178  235
'552  284  268 '400 '181   77  187 '112 '226 '365  284  '93 '226  191
'115  312 '458   57  288  424 '365  327  369   93  356  375  211 '425 '436
'555 '196   40  423  163  166   75  218 '119 '347 '183  223  256   53  243 '440
 152 '416 '562 '187 '392 '548 '469 '453 '473 '197 '460 '501 '336 '529 '561 '130 '544
 142  313 '459  101  289  446 '366  350  370   94  358  398  234 '426  459   44 '441 '103
'448  107  128  313   53  137   35  117   56  240  107  153  146   95  176  333  110 '437  334
'513  204  173  361  118   42  102   84 '140  311  204   83  187   98   95  397  148 '508  406   97
'430   79 '143  307   52  165  '50  141   54  222   84  177  142 '110  204  315 '125 '419  316   28  125
'423  108 '301  302  149  306 '208  244  199  215  148  289  171 '268 '330  308 '283 '412  309  181  264  158
 104 '468 '614 '213 '444 '581 '521 '484 '525 '249 '513 '532 '367 '581 '593 '156 '596   66 '169 '489 '554 '471 '464
'253  174 '320  133  150  306 '227  215  231   45  218  263   99 '387 '324  138 '302 '242  139  195  266  177  17…
'306  166  287  155  109  241  194  144  209  116  211  192   28  253 '253  191  269 '313  210  159  210  153  16…
'365  190  259  214   86  183  166   86  188  178  215  134   39  217 '195  250  241 '375  272  131  160  138  20…
'327  100 '252  206   90  249 '159  174  164  118  145  222   86 '220 '268  211 '235 '315  213  128  208  110   9…
'518  247  227 '367  145   50  151  '79 '189 '331  247  '60  192  152   42 '403  201 '528 '426  140   54  168   29…
'326  126  254  192   80  235  161  154  172  118  171  202   51  221 '255  211  236 '315  212  126  196  118   12…
'221  254  378   63  201  326  285  229  299   57  299  277  112  344 '338  106  360 '236  143  250  299  244   2…
'427  161  195  275   50  118  102   50  128  236  175   91  101  141 '138  311  177 '433  330   72   86   91   19…
'471  270  298  320  156 '161  208   62  236  284  287   60  145  232 '153  356  277 '481  378  179  142  203   29…
'370  154  231  219   50  175  138   84  153  182  179  132   44  191 '193  255  213 '379  276  103  143  102   1…
'464  156  159  312   64   96   69   80  105  257  156  106  138   99  129  348  138 '454  352   49   54   77   2…
'663 '304  110  531  271  278  184  329 '227 '455 '292  335  364  165  355 '548  112 '652 '549  218  259 '233  '3…
  81 '353 '499  '99 '330 '466 '406 '369 '411 '135 '398 '417 '253 '467 '478  '42 '482  103   61 '375 '439 '357  '3…
'597 '238   60  465  205  207  118  260 '161 '389 '226  265  298   94  285 '482   42 '586 '483  152  189 '167  '3…
'296  131 '277  175  107  264 '184  184  188   88  176  232   78 '244 '283 '181 '259 '285  182  152  224  134   1…
'515  173  114  369  .112   84   52  132  '96  307 '160  138  196   40  157  400   88 '504  401   69   62   97   2…
'338  154  257  187   77  212  164  116  179  145  187  164   18  220 '225  223  240 '342  240  130  179  125
'378   75 '195  258   43  200 '102  138  106  170  108  184   98 '162 '224  263 '177 '367  264   75  158   52
'528 '195  137  377  128   61   75  129 '118  322 '183  131  202   52  139  413  105 '519  416   91   49  119
'362  109  217  227   43  199  124  123  138  154  142  171   65  184 '219  247  199 '351  248   89  159   83
 226  320 '466  166  296  453 '373  357  377  101  365  405  241 '433 '466  125 '448 '183   84  341  413  323   3…
'523 '164   50  391  131  148   43  189  '87 '315 '151  199  224   41  218 '408   32 '512 '409   78  123  '93  '2…
'299  190  308  144  127  248  215  151  229  113  235  199   34  269 '260  184  290 '310  207  180  221  176
'488  212  195  337  110   53  116   54 '154  300  212   54  162  121   72  373  170 '497  394  105   29  133
```

they are either batched together, as far as is possible, to make journeys, or they are left, in the hope that it will prove possible to fulfil them by dispatching vehicles, which finish their planned journeys early, on special short trips.

If it were desired to formulate the pigeon-holing method as a set of logical rules for calculating journey plans, then the dominant rules to emerge would be the allocation of deliveries which are closest together to the same journeys, and determination of the delivery sequence within a journey by proceeding, as far as possible, between the nearest deliveries. This emphasis on the proximity of consecutive deliveries within a journey is not sufficient to completely specify a method of journey planning. Consequently, in order to examine the performance of this method on a test problem, some subsidiary rules will be added which may, or may not, completely conform to common practice; but common practice, in any case, is unlikely to be constant from time to time, and place to place. Links (a link is part of a planned journey sequence, involving direct movement between the deliveries linked) will be formed between deliveries in the increasing order of their distance apart, subject to restrictions; no delivery shall be linked to more than two other deliveries, or one other delivery and the depot, and no link shall be formed between two deliveries already linked to the same chain (a chain is a continuous set of links). Infringement of these subsidiary rules would result in a closed circuit within a journey, which is obviously inefficient. The method defined will be called the proximity rule.

To illustrate the effect of the pigeon-holing method by the effect of the

	Leeds	Lincoln	Liverpool	Maidstone	Manchester	Newcastle upon Tyne	Northampton	Norwich	Nottingham	Oxford	Penzance	Perth	Plymouth	Preston	Salisbury	Sheffield	Shrewsbury	Southampton	Stoke on Trent	Stranraer	Taunton	York
Lincoln	118																					
Liverpool	*161	232																				
Maidstone	84	35	219																			
Manchester	151	154	*304	129																		
Newcastle upon Tyne	79	134	102	119	213																	
Northampton	106	215	*119	184	257	112																
Norwich	36	97	158	70	156	57	124															
Nottingham	119	154	92	142	250	41	139	94														
Oxford	350	*343	313	344	468	285	389	322	250													
Penzance	*291	*253	*445	*252	*148	*353	*397	*297	*390	*590												
Perth	284	*277	243	278	402	219	319	256	180	*79	*524											
Plymouth	113	31	247	30	123	148	214	100	170	*367	*223	*301										
Preston	178	196	116	192	306	101	192	152	59	200	*442	130	219									
Salisbury	46	73	*192	38	124	94	145	37	127	348	*265	282	68	182								
Sheffield	115	58	188	66	195	93	195	79	104	*285	*305	*219	82	143	79							
Shrewsbury	184	216	103	207	314	106	189	158	65	217	*455	146	234	23	192	163						
Southampton	85	51	183	37	164	85	173	50	105	307	*288	241	66	155	47	34	170					
Stoke on Trent	279	220	*433	219	155	337	385	283	359	*556	145	*490	189	408	247	271	423	255				
Stranraer	209	*203	177	204	328	145	248	181	109	140	*450	74	*227	64	208	*145	87	167	*416			
Taunton	73	97	*226	64	81	135	179	78	172	398	*226	332	80	230	52	130	236	99	214	258		
York	132	197	36	184	274	66	111	123	57	281	*415	211	212	84	160	153	77	147	401	165	196	

proximity rule it has been applied to two artificial problems based on the data given in figure 29.1 for the distances between cities in the A.A. mileage chart (29.1), which are illustrated in figure 29.2.

The first problem is that of determining a sequence for a single, complete tour of the 48 cities. Doncaster and Sheffield are only 18 miles apart, are the closest pair, and are, therefore, linked first; Southampton and Salisbury are 23 miles apart, are the second nearest pair, and are therefore linked second; York and Leeds are the third nearest pair, being 24 miles apart, and are linked third; the fourth link is between Leeds and Doncaster which are 28 miles apart. These links form a chain consisting of York, Leeds, Doncaster and Sheffield; considering just the two cities at the ends of this chain, York and Sheffield, the second nearest place to York is Doncaster and the third is Sheffield; both have already been included in the chain, and to link them to York would result in a circuit; similarly, the second nearest place to Sheffield is Leeds, which is already included in the chain and to link it to Sheffield would result in a closed circuit within the overall tour. Thus, there is a degree of competition for links, and it is easy to imagine that the proximity rule may not resolve this in such a way as to achieve the best final result. The sequence resulting from the continued application of the proximity rule for the forty-eight cities in the A.A. mileage chart is shown in figure 29.3; viewed as an overall sequence, it is obvious to the briefest of visual inspections that it could be improved. Most peculiar is the link between Fort William and Penzance, which involves crossing the tour at several points, near Glasgow, between Carlisle and Liverpool, between Cardiff and Oxford, and near Barnstaple. But several other links attract attention as being, almost certainly, wrong. The length of this tour is 3,457 miles; the length of the tour that is believed to be the best, which is illustrated in figure 29.4, is 2,656 miles.

Despite obvious examples of bad sequence arising from the proximity rule, some sections of the overall tour appear to be extremely good, and it might be suggested that, if the tour could be broken up into a number of parts, avoiding the worst sections by breaking, or not forming, the obvious bad links, chains with very good sequences might be obtained. This hypothesis was tested on the same data.

As separate chains will only be formed by the proximity rule as a result of some restriction preventing the separate chains being linked into one journey, each chain was arbitrarily limited to visits to four cities, during a return journey using London as the base, or depot. (A journey distance restriction would have made the sequence within the journeys important;

Figure 29.2 48 cities used in sample problems

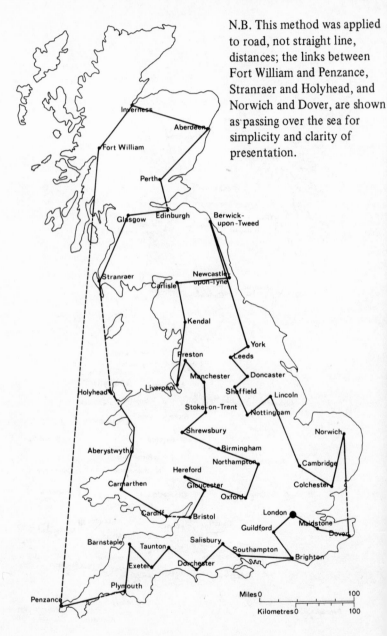

N.B. This method was applied to road, not straight line, distances; the links between Fort William and Penzance, Stranraer and Holyhead, and Norwich and Dover, are shown as passing over the sea for simplicity and clarity of presentation.

Figure 29.3 Tour of 48 cities in U.K. planned by proximity rule.

Figure 29.4 Shortest tour of 48 cities in U.K.

Figure 29.5 Journeys, restricted to 4 visits each, to 47 cities, using London as 'depot'. Journeys planned by proximity rule

but the sequence effects of the proximity rule have already been illustrated, and the purpose here was to illustrate the performance of this rule on allocation of visits to journeys, without emphasizing sequence effects). The results are illustrated in figure 29.5. Several journeys may look rather odd; the most peculiar are the journey visiting Inverness, Fort William and Stranraer, the journey visiting Aberystwyth and Carmarthen, and the journey in which a visit is made to Penzance although it otherwise only goes as far as Dorchester, when there is a separate journey beyond Dorchester. Since there are three journeys containing only three cities and one containing only two, it must be possible to reduce the number of journeys by one: and it is not difficult to find a set of journeys (illustrated later in figure 35.4) which appears better, and has one journey less; the total planned distance of this set of journeys is 6,251 miles, as against 7,150 miles for the journeys produced by application of the proximity rule. All the cities involved in the obvious difficulties when the proximity rule is applied, Stranraer, Aberystwyth, Carmarthen, and Penzance, are remote, and the furthest from the depot, London, in their own particular direction.

From these examples it would seem that proximity is not the only factor which needs to be taken into account when allocating cities to journeys; and, since the difficulties in the sequence determined by the proximity rule were also associated with the remote cities, there seems reason to doubt whether a simple rule of this type will produce an adequate answer to the dual problem of allocating cities to journeys and of finding the best sequence to visit a given set of cities.

Chapter 30

Rigorous methods of solving the travelling salesman problem

Since it appears that inefficiencies may result from application of the simple, rule of thumb, manual methods used in practice, it is of interest to examine the alternative results, benefits, and costs, which might be offered by more rigorous methods. To simplify this examination a simplified problem, finding that sequence of visits to a specified set of places which gives the shortest complete tour, will be used to illustrate theoretical points. This problem has received a considerable amount of attention in operational research literature and is known as the travelling salesman problem; the reasons for this name may appear obvious, although actual problems associated with planning journeys for salesmen are usually more akin to those of planning wholesale delivery journeys than to this simplification.

The travelling salesman problem can be stated simply as follows: find the route of minimum length which could be followed through a specified set of cities in order to visit each city and return to the start. It must be assumed that data is available describing the distances between cities. From the statement of the problem it would appear to fall into the general category of problems which are described as optimization problems, i.e. it is a problem in which the object is to find the best, or most favourable, solution from amongst, by implication, a number of possible solutions. It has already been mentioned that the number of possible sequences in which a number of cities can be arranged is extremely high.

Within applied mathematical literature, the term optimization is used to describe processes in which attempts are made to find the maximum or minimum values of a function, or expression, often known as the objective function, which may contain one or more variables, together with the values of those variables that give the maximum or minimum values of the function; optimization is also used to describe the procedures, or methods, used to seek for the optimal solutions. (References will not be given for points made during the general discussion of optimization methods which follows; Wilde and Beightler have surveyed the field (30.1)). In many optimization problems there are a number of equations or inequalities, which are known as constraints, each of which may limit the range of permitted values of one or more of the variables and, when constraints are included in the statement of the problem, the values of the variables which give the optimal value of the objective function must also satisfy the constraints.

The objective function of the travelling salesman problem is a formula for the distance of the tour, and a solution involves finding the minimum distance and the corresponding sequence of cities. There are no constraints. As a comparison, for wholesale delivery journeys the objective function to be minimized would be one expressing the formula for total cost; typically, the minimization would be subject to capacity and duration constraints.

While it is possible to define optimization problems in general terms, the ability to find a solution to a particular problem is not guaranteed by the ability to express it in terms which conform to the definition. There is no universal method for the solution of all optimization problems. Many methods are available; each has its own very specialized area of application. Individual optimization methods are limited in application to a restricted range of formulations which fall within the overall definition; to use a specific method of solution it is necessary to devise a way of formulating the problem which conforms to the restricted scope of that method; even when the formulation conforms to that required for a specific optimization method to be applicable in theoretical terms, whether a solution can be obtained in practice depends upon the size, and usually also upon the special characteristics and structure, of the problem under consideration.

Probably the best known technique for solving optimization problems is that of linear programming. To be applicable, it is necessary for the relationships in the objective function, and for those in the constraint inequalities, to be linear, i.e. the contribution of any particular factor in the objective function and constraints, where it appears, must be proportional to the amount of that factor included and must not alter the contribution of any other factors.

In terms of simple journey planning procedures an example of a linear constraint is the journey restriction imposed by the vehicle load capacity when only weight is of importance. In these circumstances, the weight contributed by each category of goods is proportional to the quantity of that category carried, and the overall weight is the sum of the weights contributed by each of the categories; the overall weight has to be maintained at a level that is less than the load capacity of the vehicle.

But the constraints resulting from vehicle load capacities are not always linear. A petrol tanker that is capable of carrying a total load of 4,000 gallons may have four separate compartments, each of which is capable of holding 1,000 gallons of petrol. It is not possible to assume, because the total volume of an order is 3,000 gallons, that the vehicle of 4,000 gallon capacity would have sufficient capacity to complete delivery of the order on one journey. If more than four brands are included in the order, then the vehicle would not be able to carry all the brands separately and simultaneously. Furthermore, even if only four (or three) brands are included in the order, nevertheless, if the delivery requirement for one (or for each of two) brand was in excess of 1,000 gallons, then the delivery could not be completed in one journey without mixing the brands. These are examples of very simple combinatorial constraints.

Because journey durations depend upon the sequence of deliveries within journeys, and upon the allocation of deliveries to journeys, duration restrictions are also combinatorial in nature. Problems of any size including combinatorial constraints cannot be tackled by linear programming methods.

The reason for requiring the objective function and constraints in linear programming to be linear in form, is that the methods of solution exploit the linear characteristics to obtain solutions much more rapidly, and, consequently, solutions to much larger problems, than could be obtained if these restrictions were not imposed. As a simple physical analogy, the linear objective function can be regarded as representing a planar sloping surface, that is, a surface which rises in one direction, but has no curves, folds, or bumps in it; the linear constraints may be regarded as straight lines drawn on this surface; the optimization problem is to find the highest point on the surface which is within the area bounded by the straight lines representing the constraints. Extending the analogy a little, the area may be regarded as being represented by an estate on the side of a hill, the constraints being represented by boundary fences, the problem being to find the highest point of the estate. Under these circumstances, it may be proved, and for this simple analogy it is obvious, that the highest point occurs at a point at which two or more of the constraints, or boundary fences, meet. Furthermore, since the surface is flat rather than curved, and the constraints, or boundary fences, are straight, a constraint, or boundary fence, that starts in an upwards direction will continue climbing until another constraint, or boundary fence, is met. By exploiting simple concepts such as these, linear programming methods are available for the solution of some quite large problems, involving several thousand variables and constraints. (When applied to practical problems, a significant proportion of the variables and constraints have usually been introduced to facilitate the adaptation of the practical problem to the required method of formulation).

Looking at the travelling salesman problem, one of its cardinal features is that, if a city is inserted between two others in the sequence, the effect on the distance to be travelled between the two original cities depends on the position of the city being inserted relative to the positions of the original two cities, rather than on the position of the city being inserted, considered on its own. Since it is the distance of the tour which is to be minimized, and which therefore corresponds to the objective function of the optimization problem, it is clear that the objective function is not linear, and therefore that linear programming does not offer, directly, a means of solution.

If the linear restrictions, imposed to achieve the simplicity which linear programming exploits, are relaxed, then the size of those problems that can still be solved is relatively small. The technique which is best used for any particular problem still depends upon the form of the objective function and constraints. But no methods of this type are directly applicable to problems with combinatorial objective functions; and while, by clever formulation, mathematical programming methods have been applied to solve travelling salesman problems (e.g. **30.2**), these have been very small problems, below the size of most practical problems, and the computational cost has been high.

Another general class of optimization methods is based on applications of the methods of differential calculus, the foundations for which were laid in the seventeenth and eighteenth centuries. A simple physical analogy of the type of problems dealt with by these methods is that of finding the highest point of a range of hills which are shrouded in fog, assuming that the height at any point can be measured without visual reference to the surroundings, e.g. by an altimeter. The natural way of trying to find the highest point of a single hill in a fog would be to walk uphill until a point was reached from which it was impossible to ascend in any direction. This point would then be a local optimum, or hill-top. However, there might be other hill-tops round about, many of them much higher, and the problem of searching for all the hill-tops in order to identify the highest is extremely difficult and time consuming.

Furthermore, methods based upon the differential calculus are only applicable if another condition is met; the surface must be continuous or appear to be so. In the physical analogy this condition may be represented by the condition that there be no crevices or precipices. Clearly, the

difficulty, quite apart from the danger, of hill-walking and finding hill-tops
in a fog is much greater if there are crevices and precipices; furthermore, it
is only possible to ensure that a pinnacle is detected in these conditions if
the search is detailed enough to detect its base.

It is obvious that the objective function of the travelling salesman
problem, which is the sum of the distances between the cities in each
particular sequence, is not continuous. Each particular sequence of the
cities has a corresponding precise value for the objective function, or tour
distance. Any change in the sequence of the cities causes an abrupt change
in the tour distance. Neither the sequence nor the tour distance can be
changed continuously. Consequently the travelling salesman problem does
not correspond to the assumption which is fundamental to the application
of methods of optimization based upon differential calculus.

One type of optimization technique which is advocated as being
particularly useful for the solution of problems associated with sequences
is dynamic programming. This is based on the application of a principle
known as the optimality principle. Stating this in terms which are relevant
to the travelling salesman problem, if a route has to pass through three
cities, then the best route between the first and third cities incorporates
the best route between the first two cities. But the practical application of
this principle depends on the number of alternative sequences to be
considered being restricted by the nature of the problem, otherwise the
problem is too large; the application runs into the 'curse of dimensionality',
as the originator of the technique, Bellman, picturesquely called it. But
the essence of the travelling salesman problem is the large number of
possible sequences, with freedom of choice between them. Consequently
dynamic programming is unlikely to offer an effective method of solving
the travelling salesman problem. Again, by clever formulation and at the
expense of significant quantities of computer time, small problems have
been solved by dynamic programming (**30.3**) but this work illustrates the
limitations of the approach.

Thus, superficial examination of three of the main categories of
methods used to attack optimization problems indicates that the travelling
salesman problem does not correspond to the conditions adopted as
necessary for successful application of technique falling within these
categories; it is not readily amenable to solution.

When the travelling salesman problem was first described and
recognized, it was thought that it might be of comparatively little interest
to pure mathematicians. It was obvious that, for any problem, there would
be one or more sequences which would give the shortest tour, and that the

best sequence could always be found, in theory, by enumerating all the possible sequences and comparing them to find the shortest. However, the applied mathematician cannot be satisfied with the knowledge that, in theory, a best sequence exists and could be found, but, as the problem has some practical significance, must be interested in developing practical methods of finding the best sequence.

If the number of cities to be visited is N, then the number of the alternatives for the first visit is N, any one of the remaining $N-1$ cities can be visited second, any one of the remaining $N-2$ can be visited third, and so on. The number of sequences is, therefore, $N x (N-1) x (N-2)$ . . . . . . $3 x 2 x 1$, or $N!$ (known as N factorial). The number of sequences of ten cities is, as has been mentioned, 3,628,800; the number of sequences of 100 cities is approximately 10^{158}. Thus, the number of sequences in a travelling salesman problem with many cities is of astronomical dimensions. (This is no exaggeration; astronomers coined a new measure of distance, a light-year, which is the number of miles travelled by light in one year; it is approximately $5 x 10^{12}$ miles. But $5 x 10^{12}$ light-years would still represent fewer miles than the number of different tours that could be formed with 100 cities). Furthermore, the rate of increase of the number of sequences with the addition of extra cities becomes extremely high; increasing the number of cities from 100 to 101 multiplies the number of sequences by 101.

With such astronomical numbers of sequences, and with the high rate of increase, any method that depends upon enumerating all the sequences and comparing them to find the best is unlikely to be practical, except, possibly, for extremely small problems. If it were possible to form, record, calculate, and compare the distance of a single 100 city sequence in a micro-second, or 10^{-6} second, which would be faster than it could be done by the fastest existing computers, enumeration of all the sequences to find the shortest would take more than 10^{144} years. Typically, the size of practical journey planning problems is too large for complete enumeration methods to offer any hope as a means of solution.

One line of attack on the travelling salesman problem which has received repeated attention involves the development of methods which depend upon the enumeration of only a small proportion of the sequences. (It might be a more realistic reflection of the literature to suggest that there are many different lines of development of partial enumeration methods). Elementary, but rigorous, methods of reducing the number of sequences which need to be enumerated are obvious; for example, if a partial sequence is found which is already longer than the shortest complete sequence found so far, then all the complete sequences containing this partial sequence can be automatically rejected without testing them individually. However, the problem of keeping records of all the sequences that have been tried and rejected in partial enumeration methods can become extremely complex, while the number of tests required, even if a careful strategy for employing them is utilized, can become computationally very demanding.

Nevertheless, partial enumeration appears to form the basis of the most effective and promising methods for finding rigorous solutions to the travelling salesman problem reported to date; but, even if highly sophisticated methods to reduce the number of sequences enumerated are employed, the computational requirements are formidable. One well documented solution of this type (30.4), using a 'branch and bound' algorithm, includes performance data which can be used as a bench mark for the computational requirements. The average computing time requirement for finding the best sequence of 40 cities, using an IBM 7090, was reported to be 8 minutes. It was estimated that each addition of 10 cities to the size of the problem would increase the computation time requirement 10 times; on this basis, problems of 50 cities would be expected to take 80 minutes, of 60 cities 800 minutes, and problems of 100 cities would be expected to take 8,000,000 minutes. The scope for practical application of this method is limited.

Chapter 31

Non-rigorous methods of tackling the travelling salesman problem

Solving a problem, in a rigorous sense, involves both finding the solution, and, by implication, proving that it is the solution; in the context of optimization problems, the requirement is not only that the optimum be found, but also that it be shown to be the optimum. This implies that, either the optimum should be shown to be so by direct comparison with the alternatives, or that simple rules exist and are applied which enable it to be shown that, without individual recognition of most of the alternatives, these cannot surpass the current candidate for recognition as the optimum. The peculiar strength of linear programming is that, in the context of the definition of the problems to which it can be applied, it is possible to find and establish the optimum with direct tests on only a small number of candidate solutions.

Outside a small set of special problem formulations, efficient methods for finding and establishing the optimum without implicit or explicit enumeration do not exist. Thus, in continuous surface optimization, many of the difficulties are not associated with finding the tops of individual hills, but with establishing that there are no summits higher than the highest already found; there is no general method for establishing this, except by enumeration, or a complete search of all the summits or even, if the number of summits is not known, a search for as many summits as can be found and elimination of these by direct comparison. These enumeration or search procedures are liable to be very expensive in terms of computational requirements.

Because proving a solution to be the optimum is so demanding, there have been attempts, in order to increase the size of problems examined, to apply optimization techniques in a non-rigorous manner, i.e. to find a candidate for the optimum, but not to establish, by thorough enumeration or search, that this candidate is the optimum. It is implicitly assumed that these candidates are good, even if not the best. Many such candidates may be found to increase the likelihood that the best candidate found is either the optimal solution, or is very close to it.

It is easy to illustrate that, for travelling salesman problems, there may be many tours which are not very much longer than the optimal tour. The 48 cities in the A.A. mileage chart, already used for previous illustrations, may be arranged in 48!, or approximately 10^{61}, different sequences or tours. The length of a complete tour of these 48 cities cannot be less than half the sum of the distances between each city and its two nearest neighbours; this lower limit to the length of the shortest tour is just over 2,000 miles long. Similarly, it is possible to identify an upper limit to the length of the longest tour by assuming that each city is linked to the two cities furthest from it; for this problem the upper limit of the length of the longest tour is approximately 22,000 miles. All the 10^{61} sequences must have lengths which lie between these two limits; the difference between the upper and lower limits is of the order of 20,000 miles. Consequently there are, on average, more than 10^{56} sequences or tours corresponding to each length, if differences of less than a mile are not distinguished.

Information about the frequency distribution of the lengths of different tours is not readily available. What little information has been established is restricted to individual problems, and its status is more that of subjective impressions than of objectively established or well documented knowledge. Nevertheless, these impressions are of considerable importance in considering computing strategies.

If tours were distributed uniformly between the possible lengths, then tolerably short tours might be expected as a result of the construction of a few tours at random, e.g. with a perfectly uniform distribution, so that all lengths were equally likely, the chance that 100 tours selected at random would not include one whose length was under 3,000 miles would be approximately 6 in 1,000.

The frequency distribution of the lengths of tours in a typical travelling salesman problem is probably not uniform, with each result equally likely, but bell-shaped, with the middle range of results being much more probable. If the frequency distribution of the lengths of possible tours for the A.A. 48 city problem were to correspond to the archetype of bell-shaped distributions, the normal distribution, then the average length of a sample of randomly selected tours would be expected to be approximately 12,000 miles. If it is assumed that the standard deviation would be 3300 miles, i.e. that the length of only one out of a thousand randomly constructed tours would be less than 2,100 miles, then the length of only two more tours would be expected to be between 2,100 miles and 3,000 miles. In these circumstances the probability that 100 tours constructed at random would not contain one of length less than 3,000 miles would be approximately three in four. If, as seems intuitively likely, there are fewer short tours than there are long tours, then selecting tours at random could by an expensive, and even an impractical, method of obtaining relatively short tours.

A number of publications refer to methods which have been developed for finding short tours, which might be optimal, but which do not include any attempt to prove that the tour found is optimal. To judge with certainty the success of these methods, in terms of how near they come to finding the optimal tour, it is necessary to apply them to problems for which the optimal tour has already been found by some other method. However, as there are only a few tours for which the optimal has been found and published, and as these are all, because of the size of the computational requirements, small problems, there have been occasional attempts to evaluate performance on larger problems, for which the optimal is not known, by comparing the performance of different approximate methods against each other.

One major category of approximate methods depends upon partial enumeration of the possible tours, but a more limited partial enumeration than is included in rigorous techniques. It would be possible to devise new methods of this type continuously, each differing in some detail or another, and it would be pointless either to try to describe a large number of such methods, or to give a full exposition of any one. Instead, an attempt will be made to give an impression of these methods by outlining the principles developed in a sequence of publications which appear to have provided both promising results and good documentation of the methods and results obtained for a variety of published problems.

Figure 31.1a shows a possible tour for a small travelling salesman problem.

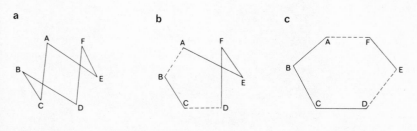

Figure 31.1a   Figure 31.1b   Figure 31.1c

Figure 31.1 Illustration of 2-chain method.

If, to reduce cross-overs, or intersections, in this tour, the links between *A* and *C,* and between *B* and *D,* were broken and were re-connected in the only alternative way which includes all the chains in the same tour, then the result obtained is shown in figure 31.1b. If, repeating the process, the links between *D* and *F,* and between *A* and *E* were broken and re-connected, then the result is illustrated in figure 31.1c. Thus, if a stage is regarded as breaking two links and re-connecting the ends in that way, of the two possibilities, which gives the shorter tour length, then the jumble of this initial tour can be converted into the shortest tour in two stages. As a general method, pairs of links are broken and re-connected if any advantage is obtained, until a tour which cannot be improved by further application of this method is found. If this method is applied to a number of randomly selected initial tours, it is quite likely that the optimal tour will be found, and, if not, that the shortest tour found will not be far short of the optimal (31.1). This will be called, for convenience, the two-chain method.

In the two-chain method the best continuous tour found from each starting tour to date is broken into two parts and re-connected if this results in an improved tour. The method can be elaborated and, it is claimed (31.2) improved, if the tour available at any moment is broken into three parts, and these are re-connected in the shortest of the eight alternative ways that includes all the parts in a single tour. This is illustrated in figure 31.2, where the alternative ways of joining three elementary chains are shown, and in figure 31.3, where it is shown how, in one small problem, the three-chain method leads to the shortest tour in one step less than the two-chain method, which is illustrated in the same figure.

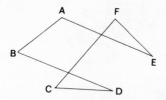

If links between *A* and *E*, *B* and *D*, *C* and *F* are broken, then the sections can be re-connected as follows:

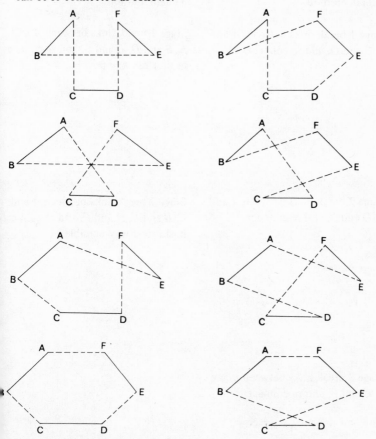

Figure 31.2 Illustration of the 3-chain method; alternative ways of linking three chains without forming closed sub-tours.

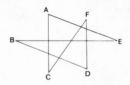

Problem with starting random tour as initial solution.

2-chain Method	**3-chain Method**
Stage 1 break links between *A* and *E*, *B* and *D*, and re-connect.	**Stage 1** break links between *A* and *E*, *B* and *D*, *C* and *F*, and re-connect in shortest way possible

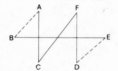

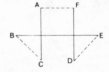

Stage 2 break links between *A* and *C*, *D* and *F*, and re-connect

Stage 2 break links between *A* and *C*, *B* and *E*, *D* and *F*, and re-connect in shortest way possible

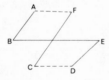

Stage 3 break links between *B* and *E*, *C* and *F*, and re-connect

Figure 31.3 Application of 2-chain and 3-chain methods to a simple prob

It has been claimed that the three-chain method is faster, and is more likely to lead to a relatively short tour, than the two-chain method. Nevertheless, it is considered desirable to apply the three-chain method to several initial tours, if it is desired to find the optimal tour, and, even when this is done, there is no guarantee that the shortest tour found will be optimal.

A similar method has been described, called 'oats', which is claimed to be somewhat faster and more effective than the simple two and three-chain methods (31.3). Again, this method is based upon the improvement of a randomly selected initial tour, and it is done in two stages. Initially, the city with the largest combined distance from its two nearest neighbours in the existing tour, is extracted from its present position, and inserted in turn between all the other pairs of cities in the tour, to test whether any shorter tour can be found in this way, and, if it can, to insert this city in the position which will give the greatest improvement for the movement of this city. This process is repeated with each city, in the decreasing order of its combined distance from the two nearest neighbours. In stage two, the same process is performed with chains, or sequences of cities, as has been done with single cities. This part of the procedure is similar to that of the two-chain method already described. Again, the best tour found starting from any particular tour (which is called a COR, or Candidate for Optimum Result), or from many, is not necessarily the optimal tour. If the process is repeated starting from many different initial tours, the chance of finding the optimal, or a relatively short, tour is rapidly increased; however, as problems become larger, the probability of finding the optimal tour decreases rapidly.

Oberuc, in his paper describing 'oats' (31.3), also gives much information about its performance, and compares its performance with that of other methods. Some of the tables and figures presented by Oberuc are repeated here. Table 31.4 contains the result of applying this method to eight different travelling salesman problems, with information both about the length of the best tours found and the computer time requirements.

Table 31.4 Results of 'oats' computer runs

number of cities	number of COR[1]	number of optimum solutions	total computer time[2] (min)	average time per COR (min)	average time per optimum	ratio of optima per COR	optimum	lower bound[3]	% optimum above lower bound
20	377	143	3.50	0.0093	0.024	0.3793	246	189	29.8
33	161	67	7.10	0.0441	0.106	0.4161	10861	9621	12.9
42	98	30	8.60	0.0876	0.287	0.3061	699	593	17.9
48	350	16	42.75	0.1221	2.672	0.0457	11461	10247	11.8
57	422	8	98.92	0.2344	12.36	0.0190	12955	11345	14.2
75	179	5	96.08	0.5367	19.22	0.0279	12372	11121	11.2
86	238	2	198.00	0.8319	99.00	0.0084	13349	11939	11.8
100	77	–	111.00	1.441	–	–	14963[4]	13248	12.9

1 COR is short for Candidate for Optimum Result. One COR is found as a result of processing each random starting tour according to the techniques described.

2 Univac 1108.

3 The lower bound is half the sum of the distances between each city and its two nearest cities.

4 This was the best answer obtained.

Figure 31.5 shows the frequency distributions of the length of the best tours found starting from different random solutions, for each of the eight problems.

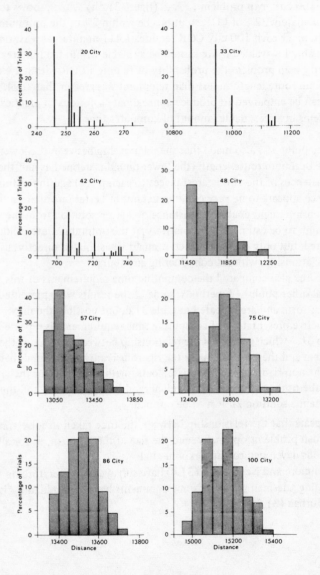

Figure 31.5 Frequency distributions of solution values resulting from application of the 'oats' method.

The conclusion drawn from these figures was as follows:

For a 100 city map problem . . . . . . (figure 31.5h) . . . . . . shows that approximately 32% of COR solutions lie within 2% of the optimum route length. Since each 100 city COR requires 1.411 minutes, at least one reasonably low valued route should be available within ten minutes. For a 100 city map problem the probability of finding a COR within 2% of the optimum route length in less than ten minutes is greater than 0.94. Thus oats can be employed to produce approximate solutions to practical problems in a reasonable amount of computer time.

The point was also made that the relationship between the lower bound to the optimum route length (the lower bound is defined as half the sum of the distances of the two nearest places to each place) and the optimum distance appears to be very close; in default of better information this relationship might enable the distance of a given solution from the optimum to be estimated; alternatively, if the optimum route is not required, but only its length, then it might be estimated directly, using this relationship, without constructing any tours.

Oberuc also compared the computing time requirements of this, and several other published methods; some of the results were presented in tabular form and are repeated in table 31.6, but possibly the most instructive presentation of computing time requirements is repeated in figure 31.7 which compares the relationship between the size of the problem and the time taken for the rigorous branch and bound method, and the non-rigorous, approximate, 'oats' method, giving, for the latter, both the time to process an individual random starting tour and the time to obtain a solution known to be optimal.

It appears that the relationship between the time taken to solve travelling salesman problems optimally, and the size of the problem, is, for all the methods developed to date, exponential.

Bellmore and Nemhauser (31.4) have surveyed the literature on the travelling salesman problem; some comments have been added by Isaac and Turban (31.5).

Table 31.6 Expected computer time required for selected travelling salesman problems

investigators	Held & Karp	Karg & Thompson	Little et al.	Reiter & Sherman	Roberts & Flores	Oberuc
year	1962	1963	1963	1965	1966	1968
computer	IBM 7090	BENDIX G-20	IBM 7090	IBM 1620	IBM 7094	UNIVAC 1108
number of cities / optimum				Time (min.)		
20 246	2	–	0.126	3.3	7.9	0.024
33 10861	–	2.29	1.8[a]	7.35	–	0.106
42 699	10	4.45	12.0[a]	28.3	–	0.287
48 11461	15[b] (11566)	–	50.0[a]	201.7	7.4	2.672
57 12955	–	16.93[b] (12985)	300.0[a]	520.3	101.3[bc] (12985)	12.63

a Times indicated are approximate, based on the solution of other problems.

b Optimal solution not found: best solution indicated.

c Average of two widely-spaced times.

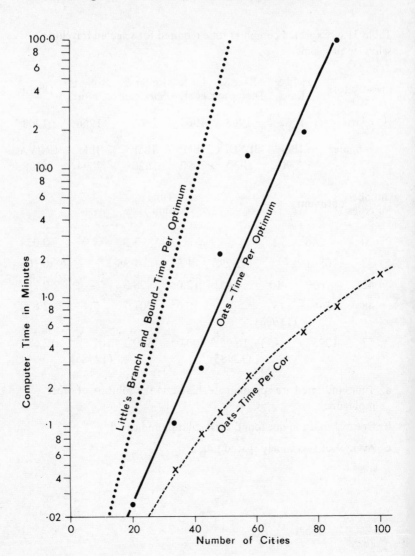

Figure 31.7 Relationship between problem size and time requirements

Chapter 32

Feasibility and computing cost

The computational methods available for finding optimal solutions to the travelling salesman problem require a computing time that increases exponentially with the size of the problem; thus, the time requirements of the 'branch and bound' method increases 10 times for each addition of 10 cities to the size of the problem, while for the 'oats' method the time required for optimal results increases by approximately 3.5 times for each addition of 10 cities. There are two implications of computing time requirements which increase exponentially with the size of the problem: the first is that, because computers occasionally break down, and cannot, in general, be dedicated to the same task indefinitely, and because of the rapidly increasing time requirement, there is a limit to the size of problem which can be solved, and this has been the limitation of theoretical solutions throughout; the second is that there is usually a more stringent limit to the size of any practical problem which can be attacked with any prospect of the financial rewards exceeding expenditure on computing time. For practical problems, if the computing cost is likely to be of similar order to that of the benefits, then the optimization objective should include the computing cost, and be of the form of maximizing the net benefit after computing expenses have been paid. When the computing expenses increase exponentially with size, and there is no possibility of the benefits increasing in the same way, then there is, inevitably, a size barrier to the application.

For rigorous methods, or even the non-rigorous 'oats' method, it is clear that, almost irrespective of the precise values of the cost parameters of the application, the cost barrier restricts applications to being extremely small; while the time barrier of practical feasibility is not far behind owing to the exponential rates of increase of computing time requirements. Foreseeable increases in computer performance are unlikely to alter these conclusions in more than a superficial way. One forecast (32.1) is that by 1975 computers will be 200 times faster and 500 times cheaper than in 1968. On the basis of this forecast, the feasible limit of the size of problem that could be solved by the 'branch and bound' method would be increased by 23 cities, while the size of problem that could be solved for the same cost would be increased by 27 cities: for the 'oats' method the corresponding increases in size resulting from these developments in computing performance would be 42 cities for the feasible limit, and 49 cities for the same computing cost. (The forecast quoted applies to the speed and cost of the electronic parts of a computer, excluding the peripherals, which usually represent a substantial proportion of the capital value; it applies less to the total cost of operating a computer system including its associated human beings, buildings and other necessities which, in total, is unlikely to decrease in cost so rapidly. However, in the discussion it is assumed that the reduction applies overall because, as an incremental task, it is almost entirely concerned with computation. Sharpe (32.2) presents much of the available evidence about past trends in the cost and effectiveness of computing equipment).

The profitable size of problems depends upon the particular pattern of benefits to be anticipated; the feasible limit of size is also somewhat indeterminate since it is possible to suspend computing tasks before they are finished and continue later by appropriate design of the methods used. However, for purposes of illustration, two limits of practical length of computing jobs will be assumed, these being 10 and 20 hours, with the figures for 20 hours in brackets. As reported and reproduced in figure 31.7, the computing time requirements of the 'branch and bound' and 'oats' methods would impose limits of size at 59 (62) and 100 (106) city travelling salesman problems respectively. The forecast increase in computing speed would increase the size limits to 82 (85) and 142 (148) city problems respectively. (There are also likely to be computer storage limits; these could be alleviated at a cost, which might include additional computing time, but are being ignored). The effect of the exponential relationship between the size and computing time is shown clearly in the way that doubling the time available barely increases the size of problem which can be solved.

The size of many journey planning problems which occur in practice is equivalent to that of travelling salesman problems with several hundreds or even thousands of cities. For practical purposes, therefore, computing methods which are aimed at finding an 'optimum' judged purely in the terms of the application, e.g. transport cost, and ignore the computing cost implications, are unlikely to have much general relevance, unless, or until, some developments in technique occur whose impact is to simplify the work by many orders of magnitude. (Future references to solutions which offer the best result judged in terms of the application only will be referred to as 'optimal', or as having the 'minimum' cost. Words such as optimal or minimum will be used without inverted commas only when the overall minimum or optimum having regard to such costs as those of computing are also included in the evaluation).

But earlier comments in this chapter, and examination or the results of, for example, the 'oats' method, suggest that solutions very close to the 'optimal' ('near-optimal' solutions) are obtainable in much less computing time than that required for 'optimal' solutions, and that the divergence between the time requirements for 'optimal' and 'near-optimal' solutions increases considerably as the size of the problem increases. Thus, depending upon the transport costs of departures from 'optimality', and the computing cost of going from a 'near-optimal' to an 'optimal' solution, the optimal solution to most problems will be 'near-optimal'.

Even so, the time requirements of the non-rigorous partial enumeration methods which have been described increase very rapidly with the size of the problem. Thus, the time required to find a local 'optimum' (time per COR, table 31.4) using the 'oats' method is of the order of 5 seconds for 42 city problems and 85 seconds for 100 city problems. Although the rate of increase in computing time requirements with size is much less than that of the rigorous methods, nevertheless, the rate of increase is still very high, and so must impose clear financial and practical limits to the size of the problem which can be tackled.

As mentioned earlier, the number of alternative sequences of N cities is $N!$ (or N factorial). This increases at a rate which is far greater than exponential (according to Stirling's Formula, the value of $N!$, when N is large, is given by $N! \sim (N/e)^N \sqrt{(2 \pi N!)}$ It is a measure of the success of the 'branch and bound' algorithm that its computing time requirements only increase at a simple exponential rate; not only does this method enable the 'optimal' solution to be found by a partial enumeration of the possible sequences, but it also enables the proportion of the total number of sequences which need to be enumerated to find the 'optimal' solution to decrease as the size of problem increases. It is only because of these features that the solution is as potentially effective as it is.

For the three-chain method, a guide to the way in which the inherent computing load may vary with the size of the problem may be gained by calculating the number of ways in which a tour may be divided into three and reconnected. A tour including N places has N links, and the number of different ways in which this tour may be broken into three separate chains is $N(N - 1)(N - 2)/6$. (Any one of the N links may be broken first, of the $N - 1$ remaining broken second, and of the remaining

N - 2 broken third; but for the purpose of distinguishing between the chains thus formed the sequence in which the links are broken is unimportant, and therefore this number of alternatives may be divided by the number of possible sequences in which the same three links may be broken, which is 6). These sets of three chains may each be re-connected in eight ways. (Consider one end of one chain; this may now be connected to any one of the four ends of the other two chains; when this first connection has been made, the other end of the original chain may be connected to either of the two ends of the chain not yet incorporated; there are, therefore, four times two, or eight, ways of connecting three chains without forming complete sub-tours). Thus, the number of ways in which any tour can be broken into three chains and re-connected is $4N (N - 1)(N - 2)/3$.

Consequently, it would be reasonable to expect the computing time of this method to be approximately proportional to the cube of the number of places included in the problem. (This excludes any more than proportional increase in computing time requirements due to the problems of manipulating larger chains, which would be difficult to avoid). In practice, the computing time reported for calculating the shortest tour that can be found by splitting a given tour into three chains and reforming, is approximately proportional to the cube of the number of places in the problem (32.3). The computing time per local 'optimum' in the 'oats' method appears to increase at a slightly greater rate than the cube of the number of cities.

While increases in computing time requirements which are proportional to the cube of the number of cities are less demanding than exponential increases, nevertheless limitations on the size of problem which can be tackled profitably, depending upon the cost parameters of the problem, remain. Thus, if the computing time requirement is 100 seconds for 100 city problems, it would become 12,500 seconds, or approximately 3½ hours, for 500 city problems.

To reduce the computing time requirements further, while still retaining a partial enumeration technique, it is necessary either to devise much better computing techniques for applying the methods already described, or else to apply a more elementary version, such as the two-chain method, which may be regarded as a degraded form of the three-chain method. The number of ways in which a tour of N cities can be divided into two chains in $N/N - 1/2$, and there is only one new way of re-connecting each of these pairs of chains. Consequently, it would be expected that the computing time requirements of this method would be approximately proportional to the square of the number of places involved in the tour.

From the point of view of computing costs this type of relationship is much more encouraging. On the other hand, it is paid for, to some extent, by a deterioration of the quality of the results obtained in comparison with the 'optimal'. The shortest tours found from a given initial tour are less frequently 'optimal' than with the three-chain method, and are far more widely scattered in solution value in relation to the 'optimal' than the three-chain method. It is claimed that it is more effective to utilize a given amount of computer time on the three-chain method than on repeating the two-chain method with different starting tours (32.3), assuming there is sufficient time to apply the three-chain method at all. It has to be accepted, therefore, that the performance of the two-chain method is worse, in terms of the length of tour found, than that of the three-chain method, in return for its decreased computing time requirement. Whether the two-chain, three-chain, or 'oats' method is preferred for a given problem will depend upon whether the limits of practical size for the longer methods have been exceeded, and, if not, upon a trade-off between the increased computing costs of the three-chain or 'oats' methods as compared with the two-chain method applied with comparatively few repetitions, and the value attributed to the respective solutions.

But the result has so far been compared with the length of the 'optimal' tour. In practice, the advantage to be obtained from journey planning by any improved method is an advantage over whatever is being achieved at present; the 'optimal' achievable is only of practical interest insofar as it gives a guide to the results which might be obtained if 'perfect' methods were developed, and is of limited use as a guide to the performance of any method relative to current performance.

It is easily shown experimentally that a human being is capable of finding quite good tours. Thus, for example, if given the task of producing a tour, few people would produce a tour which included any links which crossed one another, and this alone ensures that the tours produced are not too bad; the tour of 48 cities in Britain produced by application of the proximity rule, and already illustrated in figure 29.2, includes some links which would probably not be included in a manually prepared tour, yet it is only 30% longer than the shortest tour possible. Experiments in which individuals preparing a tour were given a light pen display and the aid of a computer programmed to feed back to them the results of the tours they were trying (32.4) showed that, under these conditions, some individuals can find 'optimal', or 'near-optimal', tours in a comparatively short time. No precise generalization about how well tours will be prepared manually is likely to be valid, but, at the same time, it is important to recognize that, in favourable conditions, or even conditions which are not acutely unfavourable, human beings are capable of devising tours which are relatively good; the scope for reducing the length of tours using fully automatic computing methods to replace manual methods appears to be, in general, relatively limited, and may be less than 25% of current results. However this statement could be misleading. It is the author's current belief that in most practical applications of this type of technique the improvement in length obtained by using a computer to improve a tour of a given set of places will be relatively small; very significant improvements are likely, however, if the problem is extended to one of allocating as many places as possible to the tour, and simultaneously finding the best tour subject to a constraint on the tour length or duration. Of course, it is the latter problem which corresponds to most of those found in practice, and not just the problem of finding the shortest tour of a given set of places. The whole problem of costs and benefits is tackled more comprehensively in part 9.

The performance of the partial enumeration methods described is not so impressive as to leave no scope for alternative lines of approach to solutions of the travelling salesman problem. But the travelling salesman problem is only being used as a standardized and simplified test problem. In practice it has already been established that the typical wholesale journey planning problem is not only one of finding the shortest, or a relatively short, journey around a set of visits, but also one of allocating visits to journeys which are subject to restrictions, e.g. on duration, and obtaining efficient planned journeys. This is typical of journey planning problems in general. Alternative approaches to journey planning problems may, therefore, be not only possible, but also desirable.

Chapter 33

Conclusions from the survey of computational methods

The examination of the available 'optimal' and 'near-optimal', or approximate, methods in the last three chapters offers only limited encouragement that development of these computational techniques, in conjunction with anticipated developments of computer technology, will offer either practicable or financially attractive ways of approaching the calculation of journey plans. However, this survey has been by no means comprehensive; several lines of development have been omitted deliberately. Some, at least, of those lines of development omitted appear most unlikely ever to be developed to a point where any practical application becomes feasible, or where they are likely to offer competition to those partial enumeration techniques described.

For example, one development which has received some attention in the literature, is known as 'combinatorial programming' (actually this is another form of controlled partial enumeration), and the 'truck dispatching' problem has been quoted as a possible area of application of this method (a list of references may be found in reference 33.1). The essence of this method, when applied to the 'truck dispatching' problem, is the selection of that set of routes, from amongst the variety of those considered possible, which will satisfy a given set of delivery demands at least cost. It requires as input data a list of all the routes which might possibly be employed, and ignores the enumeration problems of preparing this set of routes. Although this technique starts when a very major part of the total problem has already been solved, it makes a mammoth task of determining the best combination of routes to be utilized from amongst those presented to it. This is illustrated by the results in table 33.1 taken from one.paper, published in 1968, (33.1) on the development of this technique.

Table 33.1 Solution times for sample of 'truck dispatching' problems
by 'combinatorial programming' algorithms

problem size[†] m x n	solution times algorithm 1	(IBM 7094 seconds) algorithm 2
5 x 31	.050	.050
6 x 62	.167	.117
8 x 92	.567	.200
13 x 91	35.167	6.367
11 x 231	9.183	1.383
11 x 561	12.917	2.867
11 x 1023	27.267	14.383
11 x 1485	34.950	19.317
12 x 298	89.133	3.500
12 x 538	131.033	7.117
12 x 793	77.667	4.567
15 x 575	600.000*	69.483
19 x 1159	–	2400.000*

† m is the number of deliveries to be made.
n is the number of alternative routes considered; a selection of these, in
which each delivery is performed, is the solution.
* problem solving terminated without having proved optimality.

It would appear that these algorithms take longer, and increase in length
more rapidly, than the 'branch and bound' method of solving the travelling
salesman problem published some years previously by Little et al. (33.2),
if problems of the same number of cities and deliveries are compared. On
this evidence it is most unlikely that this method will become of practical
significance for many truck dispatching problems. A subsequent brief
announcement (33.3) that a new algorithm has been developed which
solved the difficult 19 delivery problem in thirty seconds is unlikely to
indicate any significant increase in the practical relevance of this approach.
　　Amongst the mass of technical literature of this type, a high proportion
is irrelevant for practical purposes in its present form, even though
practical relevance and application may be claimed for it. Unfortunately,

unlike the paper cited, much of this literature does not even include sufficient information to enable its relevance to be evaluated on objective grounds. In these circumstances, appreciation of what might be relevant is essentially a matter of judgement, which is likely to be better the greater the amount of time devoted to each judgement; but the time available for each judgement is limited by the number of papers requiring it. Consequently, despite the pessimistic appreciation of the state of development of techniques for the solution of this type of problem presented here, it is possible that, buried in the mass of irrelevant literature, some developments of serious practical potential have been missed. Scott, in a survey of methods available for dealing with the combinatorial problems that arise in the planning of urban and regional systems (33.4), comes to slightly more optimistic conclusions.

If the appreciation presented here is correct, however, only the simplest and quickest of the approximate techniques offer much promise of practical application to any but the smallest problems.

Chapter 34
Criteria for practical techniques

Several guide-lines have emerged from the survey of available computational techniques. For a method to offer scope for wide practical application it is necessary, not only that it should be fast when applied to test problems, but also that the relationship between the size of the problem and the computing time required should increase as slowly as possible, and certainly not significantly faster than the rate of increase of potential benefits with the size of problem. For most practical purposes this second guide-line may be interpreted as being that the increase in computing time requirement with increasing size of problem should be as near linear as possible.

Further, because of the high cost, and even impracticability, of proceeding to 'optimality', a cost which is recognizable not only in the absolute size of the computing time required for a given problem, but also in the exponential relationship between the computing time requirements and increasing size of problem, it is necessary to consider utilizing methods which do not guarantee 'optimal' results. Thus, it is necessary to accept and consider a trade-off between the cost of failing to achieve 'optimality', and the corresponding computational cost; the ideal result of this trade-off has already been defined as being optimality. This trade-off is distinct from, and in addition to, that between any improvements to be derived from the application of computational methods over the increased cost, if any, associated with their use in place of manual methods; detailed consideration of the trade-off between the advantages and costs of computer usage is deferred until part 9.

A trade-off between the cost of failing to achieve 'optimality' and cost of computation is necessary; but it is also necessary to take a practical view of what is meant by the costs of failing to achieve 'optimality', and even, of 'optimality'. The travelling salesman problem involves finding the shortest tour; an aim of journey planning is usually finding the quickest journey. But it has been shown that common methods of estimating distance are by no means precise; the conversion of distance into journey duration, and thence into cost estimates, appears to be less precise. The standard error of estimates of journey distance may be more than 10% of the distance estimated, while standard errors of estimates of journey duration may easily be in excess of 25% of the estimates, especially in urban areas. One implication of these uncertainties of estimation is that if the estimated distance of two tours differ by much less than the standard error of estimation, there is a significant probability that the longer of two tours, according to the estimates, is, in fact, the shorter. The tour which is 'optimal', taking into account the estimated distance, time, or cost, may not be, in real terms, the 'optimal' tour, if there are other tours which are estimated to be longer by a margin that is less than, or of the same order as, the standard error. Consequently, the various 'near-optimal' solutions are, for most practical purposes, indistinguishable; the objective of journey planning calculations need only be to obtain any 'near-optimal' solution; the tolerable difference between the 'optimal' and acceptable 'near-optimal' solutions is determined by the accuracy of the method of estimation employed.

The same point can also be taken in reverse: the real improvement in journey planning performance offered by a better method of journey planning can only be established when the standard error of the method of estimating the criterion, whether it is distance, duration, or cost, has been taken into account. There are two obvious corollaries: small improvements, relative to the standard error, may be non-existent in real terms, and the smaller the improvement relative to the standard error of the method of estimation, the greater the number of observations required to establish experimentally a significant difference. It follows that it is better not to put too much trust in improvements in journey planning, in terms of producing better routes, as a means of justifying the use of computer methods, but rather to anticipate that the main advantages may be derived from, or at least become apparent as a result of, improvements in the methods of estimating journey duration, or from exploitation of economies of scale, which have already been discussed, or from economies resulting from including journey planning in administrative systems, which will be discussed later.

Uncertainty as to what is either 'optimal' or optimal is increased by consideration of some of the other factors which complicate the journey planning situation. To give but one example which has already been mentioned, on some occasions it has been shown that the journeys actually performed by drivers not only differ from the journeys planned, but are also considerably longer. Whether this is the result of unforeseen requirements for services, lack of knowledge of the road network, or of drivers seeking routes which subject them to the least cumulative stress, the objective of journey planning is rendered that much less clear and specific.

Thus, too great an emphasis on establishing the route with the shortest estimated distance, or duration, or lowest estimated cost, may not only be unrealistic in terms of the associated computing cost, and of the established accuracy of the methods of estimation utilized, but may also emphasize discrepancies in objectives between drivers and management. It will therefore be assumed that the proper objective of computational methods should be to obtain a result which is 'near-optimal', rather than 'optimal', in terms of the estimated performance. Keeping in mind computational costs, assessments of journey distance or duration estimation accuracy, and any confusion of objectives which may be revealed in practice, it will be assumed that tours with estimated distances which are not much more than 10% greater than the estimated 'optimal' distance are, for practical purposes, likely to be indistinguishable from the 'optimal'. Within this range methods which produce shorter routes are to be preferred if the computational requirements are similar.

Chapter 35

Directed search methods

If given a map with a number of cities plotted on it, and instructed to prepare the shortest tour around them by hand, most people devote most of their effort to the initial preparation of a complete tour, and little effort to preparing variations, or to experimenting with alterations, to the first complete tour formed. Manual efforts are directed in a way which is totally different from that of the partial enumeration methods described, in which emphasis is placed on preparing systematic variations of random starting tours.

Furthermore, one common approach to the preparation of tours manually is for these to be prepared on a step by step basis; cities may be linked together in pairs discontinuously, rather than a tour being drawn in one continuous movement. This tendency may be a necessary reflection of the nature and limitations of human information processing, or computing, ability, as described, for example, by Miller (35.1).

In the attempt to represent the pigeon-holing method of journey planning as a logical process, the main rule employed was that the cities were linked together in the order of their increasing distance apart. This is a discrete, step by step, process similar to that described as being a common way of preparing journeys on a map. These are examples of what will be called here 'directed search methods'.

Typical characteristics of directed search methods, as applied to routeing or sequencing problems are:
1 the method is discontinuous or discrete, cities are linked together in pairs according to a sequence determined by some criterion;
2 once links have been established, they remain established; the remaining steps required to finish the tours are framed in such a way as to incorporate the links already made;
3 only one tour can be prepared from a given problem with a given directed search method; there is no enumeration or random variation.

The proximity, or 'link the nearest first', rule was devised in an attempt to reproduce, in a logical form, an analogy to the commonly applied manual method of preparing journey plans called pigeon-holing. This is a simple directed search method, and the result of applying it to a travelling salesman problem is illustrated in figure 29.3. The result does not appear very good to manual inspection, and, in terms of computed distance, it is approximately 30% longer than the 'optimal' tour. It is not only worse than has been accepted as a target, but is also probably worse than would be achieved by many people set to draw a tour around the same set of cities on a map. The visual impression, given by the cross-overs, that the results might be worse than those achievable manually might undermine the faith and trust in the system that would be necessary for it to be successful. And this is so even though the main advantages of journey planning by computer may not be found in the preparation of better (e.g. shorter on the basis of estimated distances) tours, but rather in such developments as improved estimation of journey duration and, consequently, improved utilization of the available time, and although it may be impossible to establish significant differences in routeing performance. But the standard of performance illustrated in figure 29.3 is not an unfortunate accident resulting from the particular form of this problem, but appears to be inherent in the application of the proximity rule.

It has already been observed that the difficulties associated with this method appear to arise when remote cities are linked; since links are made between the nearest cities first, the cities which start off by being remote become even more remote as the close cities are linked together. The remote cities are only fitted into the tour when chains have been formed which include all the close cities, and consequently the remote places are fitted willy-nilly onto the ends of the chains thus formed; in these circumstances it would be accidental if the links between the remote cities and the chain ends did not cross the chain, and there is certainly little cause for surprise if the tour formed by the proximity rule is not very good either when compared with the length of the 'optimal' tour, or when judged visually.

One of the techniques for 'optimization' which is applied on occasions is known as hill climbing and this is evocative both of the technique and of the circumstances of application. A simple way of finding the top of a single hill may be to climb always in the steepest direction. It is possible to apply a loose analogy of this type of steepest ascent, or gradient, method to the travelling salesman problem.

A lower bound to the length of a complete travelling salesman tour may be obtained, as already mentioned, by assuming that each city is linked to its two nearest neighbours. However, except under unusual conditions, this assumption would not lead to a tour, since the nearest relationship is not reciprocal, and some centrally located cities may be amongst the two nearest to several other cities. For example, among the 48 cities in the A.A. mileage charge (reproduced in figures 29.1 and 29.2, and illustrated in figure 35.1), Perth is the nearest city to Aberdeen, but the nearest cities to Perth are Edinburgh and Glasgow; Holyhead, Norwich, Penzance, and Stranraer are neither the nearest nor second nearest cities to any of the others. However, the cost of not forming such a preferred link can be envisaged as being the extra distance to travel to the alternative; before the linking process has commenced, the cost, or loss associated with not linking a city to its nearest neighbour might be envisaged as being the extra distance to be travelled to the third nearest. In the case of Aberdeen, the third nearest city is Edinburgh, which is 34 miles further than Perth, and this might be regarded as a measure of the loss if Aberdeen is not linked to Perth. Considered in this way, at the initial step the largest loss likely to be incurred amongst the 48 cities is by Inverness; the nearest cities to Inverness are Fort William and Aberdeen; the third nearest city is Perth, which is 49 miles further away than Fort William.

If cities are linked together in the order of the loss that would be incurred if each could not be linked to its nearest permitted neighbour (i.e. one which is not already linked twice, and is not already linked to the same chain) the tour illustrated in figure 35.1 is obtained; its length is 2724 miles, or approximately 2.6% more than the length of the 'optimal' tour. The only noticeable anomaly is the direct link between Dorchester and Penzance, and this is, in fact, responsible for most of the excess length.

To explore the performance of variations of this method four groups of ten travelling salesman problems each were used. The first group were between 20 and 100 cities in size and were based on distance matrices. Nine of these problems had already been used by others; the tenth was the A.A. 48 city problem. The other three groups consisted of problems using straight line distances calculated from co-ordinates generated randomly; the groups consisted of 50, 500 and 2,500 city problems. The performance of one of the methods developed when applied to these problems is summarized in table 35.2 (the method used on the distance matrix problems was not identical with that used on the co-ordinate problems (35.2)). The ratio between the lengths of the tours produced and the corresponding lower bound is fairly stable. For comparison, the ratio between the lengths of the 'optimal' tours and the lower bounds for the distance matrix problems is 1.17 (standard deviation 0.07). This comparison suggests that the results obtained may generally be within

Figure 35.1 Tour of 48 cities in A.A. mileage chart found by directed search method using Simple 'loss' criterion. Length 2724 miles, or 2.6% longer than shortest tour.

10% of the 'optimum'. Furthermore, both this test and comparison with the way in which the length of the tours is expected to vary with problem size (**35.3**), suggests that the results may improve as the problems increase in size. The computing requirements of the method applied to the co-ordinate problems increased at a rate less than $N^{1.5}$, where N is the number of cities. It appears probable that, if the need were strong enough, this method could be extended to 10,000 city problems with existing computing facilities. Further details of this work have been published elsewhere (**35.4**).

Table 35.2 A directed search method applied to travelling salesman problems.

Problem type	size of problems	ratio = $\dfrac{\text{result}}{\text{lower bound}}$		average computing time (CDC 6600) seconds
		average	standard deviation	
distance matrices	20-100	1.26	0.14	0.19 - 5.15
random co-ordinates	50	1.30	0.05	0.51
random co-ordinates	500	1.30	0.04	13.05
random co-ordinates	2500	1.28	0.01	140.2

Reverting to the calculation of plans for intermediate wholesale delivery journeys, it was shown that the application of the proximity rule tends to produce journey plans which do not appear to be very good; the plans produced appear to be most at fault when dealing with the deliveries furthest from the depot (figure 29.5). Similar difficulties were encountered in the application of the proximity rule to the preparation of complete tours, the links joining the most remote cities to the tour being the most questionable. Some consideration of the remoteness of the delivery, or its distance from the depot, seems to be required; this was achieved with the loss method applied to the travelling salesman problem by taking into account the extra distance to be travelled if the link to the nearest city could not be included in the tour.

Turning again to the 48 cities in the A.A. mileage chart, the furthest city from London (the depot for this purpose) is Inverness. A return journey from London which includes Inverness must be at least 1,058 miles long. The city nearest to Inverness is Fort William, and is 66 miles away. A return journey from London which includes Fort William must be at least 994 miles long. Two separate return journeys from London to Inverness and Fort William would involve travelling 2,052 miles, but if these two cities were visited on the same return journey it would only be 1,092 miles long, or 960 miles less; this can be regarded as the saving which is achieved by linking these two cities together to be visited on the same journey. The worst reasonable way of visiting several cities is by separate return trips to each. When two cities are linked and visited on the same journey there is a travelling distance saving due to that linkage. The distance saving may be taken as a measure of the value of that linkage.

Considering visits to Inverness and Fort William as an example, the saving in distance resulting from linking them is 960 miles, which is the sum of their individual distances from London minus their distance apart. This is a general formula for the distance saving resulting from linking two deliveries together, and its derivation is illustrated in the following paragraph.

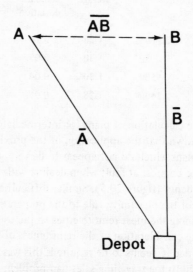

Figure 35.3. Illustration for deriving formula for 'saving'.

Consider two deliveries, A and B, distant $\bar{A}$ and $\bar{B}$ respectively from a depot (figure 35.3). Let A and B be a distance $\overline{AB}$ apart. If A and B are visited in two separate return trips from the depot the travelling distance is $2(\bar{A} + \bar{B})$. If they are visited in one journey, the travelling distance is $\bar{A} + \bar{B} + \overline{AB}$. The difference between these two distances is the 'saving',

$S(AB)$, resulting from linking A and B, where

$$S(AB) = \bar{A} + \bar{B} - \overline{AB}$$

or the sum of their distances from the depot minus their distance apart.

Proceeding in the same way it is easily shown that the 'saving' resulting from the addition of further deliveries to the journey is additive, and may therefore be taken to reflect the value of progressive extensions to a journey. The 'saving' can therefore be used as a criterion for the sequence in which links, and therefore journeys, should be formed during journey planning, using a step-by-step, directed search, process. When the savings criterion is used to plan journeys, it is notionally envisaged that the worst reasonable set of journey plans would involve visiting each delivery on a separate return journey. The saving of potential links between pairs of deliveries is then calculated, and deliveries are linked together in the decreasing order of saving, subject to journey restrictions not being exceeded by the chain thus formed, and to conditions that the deliveries being linked are not already linked to the same chain, or linked to more than one other delivery. Each separate link formed thus reduces the total distance required to visit all the deliveries by the maximum amount possible in one step, starting from the worst reasonable distance.

Application of the use of the savings criterion to plan journeys is illustrated in figure 35.4, in which the 48 cities in the A.A. mileage chart are allocated to journeys which start and finish at London and include no more than four cities per journey; this should be compared with figure 29.5 which illustrates the application of the proximity rule to the same artificial problem. Application of the savings criterion has produced journey plans with a reduction of one journey and 12.5% of the distance; it is probable that, in this case, the journey plans produced by application of the savings criterion are the best possible; however this is not always, or even often, the case.

Since the savings criterion was first advocated for planning multiple-delivery journeys by Clarke and Wright (35.5) and Webb (35.6), who arrived at this criterion independently, attempts have been made, by Gaskell (35.7) and Christofides and Eilon (35.8), to evaluate the quality of the plans produced. Gaskell applied the savings criterion and three slight variations of it to some small test problems, and compared the results obtained by the application of these directed search methods with the best that could be obtained by manipulation and visual judgement. Table 35.5 illustrates the results he obtained.

Figure 35.4 Journeys, restricted to 4 visits each, to 47 cities using London as 'depot', Journeys planned by savings criterion.

Table 35.5 Comparison of results obtained by applying different directed
search criteria (35.7)

problem no.	% excess mileage over best results known obtained by different methods*			
	1	2	3	4
	(savings criterion)			
1	8.5	11.3	7.3	0.7
2	0.9	0.9	1.4	6.1
3	3.6	4.9	1.4	4.9
4	2.2	10.8	2.9	2.2
5	10.1	16.2	11.9	7.8
6	0.6	0	4.1	7.0

*These figures are slightly different to those given originally because some
slightly improved plans have been found since (35.11).

Table 35.6 Comparison of application of 3-chain and savings criterion
methods (35.8)

problem no.	deliveries	savings criterion excess mileage (%) over 3-chain result*	time (IBM 7090 minutes) savings criterion one run	3-chain
1	6	4.4	0.1	0.1
2	13	0	0.1	0.1
3	21	2.2	0.1	0.6
4	22	0.6	0.1	0.5
5	29	10.1	0.2	0.8
6	30	0.9	0.2	0.8
7	32	3.6	0.2	0.8
8	50	5.2	0.6	2.0
9	75	2.7	1.3	4.0
10	100	2.8	2.5	10.0

*In no case did the 3-chain result fall short of the best result known, and sometimes
improved upon it. For two of the problems the result of application of the 3-chain
method was described as the 'best of 10 runs'; otherwise no indication is given of the
number of runs except that one step of the procedure was 'repeat several times and
select the best solution'. Oberuc (35.7) and Shen Lin (35.12) agree that the number
of runs to find an 'optimal' solution increases rapidly with the size of problem.

Christofides and Eilon developed a version of the three-chain method, already described in chapter 31 in terms of its application to the travelling salesman problem (35.9), for planning multiple-delivery journeys, and were therefore more likely to find the 'optimal' plans than Gaskell; they applied the three-chain method to the same problems as Gaskell, and also to some new ones. Table 35.6 repeats some of the results they obtained..

Examination of the results presented in tables 35.5 and 35.6 lends support to the view that directed search methods are likely to give results of satisfactory quality when applied to practical journey planning problems.

The three-chain method, as applied by Christofides and Eilon, is the only computational method reported so far which consistently gives results, judged by the planned length of the journeys, better than, or as good as, those obtained by the application of the savings criterion.

Examination of the computing time requirements reported for individual runs of the three-chain method shows that, not only are these long, but also they increase at a rate which is close to the square of the number of places involved; this relationship is rather better than was reported by Shen Lin, the originator of the method, when it was applied to travelling salesman problems (35.12), but the basic time appears to be longer; different computers and programs were used and this may account for all the difference, but it is quite possible that some of the difference reflects the different structures of travelling salesman problems and those of planning wholesale delivery journeys.

If, as suggested for the travelling salesman problem, the number of runs required to achieve an 'optimal' solution increases far more rapidly than the size of the problem, the total computing time to achieve the same probabili of obtaining an 'optimal' solution, or coming within a given distance of it, would be expected to increase more rapidly than the cube of the number of deliveries. The potential application of the three-chain method to practical journey planning problems is almost certainly severely limited because of the computing time requirements.

However, although the plans produced by directed search methods such as the savings criterion appear to be within the quality target set earlier, the computing time requirements reported by Christofides and Eilon are still quite large, and increase rapidly with the size of problem. The crudest examination would suggest that, as the number of potential links between deliveries, for which savings have to be considered and compared, is approximately proportional to the square of the number of deliveries (the number of distinct pairs is $N(N-1)/2$, where N is the number of deliveries), the computing time requirement of this directed search method would be proportional to the square of the number of deliveries. The results reported in table 35.6 support this assessment.

It has already been suggested, in connection with discussion of the two-chain method, that computing time requirements which increase with the square of the size of the problem will, almost certainly, limit the scope for practical application, since only in exceptional circumstances can the benefits to be derived from an application be expected to increase as fast as the square of the size of problem. (Additionally, there is usually a fixed cost associated with submitting any job to a computer, and this may limit the scope for application to small problems). But any directed search method which involves links being constructed with consideration of the relative positions of neighbours, would appear to require time to compare these relative positions; the time required to compare relative positions would be expected to depend upon the number of possible relative positions, or the square of the number of neighbours.

Journeys could be planned without consideration of the relative positions of neighbours, and therefore without the time requirement increasing so rapidly, but the quality of journey plans which could be produced under such conditions is questionable. Thus, links could be formed between deliveries in the order of their distance from one single place, for example, the depot, or a place at one extremity of the area; in these circumstances the number of distances to be considered and compared is the number of deliveries in the problem, and, consequently, the computing time requirement would be expected to be inherently proportional to the number of deliveries. But if a travelling salesman tour is constructed around the 48 cities in the A.A. mileage chart by linking cities to the chain in the order of their distance from Penzance, in the extreme south-western corner of Britain, a tour which is more than 90% longer than the shortest tour is obtained. It may be possible to find better methods, but, intuitively, the possibility of producing good tours or journey plans without considering relative positions appears very slight.

Consequently, if any improvement in the relationship between the computing time requirement and the size of the problem is to be obtained it is most likely to be found in the detail of the computational implementation. Since the computing time requirements for the application of the savings criterion repeated in table 35.6 are already so large, even for small problems, as to raise doubts about the potential scope for applying this method profitably to many situations, particularly those where journey plans are prepared daily, an examination of the problems of, and techniques for, using the savings criterion to plan wholesale delivery journeys is necessary to establish whether the scope for application is very extensive.

The scope for using savings criterion to plan wholesale delivery journeys may be taken as a general indication of the practical potential of directed search methods.

Chapter 36

Appendix

An estimate of the number of tests required to find a particular delivery in an ordered delivery list by the 'binary search' method.

Let there be N deliveries.

1 delivery could be identified on the first test, either of 2 deliveries on the second, any one of 4 on the third, and, in general, any one of $2^{(x-1)}$ deliveries could be identified on the xth test.

Let x be defined by

$$2^{x+1} > N \geqslant 2^x$$

Thus the number of deliveries which would be identified by x tests is n where

$$n = 1 + 2 \ldots \ldots + 2^{(x-1)}$$

$$= 2^x - 1$$

Thus the number of deliveries which would not be identified within x tests, and require a further test to be identified, is

$$N - n = N + 1 - 2^x$$

The average number of tests required to find a delivery is therefore A where

$$NA = 1 + 2.2 + 3.2^2 + \ldots \ldots + x 2^{x-1} + (x + 1)(N + 1 - 2^x) =$$
$$= 1 + 2^x (x - 1) + (x + 1)(N + 1 - 2^x) =$$
$$= 1 - 2^{x+1} + (N + 1)(x + 1)$$

and

$$A = [1 - 2^{x+1} + (N + 1)(x + 1)] / N$$

If N is large, $1/N$ may be neglected, and $(N + 1)/N$ tends to 1.
If $N = 2^x$

deliveries, the overall computing time required for the comparison process to discover the potential link with largest saving, during the step-by-step formation of links, may be proportional to the cube of the number of deliveries.

Thus, if the savings criterion were to be applied in the way described, the computing time requirements would be too large for many applications to be profitable, and would increase far too rapidly with the size of application, while the storage requirement would also be too large for most computers.

One way of reducing some of the immediate problems of the method of applying the savings criterion already described, if delivery points recur, is to prepare a file of the savings of potential links on a backing storage medium in a separate procedure; the rapid access storage capacity limitation is removed and calculation of the savings of the potential links is reduced to the status of an overhead, or quasi-capital, expense, to be shared between the number of times it is used.

However, this separation does not remove the problem of finding the potential link with the largest saving to confirm at each step; it was shown that the computational aspect of this problem may be proportional to the cube of the number of deliveries if the savings are maintained in the computer's rapid access store. But if, to find the largest saving at each step, it is necessary to transfer the complete file which is proportional in length to the square of the number of deliveries, from the backing storage, then the time requirement of this process will not only continue to be proportional to the cube of the number of deliveries, but will be increased, for all but the slowest computers, by the relatively slow process of transferring the savings information from the backing store into the computer.

Thus, while some of the original computational demands of the simple method of applying the savings criterion are reduced by preparing in advance a file of savings stored on a backing storage medium, the problem of finding the largest saving at each step remains, and is aggravated by the relatively slow rate of transfer of information from the backing store.

The problem of transferring information from backing storage can be reduced if the file of savings of potential links is stored, not as a square matrix of the savings between pairs of deliveries in a sequence determined by the deliveries, normally in delivery of customer number order, but as a list in a sequence determined by the size of the saving of the potential links. If this list is read in decreasing saving sequence, each potential link found which is permissible, i.e. its formation would not result in an infringement of the journey restrictions, while the deliveries at each end have not already been linked twice, nor have they been linked to the same chain, could be confirmed since it would, at that stage, be the potential link with the largest saving. Thus, an ordered savings file (a file of the savings of potential links in decreasing savings sequence will be called a savings file) would only have to be read once in the preparation of each set of journey plans, and the burden of information transfer from backing storage would be drastically reduced.

However, there are costs associated with the use of an ordered savings file. The first is that the initial preparation of the file of savings of potential links is followed by a sorting process, in which the file is rearranged into declining savings sequence; this is an addition to the initial overhead. The second is that, as the sequence of the file no longer corresponds to a sequence determined by the deliveries, as in a matrix, it becomes necessary to identify each potential link; the simplest method of doing this is to identify each potential link by the deliveries at its ends, and typically results in an expansion of the size of the file by three or more times. (It is possible, after the savings file has been prepared, to abandon the value of the saving of each potential link, since the actual value is not required during the processing, but only the sequence, in order to reduce the expansion of the file. However, it is normally convenient to retain the length of each potential link, or a means of deducing it, in order to simplify the estimation of journey distances. In addition, if there is any likelihood of additional customers requiring the insertion of additional potential links, it is better to retain the value of the saving lest any addition requires the preparation of a completely new file).

The third expense of using a savings file in savings sequence is a result of the sequence of potential links on the savings file being no longer determined by any characteristic of the deliveries, such as the delivery or customer number. When a potential link, which, if the appropriate conditions are satisfied, is the next link to be confirmed as having the largest saving, is read from the savings file, it is necessary to find the deliveries corresponding to its ends before it can be determined whether the conditions for confirmation are satisfied. This requires that a search be made amongst the deliveries, and there are a number of alternative ways of conducting this search.

If the list of deliveries is held in a sequence which does not correspond in any systematic way with the identification of the ends of the potential links on the savings file so that each delivery has to be examined, then, on average, correspondence between an end of a potential link and a particular delivery will be established after half the deliveries have been examined. If the time to examine an individual delivery is a seconds, and the number of deliveries to be examined is N, the average time to establish correspondence is $\frac{1}{2} aN$ seconds. The time required to test one end of all the potential links is $aN^2(N-1)/4$ seconds, a time which is approximately proportional to the cube of the number of deliveries. This will be described as the serial search method.

If the list of deliveries is held in a sequence which corresponds with the identification of the ends of potential links, a method of searching the delivery file for a particular delivery can be used which exploits the sequential property. In the 'binary search' or 'binary chop' method, the delivery in the middle of the ordered list of deliveries is examined first; the required delivery is then found to be lying in the upper or lower half of the list. The delivery in the middle of the appropriate half of the list is tested in turn, so that the delivery is now known to be located within a quarter of the list. The list is thus divided into parts repeatedly until the required delivery is found. The average number of times the list has to be divided to find any particular delivery, if there are N deliveries, tends to log_2N as N becomes large. (It is shown in the appendix to this chapter that the number of times the list has to be divided tends to $(log_2N) - 1$ as N becomes large; the simpler form used in the text is more convenient, and conservative). If a cycle, or division, takes b seconds, then to find the deliveries corresponding to one end of all the potential links would take approximately $\frac{1}{2}N(N-1)b \, log_2N$ seconds. Thus the computing time requirement for identifying deliveries is proportional to a higher power of the number of deliveries than the square if this method is used.

Yet another method is possible if the deliveries are not only held in an ordered list, but the location of the delivery and its information in the list can be calculated from the identification of the delivery, or by direct referencing. In this case the time to find any identified delivery is constant and the time requirement for identifying the deliveries at the ends of potential links is proportional to the square of the number of deliveries. If the time for identifying one delivery by this direct referencing method is c seconds, then the time for identifying one end of each of the potential links is $\frac{1}{2}N(N-1)c$ seconds.

A number of conclusions may be drawn from a comparison of expected performances of these three methods.

As N becomes larger, the computing time requirement for identifying a particular delivery by the first two methods increases, and it increases more rapidly by the first method (proportional to N) than by the second (proportional to $log_2 N$). Consequently, whatever the relative starting speeds, at all values of N beyond some lower limit set by the particular computing characteristics of the machine, the direct referencing (third) method will be faster than the binary search (second) method, which will itself be faster than the serial search (first) method. Examination of typical computing characteristics leads to the impression that the direct referencing method is almost invariably faster than the other two, and that, for most machines, binary search becomes faster than serial search at quite small values of N.

Since the time taken to transfer the details of each potential link from the backing store is fixed for a particular machine (and equals d/r, where d is the number of characters per potential link, and r is the effective transfer speed), for all values of N beyond some limiting value the binary and serial search procedures will take longer than the transfer of information; examination of machine characteristics suggests that this may often occur at quite low values of N; however the trend is for this limit to become larger with newer and bigger machines. For the direct referencing method the speed of the process will almost invariably be determined by the information transfer time, but overall computing performance will tend to determine the speed for the serial and binary search methods as N becomes large.

Whichever method is used the time requirement will not increase at a lower rate than the square of the number of deliveries, which is dictated by information transfer time requirements; above the levels of N where computing becomes the dominant factor, the time requirement of the serial search method will increase proportionally to N^3, and of the binary search method proportionally to $N^2 \, log \, N$.

Examination of the savings file method has so far been based on an assumption that the location of required deliveries is known in advance so that the savings file may be prepared in advance. This assumption was valid for the first attempted application of the savings file method (**36.5**); furthermore the maximum number of deliveries required on any occasion (N) in that application was under 200, which made the computing problem fairly straightforward. Very often, however, the location of the deliveries required on any occasion is not known long in advance, since it depends upon the placing of orders, although all the potential customers may be known. The savings file method can be adapted to these conditions by preparing a savings file of the potential links between all N potential customers, and comparing this with a list containing details of all n deliveries actually required and which have to be incorporated in the journey plan.

The time to identify by the serial method whether a given potential customer at the end of a potential link required a delivery would, on average, increase, since a complete search of the delivery list would be necessary to establish that a potential customer did not require a delivery. The probability that any potential customer requires a delivery may be taken to be n/N; consequently the expected number of tests to search the list to find whether a potential customer actually requires a delivery would be $n(1-n/2N)$.

If the binary search method is used to search the delivery list the number of tests required will come closer to the limiting value of $log_2 n$ the smaller n is compared with N, because the probability that a potential customer will be found to require a delivery at an early stage of the search will decrease.

The time required to test whether a potential customer requires a delivery if the direct referencing method is used will not change in these circumstances. There will, however, be an increase in the amount of immediate access computer storage required by this method, since provision must be made for a record to be held for every potential customer. This need not be so very demanding if two lists are held, one of potential customers and another the normal list of required deliveries. The potential customer list need only provide space for the address, or location, of the required delivery information to be inserted when a delivery is required. This double referencing method would not require much more time and would economize substantially on direct access storage space if the proportion of potential customers requiring a delivery on any occasion is relatively low.

The main difficulty which would be encountered in many circumstances if the savings file consisted of potential links between all potential custome would follow from the number of potential links included in the savings file. In many existing wholesale distribution depots, the number of known potential customers is several thousand, and may exceed ten thousand. If each potential link record required 10 characters (for two potential customer identification numbers and the saving) and there were 5,000 potential customers, a computer which transferred information from backing storage at an effective rate of 100,000 characters per second would require a little over 20 minutes to transfer all the potential link information from the savings file. (On the basis of the assumptions used th backing storage requirements of the savings file would be 125 million characters). This would be the minimum time requirement, and if either the serial or binary search methods were used, unless there were very few deliveries required, the total time requirement would probably be rather greater. Once again, for many applications this requirement would be impracticably large. (If the direct referencing method were used it might be possible to reduce the effective time requirement of the information transfer process by multi-programming; even under these circumstances the time requirement would still be substantial).

It is possible to reduce the size of the savings file by eliminating some potential links which are unlikely ever to be utilized, for example those between potential customers in diametrically opposite positions in the depot area, and therefore with a saving which is very little different from zero. Practical considerations may confuse this issue: on the one hand the true objective is that of reduction of transport cost, and a journey which includes two visits which result in no mileage saving may nevertheless contribute to a reduction of administrative and loading times at the depot, and hence to a reduction in vehicle time requirements and cost; on the other hand long journeys between deliveries may be unacceptable as appearing to be without adequate justification to management or men. In either case, editing the savings file may involve a substantial amount of costly skilled attention, and may need to be extremely drastic to achieve sufficient reduction in processing time.

A number of considerations lead to common use of a different procedure for reducing the size of the savings file. Instead of the contents of the savings file being the savings of all the potential links between all potential customers, the contents are the savings between the centres of elementary areas, or zones, within the depot area, and it is assumed that the saving between the centres of two zones represents the savings of all the potential links between potential customers in the two zones. Advantages of this assumption include:—

1   the size of the savings file can be regulated by varying the number, and incidentally the size, of zones;

2   the zones can be arranged to represent all parts of the depot area, whether containing potential customers or not, so that new customers, whatever their location within the depot area, can be included in the planning process immediately, and without modification to the savings file;

3   the methods of finding distances between zone centres utilizing specified road networks, which are used in traffic survey methods, can be used in the preparation of the savings of the potential links without much difficulty;

4   it is possible to envisage that files of information about the road network and distances between places will be collected and, in time, this will reduce

the magnitude of the task of collecting and preparing data about the road network; additionally, the spread of postal coding, which identifies addresses within small streets or blocks, may allow distances already prepared to be retrieved and utilized.

There are, however, disadvantages resulting from the use of zone centres as the ends of potential links.

1 The number of zones is dictated by processing speed or cost considerations; a larger depot area will tend to be reflected in the use of larger zones.

2 As the size of zones is increased, and the number decreased, the accuracy of distance estimation deteriorates; this aspect of journey planning has already been discussed. Whether the deterioration is significant or not depends upon the relative accuracies of estimation of different elements of the task.

3 If there are several potential customers in both zones represented by the ends of a potential link there may be difficulty in determining the links to confirm.

4 If several deliveries may ever be required within one zone the methods of searching the file of required deliveries become more complex. The exact form of tests for correspondence between customers requiring deliveries and the zones which contain them must be changed; for example, the customer identification may be split into two sections, one corresponding to the identification of the zone in which it is located, or the test for correspondence may depend upon tests for both ends of the range of customer numbers identified with a single zone. In the binary search procedure, once a delivery corresponding to a zone has been identified, it is necessary to search for others in both directions from the one identified (unless the adjacent deliveries have been tested before the first relevant one is identified). In the direct referencing method it is necessary to use double referencing with a zone list which, if it contains any required deliveries, contains the address, or location, of the first delivery of the list of deliveries required within that zone; the list of deliveries corresponding to a specific zone may have to be searched serially to determine whether any of the deliveries are still unlinked and, if so, whether they can participate in the potential link currently being processed. Thus the main asset of the direct referencing method of searching, its discrimination, is reduced if zones commonly contain several deliveries. (An increase in delivery density, which would be expected to lead to an increase in transport efficiency, would also lead to an increase in the number of deliveries required within a zone).

The use of zones, and calculation of the saving of potential links between zone centres, in the savings file method enables it to be adapted to the processing speed requirements of all types of potential application, although with possible disadvantages with regard to the quality of the plans. That the processing problems associated with using the savings file method may be substantial is illustrated by the details given by representatives of I.B.M. during a presentation of the I.B.M. 360 Vehicle Scheduling Program (36.2). Preparation of the savings file for a problem in which the area was represented by 300 customer zones, with 20 barriers and 2 congested areas where special allowances were made, took 6¼ hours on a 64K I.B.M. 360 Model 30. Preparation of journey plans using this savings file for 10 vehicles making 90 deliveries takes some three to four minutes machine time.

Two particular disadvantages might become noticeable if zone sizes have to be increased to reduce the number of zones, the number of potential links in the savings file, and hence reduce the processing time. Firstly, the estimates of journey distance may deteriorate to a point where they contribute significantly to the planned idle time. Secondly, the planned sequence within zones and between adjacent zones may be very poor; often this will only matter insofar as it reduces confidence in the planning method or as it contributes to a deterioration in the accuracy of journey distance estimation, since the detailed sequence can often be adjusted without difficulty by the driver. However, if deliveries have to be made in the planned sequence because, for example, they can only be unloaded in the planned sequence, the planning performance of this method, on its own, may become unsatisfactory.

Chapter 36

Computational problems of applying the savings criterion: the savings file method

Application of the savings criterion requires that the savings of potential links be compared to find the potential link with the largest saving at each step.

If a saving is generated for each potential link, and there are N deliveries, then the computing time requirement for generating savings is inherently proportional to the number of potential links, which is $N(N - 1)/2$, and, hence, approximately proportional to the square of the number of deliveries. The computing time requirement of calculating the savings of potential links may be very significant. The time taken to compute the shortest distance between each pair of deliveries an essential preliminary to the calculation of the savings, if the road network method is used and there are several hundred deliveries, could be of the order of hours rather than minutes; even if the straight line method of calculating distance is used, the computing time for this stage could be of the order of minutes rather than seconds (36.1).

If all the savings are calculated first, before being compared, then storage space has to be available for them; this would be beyond the capacity of the rapid access storage of many computers when applied to many problems (36.4).

The time required to establish the first link, if the saving of each potential link has to be compared with the largest so far found, would be proportional to the number of potential links, or approximately proportional to the square of the number of deliveries. It might be possible to reduce the comparison process before subsequent links are established, for example, by storing the results of some of the comparisons made when the first and subsequent links are established; but, if not, or unless this is very effective, the computing time requirement of each step may be proportional to the square of the number of deliveries. (It is true that some deliveries are soon fully incorporated into chains, and therefore savings of potential links containing these are no longer of interest, but tests are required even to establish whether they are of interest or not). Since the number of links is approximately equal to the number of

$$A^* \sim (x + 1) - 2 = x - 1;$$

if
$$N = 2^{x+1} - 1$$

$$A^{**} \sim (x + 1) - 1 = x:$$

Consequently, as N becomes large, A tends to $(log_2 N) - 1$

An upper limit to the number of tests required could be derived directly: any delivery in the list can be found if the list is divided and tested $log_2 N$ times; this is an overestimate of the average requirement since some deliveries are identified earlier.

Chapter 37

Computational problems of applying the savings criterion: the convergent limit approach

In the exposition of the savings file method it has been shown that several of the techniques adopted to circumvent serious processing problems resulted in the appearance of alternative problems which had, in turn, to be circumvented; and although it is possible to devise a method which is relatively widely applicable and satisfactory, the chain of argument is so tortuous as to prompt a re-examination of some of the basic assumptions.

A basic feature of the use of the savings criterion, as explained, was that links should be formed in saving sequence, starting from the largest, to obtain the maximum possible saving of mileage at each step, starting from the 'worst reasonable' distance. Although this statement gives the most obvious justification of the savings criterion, it imposes unnecessarily stringent conditions for its application; identical results may be obtained if links are formed in many different sequences as result of the application of less restrictive conditions. A potential link between two unlinked deliveries which has the greatest saving of any potential link including either of these deliveries will be formed as a result of the application of the savings criterion; the sequence in which it is formed is unimportant. Thus, the savings of the potential links between Penzance and Plymouth, and between Aberystwyth and Carmarthen, among the A.A. 48 cities, illustrated in figures 37.1 and 37.2, are larger than those of any other potential links including any of these cities. The end result of the application of the savings criterion would be the same whichever of these two links was formed before the other, or even if either were the first link to be formed. If either or both of the deliveries involved in a potential link are already linked once, and hence form part of a chain, an additional condition for that link to be confirmed (it is taken for granted that the potential link is permissible, i.e. that neither delivery is already linked twice, and the two deliveries are not already linked to the same chain) is that the saving of the potential link is greater than that of any potential link including the deliveries at the other ends of the chains to which they are linked. If this second condition is infringed it is possible that linkages with a larger saving at the other end of the chains will be prevented by the journey restrictions.

The overall effect of this relaxation of the sequence in which potential links may be confirmed is to reduce the amount of computational work required to compare the savings of potential links before confirming one. A complete search to find the potential link with the largest saving is not necessary.

The saving of a potential link between two deliveries is defined as being the sum of the distances of the deliveries from the depot, minus their distance apart. It follows that the further deliveries are from the depot, and the nearer they are together, the larger the saving of a potential link between them. If distance from the depot and closeness together can be utilized to guide the search amongst potential links and their savings, and potential links with large savings are recognized by these characteristics, then it might be possible to achieve further economies in the searching process. This is best illustrated with an example, which has already been introduced in chapter 35, and is the application of the savings criterion to plan journeys, including no more than four of the A.A. mileage chart cities (37.1), based on London. The mileage chart and another map is illustrated in figures 37.1 and 37.2.

It can be seen from examination of the bottom row of the mileage chart that the furthest city from London is Inverness, the distance being 529 miles. It can also be seen by inspection that the nearest is Fort William. The saving of a potential link between Inverness and Fort William is 960 miles. Although it has not been proved, this is the potential link with the largest saving, and it has been found with comparatively little effort.

To prove that the potential link between Inverness and Fort William is that with the largest saving, the saving of the potential link between Inverness and Fort William, of 960 miles, can be used as a target and as a criterion for elimination of other sets of potential links. Since the saving of a potential link is the difference between the sum of two distances and another distance, the sum must exceed the target saving, and at least one of the two distances summed must be more than half the target saving. Thus, the only potential links that could have savings in excess of 960 miles would be those including at least one city further than 480 miles from London. Examination of the distances of cities from London shows that only three are further than 480 miles from London; they are Inverness, Fort William and Aberdeen. Only potential links including at least one of these three cities could have a saving greater than 480 miles. Thus, once a saving which may be the largest is found, it is possible to eliminate many potential links from consideration by limit tests.

The limit tests can be established more formally. Let $S(XY)$ be the saving of a potential link between any two points X and $\overline{Y}$; let $\overline{X}$ and $\overline{Y}$ be the distance of X and Y from the depot, and $\overline{XY}$ be their distance apart, then

$$S(XY) = \overline{X} + \overline{Y} - \overline{XY}$$

I₁ ⁺ is assumed that X is further from the depot than Y,

i.e. that $\overline{X} \geqslant \overline{Y}$

Figure 37.1 Distances between 48 cities in Britain

Column labels (diagonal), in order:
Aberdeen, Aberystwyth, Barnstaple, Berwick-upon-Tweed, Birmingham, Brighton, Bristol, Cambridge, Cardiff, Carlisle, Carmarthen, Colchester, Doncaster, Dorchester, Dover, Edinburgh, Exeter, Fort William, Glasgow, Gloucester, Guildford, Hereford, Ho...

```
'427
'573 '214
'172  306  441
'403  114  181  263
'540  244  198  388  160
'480 '121   93  348   88  136
'443  211  239  291  100  105  148
'484  107 '137  362  102 '177  '44  174
'208  219 '365   88  195  351 '272  256  276
'472   45 '201  351  129 '242 '108  225   68  263
'491  252  249  339  141 '101  169   48  209  304  260
'326  172  274  175   93  214  181  117  195  139  206  165
'540 '181   86  407  145  113   61  172 '104 '332 '169  178  235
'552  284  268 '400 '181   77  187 '112 '226 '365  284  '93 '226  191
'115  312 '458   57  288  424  327  369  356  375  211 '425 '436
'555 '196   40  423  163  166   75  218 '119 '347 '183  223  256   53  243 '440
 152 '416 '562 '187 '392 '548 '469 '453 '473 '197 '460 '501 '336 '529 '561 '130 '544
 142  313 '459  101  289  446 '366  350  370   94  358  398  234 '426  459   44 '441 '103
'448  107  128  313   53  137   35  117   56  240  107  153  146   95  176  333  110 '437  334
'513  204  173  361  118   42  102   84 '140  311  204   83  187   98   95  397  148 '508  406   97
'430   79 '143  307   52  165 '50  141   54  222   84  177  142 '110  204  315 '125 '419  316   28  125
'423  108 '301  302  149 '208  244  199  215  148  289 '171 '268 '330  308 '283 '412  309  181  264  158
 104 '468 '614 '213 '444 '581 '521 '484 '525 '249 '513 '532 '367 '581 '593 '156 '596   66 '169 '489 '554 '471 '464
'253  174 '320  133  150  306 '227  215  231   45  218  263   99 '387 '324  138 '302 '242  139  195  266  177  170
'306  166  287  155  109  241  194  144  209  116  211  192   28  253 '253  191  269 '313  210  159  210  153  163
'365  190  259  214   86  183  166   86  188  178  215  134   39  217 '195  250  241 '375  272  131  160  138  201
'327  100 '252  206   90  249 '159  174  164  118  145  222   86 '220 '268  211 '235 '315  213  128  208  110   97
'518  247  227 '367  145   50  151  '79 '189 '331  247  '60 '192  152   42 '403  201 '528 '426  140   54  168  294
'326  126  254  192   80  235  161  154  172  118  171  202   51  221 '255  211  236 '315  212  126  196  118  123
'221  254  378   63  201  326  285  229  299   57  299  277  112  344 '338  106  360 '236  143  250  299  244  250
'427  161  195  275   50  118  102   50  128  236  175   91  101  141 '138  311  177 '433  330   72   86   91  198
'471  270  298  320  156 '161  208   62  236  284  287   60  145  232 '153  356  277 '481  378  179  142  203  296
'370  154  231  219   50  175  138   84  153  182  179  132   44  191 '193  255  213 '379  276  103  143  102  172
'464  156  159  312   64   96   69   80  105  257  156  106  138   99  129  348  138 '454  352   49   54   77  216
'663 '304  110  531  271  278  184  329 '227 '455 '292  335  364  165  355 '548  112 '652 '549  218  259 '233 '39
  81 '353 '499  '99 '330 '466 '406 '369 '411 '135 '398 '417 '253 '467 '478  '42 '482  103   61 '375 '439 '357 '35
'597 '238   60  465  205  207  118  260 '161 '389 '226  265  298   94  285 '482   42 '586 '483  152  189 '167 '32
'296  131 '277  175  107  264  184  188   88  176  232   78  '244 '283  181 '259 '285  482  152  212  224  134  12
'515  173  114  369  112   84   52  132  '96  307  160  138  196   40  157  400   88 '504  401   69   62   97   24
'338  154  257  187   77  212  164  116  179  145  187  164   18  220 '225  223  240 '342  240  130  179  125   15
'378   75 '195  258   43  200 '102  138  106  170  108  184   98 '162 '224  263 '177 '367  264   75  158   52   10
'528 '195  137  377  128   61   75  129 '118  322 '183  131  202   52  139  413  105 '519  416   91   49  119   26
'362  109  217  227   43  199  124  123  138  154  142  171   65  184 '219  247  199 '351  248   89  159   83   12
 226  320 '466  166  296  453  357  377  101  365  405  241 '433 '466  125 '448 '183   84  341  413  323    3
'523 '164   50  391  131  148   43  189  '87 '315 '151  199  224   41  218 '408   32 '512 '409   78  123  '93  2
'299  190  308  144  127  248  215  151  229  113  235  199   34  269 '260  184  290 '310  207  180  221  176  1
'488  212  195  337  110   53  116   54 '154  300  212   54  162  121   72  373  170 '497  394  105   29  133  2
```

then XY, the distance apart, must be at least as great as the difference between the distances from the depot,

i.e. $$X\overline{Y} \geqslant \overline{X} - \overline{Y}$$

and, substituting this limit for the distance apart in the savings formula above

$$S(XY) \leqslant \overline{X} + \overline{Y} - (\overline{X} - \overline{Y})$$

or $$S(XY) \leqslant 2\overline{Y}$$

Thus, the saving of a potential link cannot be more than twice the distance from the depot of the nearer end, rather than the further end as was suggested earlier.

If $S(AB)$ is the largest saving found so far, it follows that, if

$$\overline{Y} < \tfrac{1}{2}S(AB)$$

no potential link including Y has a larger saving than $S(AB)$.

Furthermore, if a potential link with a larger saving is found,

i.e. $$S(PQ) > S(AB)$$

then the new limit test is

$$\overline{Y} \geqslant \tfrac{1}{2}S(PQ)$$

before Y could possibly be involved in a potential link with a larger saving. This is a more stringent test than before; the distance limit tests are convergent.

	Leeds	Lincoln	Liverpool	Maidstone	Manchester	Newcastle upon Tyne	Northampton	Norwich	Nottingham	Oxford	Penzance	Perth	Plymouth	Preston	Salisbury	Sheffield	Shrewsbury	Southampton	Stoke on Trent	Stranraer	Taunton	York
Lincoln	67																					
Liverpool	73	118																				
Maidstone	20	*161	232																			
Manchester	40	84	35	219																		
Newcastle upon Tyne	92	151	154	*304	129																	
Northampton	24	79	134	102	119	213																
Norwich	73	106	215	*119	184	257	112															
Nottingham	67	36	97	158	70	56	57	124														
Oxford	60	119	154	92	142	250	41	139	94													
Penzance	8	350	*343	313	344	468	285	389	322	250												
Perth	43	*291	*253	*445	*252	*148	*353	*397	*297	*390	*590											
Plymouth	2	284	*277	243	278	402	219	319	256	180	*79	*524										
Preston	6	113	31	247	30	123	148	214	100	170	*367	*223	*301									
Salisbury	5	178	196	116	192	306	101	192	152	59	200	*442	130	219								
Sheffield	3	46	73	*192	38	124	94	145	37	127	348	*265	282	68	182							
Shrewsbury	6	115	58	188	66	195	93	195	79	104	*285	*305	*219	82	143	79						
Southampton	4	184	216	103	207	314	106	189	158	65	217	*455	146	234	23	192	163					
Stoke on Trent	3	85	51	183	37	164	85	173	50	105	307	*288	241	66	155	47	34	170				
Stranraer	9	279	220	*433	219	155	337	385	283	359	*556	145	*490	189	408	247	271	423	255			
Taunton	209	*203	177	204	328	145	248	181	109	140	*450	74	*227	64	208	*145	87	167	*416			
York	73	97	*226	64	81	135	179	78	172	398	*226	332	80	230	52	130	236	99	214	258		
LONDON	132	197	36	184	274	66	111	123	57	281	*415	211	212	84	160	153	77	147	401	165	196	

Figure 37.2 48 cities used for sample problems

345 Computational problems of applying the savings criterion: the convergent limit approach

Returning to the example, the only cities further than 480 miles from London are Inverness, Fort William and Aberdeen, and all potential links, except those between these three, can be eliminated from consideration as possibly having savings greater than 960 miles by testing the distance of the ends from the depot.

So far, only the distance of the cities from London has been used as the basis of limit tests, but it has been mentioned that nearness together is also important. For another city to form a potential link with Inverness which has a larger saving than that between Inverness and Fort William, either that city must be closer to Inverness or, if it is further from Inverness than is Fort William, it must also be further from London. Since Aberdeen is both nearer to London than Fort William and further from Inverness, the potential link between Inverness and Aberdeen must have a smaller saving than that between Inverness and Fort William; by the same arguments the potential link between Fort William and Aberdeen must also have a smaller saving. Thus, it has been established that the potential link between Inverness and Fort William is that with the largest saving without calculating the savings of any other potential link.

The limit tests which may be utilized on the distance apart may also be established more formally. If a potential link between X and Y has been found where $\overline{Y} \geqslant \frac{1}{2}S(AB)$ it is possible to derive a limit to the value of $\overline{XY}$, the length of the potential link.

Since	$S(XY) = \overline{X} + \overline{Y} - \overline{XY}$,
then	$S(XY) \geqslant S(AB)$
if	$\overline{X} + \overline{Y} - \overline{XY} \geqslant S(AB)$,
or	$\overline{XY} \leqslant \overline{X} + \overline{Y} - S(AB)$.
If	$\overline{A} + \overline{B} \geqslant \overline{X} + \overline{Y}$
and	$S(XY) \geqslant S(AB)$,
then	$\overline{XY} \leqslant \overline{AB}$.

Thus, a potential link with a relatively large saving may be found by selecting any delivery which is a relatively long way from the depot, and finding another close to it; and the saving thus found may be used as a basis for convergent limit tests which enable the exceptional potential links including either end which may have a larger saving to be identified simply. This method of search appears to conform to the generalized description of 'backtrack programming' methods given by Golomb and Baumert (37.2).

The use of this method to plan journeys for the A.A. mileage chart cities, using the map and chart, is straightforward. The furthest city from London is Inverness, the nearest city to Inverness is Fort William at 66 miles away, and the saving of this potential link is 960 miles. Only Aberdeen is greater than 480 miles from London and it is not nearer than 66 miles to anywhere, consequently Inverness and Fort William is the potential link with the greatest saving. The second nearest city to Inverness is Aberdeen at 104 miles and this potential link has a saving of 913 miles; only Fort William, besides these two, is further than 456 miles from London, but Fort William is further from Aberdeen than is Inverness, consequently the potential link with the largest saving is Inverness and Aberdeen. Inverness is now linked twice and need be considered no more. The city furthest from London is now Fort William; both Perth and Glasgow are 103 miles from Fort William, and, as Perth is furthest from London, the potential link between Fort William and Perth has the larger saving, at 809 miles. Only Aberdeen, besides these two, is further from London than 404 miles, and this can only be linked to Perth as Aberdeen and Inverness are already linked to the same chain. The saving of the potential link between Aberdeen and Perth is 822 miles and consequently this is the potential link with the largest saving. The first journey therefore involves Fort William, Inverness, Aberdeen and Perth.

It is possible to place the primary emphasis, in the searching process, on the distance apart rather than on the distance from the depot. However, the most obvious disadvantage would be that there are more distances apart than distances from the depot to be examined. If there are N deliveries, then there are N distances from the depot, but $\frac{1}{2}N(N-1)$ distances apart, to be examined and compared.

Whichever way primary emphasis is placed, if the distances are held in an ordered sequence it is possible for most of the examinations to be implicit rather than explicit. If a list of the deliveries is maintained in decreasing order of the distance of the deliveries from the depot when the search is concentrated upon depot distance, then, once the distance of one delivery from the depot has failed a limit test, all the deliveries below it on the list must also fail the same test. Thus, many deliveries may be eliminated from consideration at any step by proxy limit tests. This could be exploited with profit in the next steps of the sample problem.

The proxy convergent limit tests on the distance of deliveries from the depot, together with the separation tests on the distance of deliveries from each other, make it possible to find potential links which have a greater saving than any other potential links including either of these deliveries to be found very quickly. The best way of applying these techniques depends very much upon the conditions and, especially, the means to be used. Thus, for example, a very close pair of deliveries are far more easily recognized by visual examination than by calculation. Application of a method based on these techniques manually using a table of distances has been outlined.

If straight line distances can be taken to correspond to travelling distances a similar method may be utilized to plan journeys for deliveries which are plotted on a map, using compasses, dividers and a ruler. If straight line distances are insufficiently accurate, despite the difficulties associated with the other problems of journey duration estimation, then it is possible to devise a method which uses straight line distances to reduce the range of potential links to be examined, and a distance table for the final comparisons.

Similar methods can be applied by computer. If distances are estimated by the straight line method, then it may be found convenient to use polar co-ordinates centred on the depot, since these include the distance from the depot as one component, and the other component, the bearing, may be used to find the angular separation between two places which may be used as the basis of a convenient approximation to the distance separation.

Application of the method as outlined by hand shows that it serves to simplify both the task of finding a potential link with a very good saving, and that of limiting and simplifying the search for potential links with better savings; and this is true whether a distance table or a map and drawing instruments are used. (Manual application of the savings criterion by convergent limit methods is possible but tiring; the computational load becomes very great when the journey restrictions are significant). This is not very helpful evidence about the computing time requirements and performance of convergent limit methods of applying the savings criterion by computer, but some more objective observations follow.

The preliminary processes for the application of convergent limit methods are comparatively simple; a typical procedure would start with identification of the location of deliveries according to a cartesian co-ordinate system (e.g. National Grid) as data; the data would be converted into polar co-ordinates and the deliveries would be sorted into the sequence of their distance from the depot. This contrasts with the preliminary demands of the savings file method, which include the preparation of data concerning distances between adjacent modes if the road network method is to be used, calculation of the distances between zone centres (or preparation of co-ordinate data and calculation of distances of all potential links by the straight line method if this is to be used, bearing in mind the need to limit the size of the savings file for computational reasons) and hence, calculation of the savings of the potential links, and finally, sorting of the potential links into declining savings sequence.

The way in which the time requirements of the calculation process may be expected to vary with the size of the problem may be illustrated by considering three different aspects of the procedure:

a   the time requirements of the preliminary process would be expected to be proportional to the number of deliveries, or size of the problem; only the sorting process, a very small part of the total, would be expected to take disproportionately longer (e.g. proportional to $N \log N$, where N is the number of deliveries) as the number of deliveries to be sorted increases;

b   the probable time requirement of the procedure, using convergent limit tests of distance from the depot and between deliveries, to detect whether a delivery could possibly be part of a potential link with a higher saving than the best already found, depends upon the expected number of deliveries tested before the limit is reached; it is shown in the appendix to this chapter that the expected number of deliveries subjected to the limit tests may be proportional to $N^{1.5}$, when N is large;

c   the probable time requirement for savings calculations and tests, when the depot distance and delivery separation limit tests indicate the possibility that a potential link with a greater saving has been found, is shown in the appendix to be approximately proportional to $N \log \sqrt{N}$; it is also shown that the time requirement for this process is likely to be larger, often substantially larger, than that of the distance testing process when N is below a limiting value, which depends upon the relative unit speeds of the machine being used on the distance and angle testing procedures, and on the calculation of savings.

These arguments and calculations suggest that the computing time requirements of this method may increase at a rate that is approximately proportional to $N^{1.5}$, when allowance is made for growth of the parts of the procedure not examined here.

This prognostication may be compared with that for the savings file method; if deliveries are treated as the ends of potential links the computing time requirement would be proportional to $N^2 \log N$, but, if these computing time requirements are excessive, then if zone centres rather than deliveries are used as the ends of potential links, the computing time requirements are proportional to the square of the number of zones and to $\log N$. (Use of the 'binary search' method of matching zones to deliveries has been assumed).

The approximations in the appendix may give some basis for estimating the order of the total computing time requirements of this method; if these approximations are any guide, assuming the total time requirement is thirty times larger than for the elements estimated, and that, depending upon the machine, a savings calculation (the major computational time requirement involves taking the square root of the sum of the squares of two numbers) takes between 100 microseconds (100×10^{-6} sec.) and 10 milliseconds (10×10^{-3} sec.), and that a distance and separation limit cycle takes between 5 and 500 microseconds, then preparation of a set of journey plans for 400 deliveries would be expected to take between 9 and 900 seconds.

Some observations of computing performance of programs which have been written using convergent limit methods suggest that these estimates may not be too far astray.

The first programs using a convergent limit method were written within Leo Computers Limited (now absorbed into International Computers Limited) for Leo III from 1963 onwards. Leo III was a computer with a data-processing orientation and it was considered best to use fixed-point arithmetic for these programs because of the computational requirements of floating-point arithmetic. The time required to perform a savings calculation using fixed-point arithmetic was probably in excess of 10 milliseconds. It was difficult to observe the time taken as the central processor time was only monitored automatically to the nearest minute. The calculation time appeared to be very variable, averaging around 2 seconds per delivery. The type and complexity of the journey restrictions appeared to be responsible for large variations in computing time. Later, similar programs were written for the KDF 9 computer within English Electric-Leo-Marconi Computers Limited (also now absorbed into International Computers Limited). The KDF 9 was a calculation oriental computer with a 6 micro-second store cycle time. Again, timing facilities were not good, but to calculate journey plans for 400 delivery problems appeared to take around 80 seconds. A crude program has been written in fortran for use on a CDC 6600 computer. The time requirements vary approximately as $N^{1.5}$, where N is the number of deliveries. A 400 delivery problem takes 5.2 seconds. Taken altogether, these observations suggest that the estimates of the computing time requirements in the last paragraph may be too high.

This evidence suggests that for most purposes a convergent limit approach is likely to result in faster calculations than the savings file method.

No attempt has been made to specify one particular method as being The Convergent Limit Method; many reasons for this will emerge in the next chapter. In this chapter, however, it should be pointed out that, even to apply the savings criterion to a very simple problem, a great variety of methods is possible in which computing speed and simplicity may be traded for one another. For example, some programs have been designed to select the delivery furthest from the depot, thence find the potential link including that delivery with the largest saving, and then test whether this potential link is that including the other delivery with the largest saving. This approach generally enables the link, including either of these two deliveries, which has the largest saving, to be identified very quickly. However, sometimes neither the delivery furthest from the depot, nor the delivery with which it combines best, form any potential links with a large saving. The process may then go through several stages before a potential link that can be confirmed is found, and these stages may be identical for many consecutive steps each time the search is restarted. A corresponding ground pattern is of the furthest delivery being isolated, with the nearest deliveries to it being a conglomeration of deliveries much closer to the depot in the same direction, while the other deliveries which are a long way from the depot are in other directions. Repetitive, and wasteful, searches over the same ground are a common feature of convergent limit methods; they may be avoided by, for example, either storing the results of the test sequence, and jumping to the penultimate stage, working backwards if necessary; or starting the search from another point when the same pattern is repeated more than a limited number of times. The limit of computational complexity that is worth while depends upon many details of the application, the equipment and its costing, and there is no single method which is the best.

Chapter 37

Appendix

Relationship between problem size and the computational requirements of the convergent limit method.

An attempt will be made to illustrate the nature of the relationship between problem size and computational demands by estimating, very roughly, the number of deliveries which may be expected to satisfy the depot distance and delivery separation convergent limit tests in one part of the procedure.

The number of deliveries satisfying the depot distance test determines the number subjected to both the depot distance and delivery separation tests. The number of deliveries satisfying the delivery separation test determines the number of deliveries for which the saving has to be calculated in full. Calculating the number of deliveries satisfying either or both tests throughout a procedure would require both detailed specification of a method of calculation, and lengthy calculations based upon somewhat dubious assumptions. To simplify the problem it will be assumed that the first stage of the procedure at each step consists of finding that potential link which includes the delivery furthest from the depot and which has the largest saving; it will also be assumed that the time requirements of this stage reflect those of the complete calculation. The expected number of deliveries passing the depot distance and delivery separation tests for this stage will be estimated in order to illustrate the type of relationship which may exist between the computing requirements of the directed search procedure and the size of the problem.

Let the number of deliveries required be N, and the distance of the furthest delivery, A, from the depot be r. If it is assumed that the area is approximately circular, and the delivery density is uniform, then the average distance apart of deliveries will be of the order of

$$\sqrt{(\pi r^2/N)}.$$

If the nearest delivery (B) to A is the average distance away, then the expected distance of this delivery from the depot is of the order of

$$r[1 - 2/\sqrt{(\pi N)}],$$

if it is assumed that it is equally likely to be at any position on the circumference of the semi-circle of radius $r\sqrt{(\pi/N)}$ and centre A. The expected saving of this potential link is, therefore,

$$S(AB) = r + r (1 - 2/\sqrt{(\pi N)} - r\sqrt{(\pi/N)}$$
$$= r[2 - (2 + \pi)/\sqrt{(\pi N)}].$$

Consequently the limit of search for other potential links having a greater saving is a distance $\frac{1}{2}r[2 - (2 + \Pi)/\sqrt{(\pi N)}]$ from the depot, or $\frac{1}{2}r(2 + \pi)/\sqrt{(\pi N)}$ from the furthermost delivery.

If the delivery density in this anulus of outer radius r, width $\frac{1}{2}r(2 + \pi)/\sqrt{(\pi N)}$ is equal to the average, then the expected number of deliveries within it would be approximately.

$$2\pi r(2 + \pi)Nr/[2\pi r^2 \sqrt{(\pi N)}],$$

or $(2+\pi)\sqrt{(N/\pi)},$

which is close to $2.9 \sqrt{N}$, but will be assumed to be approximately $3\sqrt{N}$.

If the nearest delivery (B) to the delivery furthest from the depot (A) forms the potential link including A with the largest saving, and if the distance between A and B is the average distance between adjacent deliveries, then the expected number of deliveries to pass the depot distance test when there are N deliveries in total is $3\sqrt{N}$. If some other delivery X were to form a potential link AX with a larger saving than AB, then the expected number of deliveries passing the depot distance test would be less.

If, at any step, there are p deliveries, then the number of successful depot distance tests for this stage of the calculation would be $3\sqrt{p}$. If it is assumed that there are N deliveries in the problem, and that these are incorporated in journey plans in N steps, and that one delivery is removed from further consideration at each step, which are heroic but not too unrealistic assumptions, then the total number of depot distance tests required for this stage would be $\Sigma 3\sqrt{p}$, where p takes all integer values between 1 and N.

Using the integral as a means of evaluating the sum approximately, the expected number of depot distance tests for this stage of the procedure throughout the calculation would be

$$2N^{1.5}$$

For a 900 delivery problem there would be a total of 404,550 potential links. To find the potential link including the delivery furthest from the depot with the largest saving the expected number of depot distance tests would be approximately 90. The total number of depot distance tests for this stage of the procedure throughout the calculation would be approximately 54,000. This would also be the expected number of delivery separation tests.

Although this estimate only applies to the number of tests required for one stage of the procedure, it supports a hypothesis that the number of convergent limit tests is proportional to $N^{1.5}$, where N is the number of deliveries in the problem.

When there are p deliveries it is to be expected that approximately $3\sqrt{p}$ deliveries may satisfy the depot distance limit test and thus may form a potential link with a greater saving than the one already found.

If, amongst the potential links formed between the deliveries to be tested and A, all possible levels of saving are equally likely, then it is to be expected that, on average, the potential link with the best saving will be found after $log_2 3\sqrt{p}$ improvements. (This assumption probably results in the number of improvements being exaggerated, since the delivery list is arranged in decreasing distance from the depot and the probability of a good saving therefore decreases as the search progresses).

If the delivery separation tests are fully efficient, which is unlikely, but the error may offset to some extent the biases in the assumptions about the distribution of the size of the savings, then the expected number of successful delivery separation tests, and therefore of savings calculations, is of the order of $log_2 3\sqrt{p}$.

The expected total number of savings calculations for this stage of the procedure, if it is assumed, as before, that there are N deliveries in the problem, that these are incorporated into journey plans in N steps, and that one delivery is removed from consideration at each step, is $\Sigma log_2 3\sqrt{p}$ where p takes all integer values between 1 and N. The corresponding integral may be taken as an approximation to this sum, in which case the total number of savings calculations would be expected to be approximately

$$N[(log_2 3\sqrt{N}) - \tfrac{1}{2}].$$

The expected total number of savings calculations for this stage of the procedure increases only a little faster than the number of deliveries. Furthermore, for a 900 delivery problem, with a total of 404,550 potential links it would only be necessary to calculate the saving of 7 potential links to identify the one including the delivery furthest from the depot with the largest saving, and to calculate the savings of less than 6,000 potential links altogether for this stage of the procedure.

For most computers, if the deliveries are held in a list in the sequence of decreasing distance from the depot, and the angular separation is used as a basis of a delivery separation test, the two tests will be very much faster than a savings calculation. The ratio of the expected number of tests to that of thé expected number of savings calculations for the stage of the procedure examined is

$$2N^{1.5}/N[(log_2 3\sqrt{N}) - \frac{1}{2}]$$

For a 900 delivery problem the approximate value of this ratio is of the order of 9; for most computers this would be less than the ratio of computing times between the calculation of a saving and the performance of a depot distance and delivery separation test. Consequently, for this size of problem the saving calculation is likely to be dominant, and the rate of increase of computing time with size of problem for this stage of the procedure will be closer to $N log\sqrt{N}$ than $N^{1.5}$. The expected number of tests increases faster than the expected number of savings calculations with size of problem, so that at some stage the computing requirements of the tests would become dominant; but for many computers this would only be at extremely large values of N; with 16,000 deliveries the ratio of tests to savings calculations would still only be of the order of 30.

Furthermore, for a 900 delivery problem the total time requirement for the depot distance and delivery separation tests, if they take 100 microseconds (10^{-4} secs) for each test cycle, and for savings calculations, if these take 4 milliseconds (4×10^{-3} secs) each, for this stage of the procedure, would be approximately 5.4 seconds and 24 seconds. The total time requirement for the complete calculation would have to exceed 30 times that of this stage for it to exceed 1 second per delivery.

Chapter 38

Computational methods of planning wholesale delivery journeys in perspective

Simple applications of the savings criterion lead, in some circumstances, to journey plans with peculiarities which are only too visible. In general, these peculiarities occur when, especially due to boundary effects or journey restrictions, the combinatorial nature of the underlying problems are re-emphasized.

A simple and rather artificial example may be used to illustrate the way in which the combinatorial nature of the problem may reappear. Journey plans are required for deliveries to the six places shown in figure 38.1.

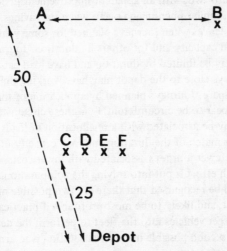

Figure 38.1. Illustration of failure of savings criterion.

A and *B* are 50 miles from the depot and 12 miles apart. *C, D, E* and *F* are 25 miles from the depot and 2 miles apart. The loads to be delivered at each place are equal, and the load capacity of the vehicles is 3 deliveries. Journeys are restricted in duration to the equivalent of 150 miles, each delivery taking a time equivalent to that required for travelling 15 miles.

The potential link with the largest saving is *AB*, with a saving of 88 miles. The journey from the depot to *A* and *B* and back to the depot involves a travelling distance of 112 miles, and equivalent duration of 142 miles; no further delivery can be added to this journey without exceeding the permitted duration; the load would be only 2 deliveries, as compared with the capacity of 3 deliveries. Another journey would be formed incorporating, say, *C, D* and *E*, fully utilizing the load capacity, and result in a journey of distance 54 miles and equivalent duration 99 miles. There would be a third journey to *F* with a distance of 50 miles, equivalent duration 65 miles and load of 1 delivery. Three journeys are planned as a result of the application of the savings criterion to this problem, involving a total distance of 216 miles and duration equivalent of 306 miles. An obvious alternative exists of plans for two journeys delivering to *C, A* and *D*, and E, B *and* F respectively, with a total distance of approximately 200 miles and duration equivalent of 290 miles. Peculiarities such as this are common phenomena among the last journeys planned for a batch of deliveries by the savings criterion; three 'rump' journeys may be produced which may be easily combined into two, with an apparent improvement in cost.

More seriously, similar phenomena occur when the savings criterion is applied in circumstances when journeys planned for some vehicles may be limited by the load capacity and for others by duration. Journeys further from the depot may be limited by duration and have load capacity to spare, while those journeys close to the depot may have working time, but not load capacity, to spare. Journeys planned by application of the savings criterion often appear to be circumferential; in these circumstances more radial journeys may be associated with a re-allocation of loads and routes which, via a better match of the duration and load capacity utilization, may result in plans for fewer journeys associated with lower costs. Before, however, too much effort is put into solving the computational problems involved, it should be recognized that there are two possible managerial solutions. The first, and likely to be most profitable if practicable, is to introduce some larger vehicles into the fleet to perform the deliveries close to the depot. The second possible managerial solution is to arrange for some vehicles to perform two or more journeys in a day, either by re-loadin or by the use of tractors and trailers. If neither of these solutions is possible or attractive, then a computational method of producing a better match between the planned load and duration utilization of vehicles may offer better journey plans than the savings criterion.

The road structure in many cities and regions is radial in form, with commercial centres along the main radial arteries and but poor

circumferential connections between them. Trade may have been
deliberately solicited and developed along radial routes. In these
circumstances, as well as when there is an imbalance between the load
and duration limitations, more radial routes may be preferable to the
circumferential ones produced by the savings criterion.

Adaptations of the savings criterion have been suggested (e.g. **38.1,
38.2**) which would tend to result in more radial routes being planned;
essentially it has been advocated that the criterion, $K(AB)$, for linking
deliveries A and B should be

$$K(AB) = \bar{A} + \bar{B} - p\overline{AB};$$

if $p = 1$, $K(AB) = S(AB)$, and routes tend to be circumferential; if $p > 1$,
then more radial routes will be produced. A simpler alternative is to
restrict the length of links between deliveries. While these methods may
serve to give the type of solution required, they will tend to do so almost
by accident rather than by design; journey durations and load capacities
will not be purposefully matched.

Planned journeys are normally limited by some restriction, even if it is,
for example, lack of available work. Since it is normally cheaper to use
larger, rather than smaller, vehicles, providing the capacity can be utilized,
it is preferable to avoid, if physically possible, a situation in which load
capacity is the predominant journey restriction. However, unless vehicles
are much larger than the normal requirements, or unless the demands for
carriage are virtually constant, it is likely that some journeys will be limited
by load capacity. One way of utilizing the vehicle time available as a result
of occasional curtailment of journey plans by the load capacity is to employ
these vehicles to perform second journeys, but in these circumstances the
tendency will be for second journeys to be relatively short and confined, on
most occasions, to only a small proportion of vehicles. If, however, the size
of vehicles utilized is restricted by statutory, physical, or similar
considerations, then second, and even third or subsequent journeys may
be common. Vehicles carrying out wholesale petrol deliveries commonly
perform several journeys per day. Many of these vehicles are of the maximum
size permitted; but physical access restrictions, for example, dictate that
some should be smaller, and yet another restriction may arise from the
difficulty of measuring the quantity delivered if too many deliveries are
made from any compartment.

When second, or even third, journeys are common, it may be possible to
plan these journeys independently, and allocate them to vehicles
subsequently. However, attempts to use this approach may encounter
major difficulties. If, for example, vehicles have distinct characteristics,

such as the numbers and sizes of compartments in which different brands of petrol may be carried, which must be considered when journeys are planned, then each journey must be planned from the outset for individual, or a class of, vehicles. Similarly, if journeys, when planned without duration restrictions, tend to require more than half the available duration, then, since it is impossible to allocate more than one journey requiring more than half of the available duration to a vehicle, the plans will not result in satisfactory utilization of the available time. Similar problems arise if, for example, two journeys, which may both be allocated to the same vehicle, include deliveries subject to delivery time restrictions. Consequently, it may be necessary to allocate the first journeys to vehicles when planned, so that second journeys can be planned subject to time restrictions imposed by the remaining portion of the available duration so far unallocated.

If deliveries are linked in strict savings sequence, few journeys, in general, are completed sufficiently early in the process for second journeys, as they are formed, to be allocated to vehicles with completed first journeys. However, the possible relaxation of the rules governing the strict sequence of link formation without altering the final result, mentioned at the start of chapter 37, may often be exploited to complete some journeys earlier, thus facilitating the allocation of second journeys to vehicles. But there is no logical reason why earlier completion of planned journeys, offered by this relaxation, should always ensure that completion is early enough to avoid all problems of allocating additional journeys to vehicles before the plans for their previous journeys have been completed.

Thus, while the savings criterion enables the combinatorial nature of many problems of planning wholesale delivery journeys to be circumvented, only slight changes in the form of the problem result in the re-appearance of the combinatorial nature. Examination of chapters 20 and 21 will show that there is a vast range of objectives and circumstances of which many occur in the planning of wholesale delivery journeys. The savings criterion cannot be regarded, therefore, as a completely general technique for planning wholesale delivery journeys.

Just as the savings criterion is limited in scope, so, at another level, are detailed computing tactics. For example, any change in conditions which renders radial journeys more attractive, or even only more likely, might be reflected in a change in the search tactics which would place more emphasis on early examination of radial potential links. Similarly, if a complex load restriction, such as the allocation of different petrols into different compartments of a tanker, were to reduce drastically the number of combinations of deliveries which could be allocated to the same journey, it might save computing time to test for compatability of deliveries before assessing the value of the potential link between them. If the full compatability test is complex and slow, it might be quicker, overall, to use a rough preliminary test which accepts some deliveries which are, in fact, incompatible; to follow the rough test with a test assessing the value of a link; and then test finally for compatability only when the most attractive potential link appears to have been found.

A conventional objective of mathematical or quasi-mathematical reasoning, formulae and methods is a degree of generality. Discussion is usually aimed at a set of problems, and even the pure mathematician is concerned that the set should contain many members, even if these are only notional problems. In most circumstances the power of a method is judged by its comprehensiveness. Linear programming, for example, is regarded as a powerful method because it has been applied to many problems of different types, once they have been suitably formulated.

High regard for general methods, and especially 'general programs', has also developed in computing circles, particularly in relation to the application of quantitative techniques of a mathematical or statistical nature. Practical justification for emphasis upon general methods and programs may be found in the relative shortage and expense of mathematicians and computer specialists.

Journey planning problems are essentially combinatorial in nature. No general methods of finding the 'optimal' solution to combinatorial problems of any size within a practicable or financially attractive computing time exists, nor does there seem to be any short-term prospect of one being developed.

However, directed search methods appear to offer prospect of a general strategy. They can be developed, at least for some problems, to give results which are sufficiently close to the 'optimal' to be indistinguishable from it for typical standard errors of estimation of the parameters involved. The introduction of a step process enables the high rate of increase of computing time requirement with size of problem to be reduced drastically.

There is no general directed search method, however, and the actual computing strategy and tactics adopted for applying a particular directed search technique may make a great difference to the computing time requirements, and, therefore, its practicability. In the application of the savings criterion, as an example of a directed search technique, it appears that the savings file method is only likely to be preferable to a convergent limit method in special circumstances. The best design of a convergent limit method is itself dependent upon the shape of the particular problem under consideration; it is a strategy rather than a specified procedure.

The picture conjured up, of vast numbers of different computer programs for similar applications being desirable, must be disconcerting when added to the large numbers of programs produced for virtually identical applications due to the widespread 'not programmed here' mentality. Under these circumstances the program design and implementation costs may be (or, perhaps, should be recognized to be) too high to justify widespread application of computer based journey planning methods, unless these costs can be shared. Even then, many of the detailed technical problems have yet to be faced, let alone solved.

In contrast, the possibility of widespread sharing of journey planning facilities recalls the case made out earlier for widespread sharing of distribution transport facilities. The journey planning costs of shared distribution transport facilities would not only be reduced by reducing the number of systems required, but the systems would also be simpler. With sufficient delivery density, few journeys between successive deliveries would be of any length, and most would not add significantly to the minimum time required for starting the vehicle, moving it, and finding a new parking place. Similarly, with increases in delivery size, the number of deliveries per journey would be reduced. In these circumstances many of the detailed problems of estimating journey duration and planning journeys are likely to be simplified considerably. Thus, it is possible to envisage that with sufficient delivery density the detailed sequence of deliveries in an urban area would make little or no difference to the journey duration, or, if it did, that the reasons would be local in either place or time. Many local problems, such as congestion, road repairs, or even the details of traffic management schemes, are likely to remain extremely costly to incorporate into the journey planning process, and may be best left to the discretion of drivers.

It is possible to produce satisfactory solutions to many journey planning problems; an example of a solution to an unusual problem is given in the next chapter to reinforce this point. But the number and complexity of such problems awaiting solution is likely to be reduced drastically by the concentration and sharing of transport services.

Chapter 39

A computational method of scheduling bulk conveyances of mail

The general circumstances and tasks of the C.C.S. fleet in the London Postal Region of the General Post Office were described in chapter 22 (and also in reference 39.1), but some of the salient details will be recapitulated here.

The primary task of the C.C.S. fleet is the performance of approximately 30,000 scheduled journeys per week for the conveyance of mail between 360 terminal points, mainly rail termini and sorting offices. The work is continuous, although there is very little on Saturday nights and Sunday mornings. Work demands peak during each week day: over 600 vehicles are utilized, being driven, throughout the period, by over 1,200 men. The time and place of departure from, and arrival at, the origin and destination of each scheduled journey, or service, is specified. The journey planning task consists of the production of duty schedules which allocate to each driver a set of journeys, or services, and which conform to all the conditions and restrictions, while making best use of the available time and effort.

According to the detailed agreements governing shift working, night work may not be scheduled to start after 10 p.m., and early morning shift drivers may not be scheduled to start work before 6.00 a.m. Furthermore, it is, usually, expensive to allocate further work to night shift drivers after the early shift drivers become available for work, not only because the night shift drivers are working overtime, but also because, owing to the duty pattern, they are due for additional rests or meal breaks very early in any extended period of duty. These provisions enable the preparation of schedules to be carried out in twenty-four hour batches, since there is, in effect, a defined break, at the end of the night shift, in the continuity of the work. Thus only one day's schedules need be prepared at one time.

Some rough idea of the magnitude of the number of possible solutions can be gained if it is assumed that the starting times of the 5,000 scheduled journeys or services performed on each weekday are spread evenly over the twenty-four hours, and that any service scheduled to start in one hour may be followed by any one scheduled to start in the next; under these assumptions the total number of possible solutions would be $(200)^{24}$. Preparation of duty schedules for this fleet requires the selection of a good solution from an astronomical number of possible solutions.

The obvious way of applying a directed search approach would be to schedule services to follow one another according to a criterion reflecting the variable costs of possible matches. Judged at the most elementary level, the cost of allocating consecutive services to the same duty schedule is the cost of the scheduled idle time plus that of scheduled empty running between the end of one service and beginning of the next, and the criterion needs to reflect, in some way, this cost.

If the cost measure described is used as a criterion, and an attempt is made to minimize the incremental cost of adding each service to the duty schedules, the effect produced might be similar to that produced by the proximity rule described earlier, in that this criterion might be expected to produce some duty schedules with much scheduled idle or empty running time between some successive services. In this case extended periods of idle time between services are not necessarily as expensive as might appear at first sight since, depending upon a number of factors, it may be possible to utilize extended periods of idle time in other ways. A number of emergency, unscheduled, demands for service arise which can be performed during periods without scheduled work, providing these are long enough, while duty schedules have to include provision for rest periods or meal breaks, and it may be possible to utilize periods which are otherwise scheduled to be idle for this purpose. Thus the cost of scheduled idle time, in this case, tends to decrease if the period becomes long enough to utilize for other purposes. Hence the criterion utilized is the direct measure of the variable cost between scheduled services. Cost is calculated in terms of minutes of idle time plus a constant, reflecting running costs, multiplied by the empty running time. Each service is allocated to that duty schedule for which it will result in the least increase in scheduled cost.

The step-by-step approach in this case is achieved by allocating services to duty schedules in the sequence of the scheduled starting time of the services. To this end, service requirements are sorted, prior to the allocation process, into the sequence corresponding to their starting times. Each service from the file of service requirements, arranged in the sequence of starting times, is allocated in turn.

The convergent limit strategy suggests that a good candidate match between service and duty schedule, according to the criterion, be found quickly, and that this should be used as the basis of a test to eliminate possible worse matches as quickly and simply as possible. Neglecting, temporarily, the distance between the finish of one service and start of another, a service can only be allocated to a duty schedule if the duty is scheduled to be idle at the starting time of the service (since services are being allocated in starting time sequence, if a duty schedule is idle at the start of a service which has yet to be allocated, the duty has no further service commitments). Consequently, if duty schedules are held in a list in a sequence which corresponds to the time when they are next due to become (or became) idle, then, by reading through the list until the first duty scheduled to become idle before the start of the service currently being allocated is identified, the shortest period of idle time resulting from the allocation of that service is found. Furthermore, the search through the list could be reduced in length, although rendered more complex in that a search in both directions might be necessary, if the position corresponding to each service start time in the scheduled duty list is stored from step to step. Since the next service starts either later, or at the same time, the search can usefully start by proceeding from the last to the current service start time, and only if a possible match is not found in this section of the scheduled duty list need a backwards search be undertaken, starting at the point in the duty schedule list corresponding to the starting time of the last service allocated.

If the difference in starting and finishing points of different services, and particularly those which might follow one another, is ignored, then this method would provide an immediate match between service and duty schedule. In practice, the difference in start and finish locations cannot be ignored, but the pattern of search utilized is basically that already described. The search for a possible duty schedule to which a service with a given starting time can be allocated proceeds through the list of duty schedules until one is found which has sufficient scheduled idle time for the empty running necessary between the finish of its previous tasks and the start of the new service. The test used to determine whether there is sufficient time for the empty running need not depend initially upon accurate estimation of the distance. Approximate tests may be used to screen the candidate schedules, e.g. if cartesian co-ordinates are used to identify locations, the empty running distance must be greater than, or equal to, the distance along each axis, and there must be sufficient time available to travel at least as far as the larger of these distances for a match to be possible. Whether, and which, screening tests are desirable depends upon the frequency of testing, the difference of the computational time requirements between the full and screening tests, and the probability that any screening test will save the failure of a full test, or that it will add to the computational load, as happens when both succeed.

When the duty schedule is found that involves the shortest scheduled idle time between the finish of its previous tasks and the start of the service being allocated, it may be taken as a candidate for the least cost match and used as a reference (the reference schedule); indeed, this schedule will be the least cost match if there is no empty running cost to be added to the costs of idle time. If there is some empty running, then a lower cost match involving more scheduled idle time may exist, providing it involves less empty running. A limit to the extent of the search for a cheaper match may be calculated from the cost of the first match with the reference schedule, and involves calculation of the amount of idle time with no empty running which costs as much as the idle time and empty running of the match already found. Thus, if s is the time, for the reference schedule, between the finish of the previous task and the start of the new service to be allocated, t is the time, which is part of the idle time, to be used in empty running, and x is the additional cost of empty running relative to idle time, then the cost of this match is K where

$$K = s + xt;$$

and the cost of any other match is K^* where

$$K^* = s^* + xt^*.$$

K^* is less than K if

$$s^* + xt^* < s + xt.$$

The maximum possible value of s^*, s^{**}, occurs if there is no empty running, and

$$s^{**} = s + xt.$$

Since, because of the method of search, s^* is greater than s, the search must terminate relatively quickly and is confined to duty schedules which are due to become idle during the period xt; the smaller the relative unit cost of empty running, and amount of empty running for the reference schedule, the shorter the search. During the search approximate tests can be used to determine whether the distance from the last position of each duty schedule from the start of the new service is greater than the empty running required of the reference schedule. If, and when, a cheaper match is found during the searching process, the duty schedule involved is made the reference, and a new limit to the search is calculated from the 'cost' of the new reference schedule. This limit is more stringent than the previous one, and the searching process follows the convergent limit strategy.

One of the most cumbersome aspects of this method is handling the list of duty schedules, and, in particular, maintaining it in the sequence of the time each duty is scheduled to become idle. When a new service is allocated to a duty schedule, that schedule has to be removed from its present place in the list, and re-inserted in the position appropriate to the finishing time of the service now allocated to it. The list has to be examined to find the appropriate point to insert it, and, if the list is maintained without gaps, all the schedules due to become idle between the old and new times of the schedule being moved have to be shifted to close the space from which the schedule has been deleted, and open up a space at the new position. If the average number of schedules moved for each service is 200, and the number of services is 5,000, then this activity implies the movement of a million duty schedule records while preparing the schedules for one day. To enable simple searching procedures to be used, the duty schedule records should be of fixed length, but it is difficult to store information in fixed length records without wasting space, and, even with fast machines, the size of the record movement task encourages brevity in the records to be moved. To reduce the problems of handling the duty schedule list it is divided into two parts: one is the full list of duty schedule information in any convenient order, and the other is a time-ordered list of duty schedule availability information, containing only the time when each duty schedule will next be available, and the location of all other information about that duty schedule in the full list. In this case, at the cost of having to find the location of basic information about a duty schedule by an indirect indexing process, the manipulation of the ordered list is confined to moving a time and address for each duty schedule moved. As computers become faster and cheaper the size of problems to which it will be worth applying such techniques in order to reduce computing time will be larger.

Although application of the convergent limit approach described reduces the length of the searching process, nevertheless there are substantial complications due to the restrictions. For example, a reference schedule, when found, may be unable to perform this service because it is a lengthy one and extends beyond the period within which a meal break must be allocated to this schedule. On the other hand, the next service to be allocated might be short enough for this duty schedule to perform it before the required meal break. Similar problems occur at the end of duties, and both of these problems are complicated by specific location requirements; meal breaks must be scheduled to be taken at one of eighteen canteens, while each duty has to terminate at the garage at which it starts.

Restrictions and rules of this type not only add to the complexity of programs designed to implement them, but they may, if handled in the wrong way, destroy the efficiency of any rapid searching process of the type described. Thus, in the procedure for finding the best match of duty schedule to service described, if the reference duty schedule cannot perform the service because, for example, it must be allocated a meal break before the end of the service, or the finish of the service is too far from any canteen for a meal break to be started by the latest permitted moment, then the whole of the search based on that match is wasted. Possible matches may have been rejected because, for example, more empty running would be required than for the reference schedule, and these possible matches might be very attractive in the light of feasible alternatives to the rejected reference schedule. Further, if the ordered duty schedule list is cluttered with schedules which cannot, in practice, perform any more services without a meal break, then the amount of redundant testing in the present position is increased, but the choice of duty schedules available later, after the meal breaks have been finished, is restricted; on the other hand, if duty schedules are allocated meal breaks when they might perform further services before the break, it is possible to create peak demands for duty schedules, and therefore drivers and vehicles, merely because many have been diverted to meal breaks which could have been taken later. If duty schedules are left awaiting allocation during the scheduling process, processing time will be increased; if schedules are allocated before it is absolutely necessary, inefficient duty schedules may result.

Approximate tests are used to detect whether any duty schedule being examined during the matching process is already overdue for a meal break, or for the end of duty; if this test indicates that action is necessary, the search is suspended while the appropriate action is taken. When the least cost match is found, more detailed testing is used to confirm that the allocation is possible; if, at this stage, more precise tests find that the allocation is not possible because, for example, a meal break would be overdue, then the second best match found, if any, has been stored for this eventuality and is treated as the best. Only when these two matches have failed detailed tests is the searching process repeated.

New schedules are only started, in the basic process, if a service cannot be performed by an existing schedule. However, to add flexibility to the scheduling process, an optional facility may be used to specify that schedules be started at particular garages and times.

Unforeseen difficulties may serve to upset the efficiency of a search method of the type described. Implicit in the argument used to justify the assertion that the search process would terminate quickly is the assumption that the distributions of the places and times at which services finish are random; if this assumption does not hold then the search process may become extremely inefficient. Thus, for example, at one stage fifty services, concerned with the bulk collection of mail from large firms, are due to finish at the same sorting office simultaneously. Once these services have been allocated to schedules, fifty duty schedules become available for further work at the same place and time. When matches between these duty schedules and another service being allocated are clearly unfeasible and fail either the time or empty running distance tests, little nuisance is involved. When, however, matches between a service and the fifty duty schedules become feasible, all fifty schedules are examined in turn to find the best match. Further, if one is found provisionally to be the best match, and then fails the detailed feasibility test, the testing and searching procedures are repeated until each schedule in this batch has been rejected. Thus, to allocate one service it is possible for each of these fifty identical duty schedules to be identified as the cheapest match, after comparison with the remainder of these schedules, and then for each to be rejected in turn. In the application described this aberration was first found during program testing when it was thought that a program error was leading to a cycle in the program, whereas the program had merely been designed on the basis of faulty assumptions. Even if the fact that services sometimes finished in batches had been recognized in advance, it is doubtful whether the resulting reduction in the efficiency of the computing method would have been appreciated. Once recognized, and the significance appreciated, the difficulty was easily removed by testing whether each duty schedule is due to become available at the same time and place as the last one tested and, if so, by-passing it.

A computer system was designed for preparing the duty schedules for this fleet, starting in 1963. Results which were capable of being evaluated took approximately two years to obtain, and refinements, union negotiations and other preparatory activities took approximately as long again before the system was applied in practice and with success. The running time of the program was fifteen minutes on a Leo 326 (two microsecond store cycle time, and very fast on data transfer and manipulation, but still requiring milliseconds for a square root calculation) for the allocation of 5,000 services to, for a twenty-four hour day, approximately 800 duty schedules. Within the small range tried, it appeared that the computing time requirement was approximately proportional to the number of services.

Part 9

Administrative and financial aspects of journey planning by computer

Chapter 40

The commercial background to systems design for wholesale distribution by manufacturing companies

Generalizations about administrative systems associated with such a heterogeneous activity as road goods transport are unlikely to be helpful in the absence of references to more specific conditions. This discussion of administrative systems is, therefore, devoted to the problems of wholesale distribution by manufacturers, since it is one of the larger identifiable activities which has already been used for illustration. But the specialized nature of this discussion should not be allowed to obscure either the general need for administrative systems in association with transport activities, or their importance. A major portion of the systems design and computer programming effort associated with the development of a computer system for preparing duty schedules for the bulk transfer of mail around London (chapters 22 and 39) was devoted to ensuring capture and retention of service requirements and to interpreting and editing the schedules prepared so that they could be reproduced and serve as instructions to drivers; inadequate attention to these administrative aspects would have rendered work on the computational aspects pointless. Transport activities concerned with the collection, conveyance and delivery of 'smalls' or 'sundries' also require to be associated with administrative systems, for example, to deal with payments and provide a basis for proving performance or settling claims for loss or damage. The need for, and importance of, administrative systems is general and not confined to wholesale distribution.

Firms distributing their finished products to wholesale and retail outlets use a great variety of commercial systems, each with its own special characteristics and virtues. Particular systems are rarely adopted solely for reasons associated with economy and simplicity of data processing; most data processing systems are designed primarily to serve other functions, such as marketing or accounting; consequently, a preliminary account of some of the requirements of these functions follows.

It is a basic assumption of most marketing policies that the timing and composition of orders can be influenced. Personal contact is often considered to be a fundamental component of the mix of marketing policies, especially personal contact when orders are being prepared. Personal contact may take the form of a visit by a representative, or of a telephone conversation; either way, it generally implies that the order taking system will commence at or near the customer. Only when re-orders are likely to be infrequent is it general practice for customers to be left to place orders remotely, e.g. by post.

Customers are usually believed to set great store upon certainty of delivery, and often also upon delivery occurring very soon after the order is placed. Emphasis is upon speed and certainty of delivery is given as a reason for warehouses being placed close to customers and for own-account delivery fleets.

The marketing function may wish to use a flexible pricing system to influence the size, frequency, regularity and other features of orders. The accounting function may wish to give discounts for prompt payment. Mistakes in charging are often resented; customers may not correct errors in their favour, consequently mistakes may also represent a direct net loss to the company. The correction of mistakes is often disruptive of the normal data processing system and may be very expensive. Invoicing and billing calculations may therefore be considered a matter for specialists, to be carried out under the control of specialists, in a centralized sales accounting department.

Some customers object to being owed money by suppliers as a result of over-payments due to failure to include all credits in the invoices. In many organizations no one is authorized to make payments to suppliers at the time and place of receipt of goods. Nor is it general practice for suppliers' agents delivering goods to be authorized to receive payment for them. Payments are usually made in arrears. It is a concern of the accountancy function to control both the credit extended to customers, and the cost of trying to extract payments from them, e.g. by sending invoices and accounts.

Invoicing systems are often divided into two categories, known as pre- and post- invoicing systems. The point of distinction is whether invoices are prepared before or after items ordered are picked from stock, or availability in stock is checked. In a typical pre-invoicing operation, orders are converted into invoices and delivery notes and goods are picked from these. Invoices and delivery notes may be copies of one another; occasionally a single document, backed up by statements, serves both purposes. In post-invoicing systems, delivery notes are prepared from orders, if they are not just duplicate copies; and goods are dispatched with the delivery notes. Either orders are then converted into invoices, or invoices are prepared from receipted delivery notes, in which case they usually incorporate credit for items returned and only charge for goods accepted.

Common advantages of pre-invoicing systems are that documentation, apart from credits for items not accepted and empties returned, only requires one process, and that information of sales, dispatches, and, by inference, stocks, is available at the earliest opportunity: disadvantages are that orders cannot be dispatched until documentation has been prepared and is available at the depot, and also that corrections or credits must be issued for goods not available, delivered, or accepted, and for empties.

The main advantage of post-invoicing is lack of complication between receipt and dispatch of orders, which means that, typically, the interval between receipt and dispatch of orders is much shorter; consequently, post-invoicing is a very common practice, especially when orders are received at a local sales office associated with a local warehouse and transport depot. However, post-invoicing commonly requires two entirely separate procedures, the preparation of delivery notes and of invoices; post-invoicing is also usually associated with later, or less certain, sales and stock information, and with invoices being dispatched much later, relative to deliveries, than with pre-invoicing; other things being equal, later invoicing would be associated with later payment, and increased customer credit.

Typically, post-invoicing systems are preferred when orders are received locally, the order cycle is irregular or infrequent, items ordered are often not available and there are empties or other reasons for frequent credits.

Pre-invoicing systems are likely to be preferred if orders are received centrally, e.g. by post, whether direct or from representatives, so that immediate use may be made of centralized machinery, and if, for one reason or another, corrections to the invoices are unimportant or rare; corrections may be unimportant or rare if orders are placed regularly or frequently so that corrections may be made on subsequent invoices, if reliance is placed upon statements for reconciliations, or if conditions giving rise to corrections or credits, e.g. individual items ordered being out of stock, or the return of empties, are rare.

Control of warehouse stocks to ensure continuous availability of all

items, without excessive stockholding, is more effective the more recent
the information about movements available. The natural source of such
data is from orders or delivery notes, and it can be processed economically
when invoices are prepared. Because of the delays associated with post-
invoicing systems, however, a separate system for stock-recording is common.
The total requirement of each item for the deliveries allocated to a journey
may be summarized for assembling loads in the warehouse (except when
individual orders are assembled separately, usually for special reasons) and
these summaries are then relatively easily summarized themselves into
stock depletions. Early knowledge of requirements for stock replenishment
also assists efficient production planning.

The selling and marketing functions are assisted in their task by a rapid
flow of information about customer purchases, oriented towards customers
for representatives' calls, items for promotional policy, and towards other
factors, such as region as an indicator for local management or of local
preferences. The same information, in a slightly different form, is the
earliest indicator of gross revenues.

Methods of resolving conflicting requirements for speed of data
processing, whether for customer service or company control, and economy,
differ greatly between companies. In recent years, computers have often
been introduced to carry out some of the data processing tasks, but, in
general, the introduction of computers has not been accompanied by a
change in broad system, e.g. from post-invoicing to pre-invoicing, but
rather by attempts to speed up, centralise, extend, integrate, rationalize
and, thereby, reduce cost. The primary objectives given for the introduction
of computers have usually been the reduction of processing costs, and
extra control of sales accounting, with increased managerial control and
information frequently being added as subsidiary reasons.

A major problem in obtaining economies from any computer based data
processing system is that an additional process is introduced, the conversion
of information into a form suitable for machine reading. Costs of the
elementary conversion process, punching paper tape or cards, can easily
amount to several d. per order; more sophisticated equipment is
available, e.g. optical readers, and machines which produce both typewritten and paper tape or card copies of the same information, but they do
not eliminate the conversion cost, although it may be reduced thereby.

Data conversion tends to be cheaper in bulk. Better utilization of
personnel and machinery can be obtained, and proper provision can be
made for sickness, holidays and other absence, training, and supervision of
operators at less proportional expense.

One of the major causes of expense in data conversion is the need for accuracy. It is common practice to punch and verify separately order information which is being converted for post-invoicing, since customers do not like being charged for what they have not received, and tend to resent the need to correct mistakes which are to their own advantage. Opinions differ as to whether data conversion for pre-invoicing need to be the same standard of accuracy. According to the argument in which it is maintained that data conversion for pre-invoicing need not be so accurate as that for post-invoicing, the objectionable mistake occurs when an inconsistency is introduced between corresponding invoices and the delivery notes, but in a pre-invoicing system they are the same; data conversion inaccuracies in pre-invoicing systems increase the discrepancies between goods required and goods delivered, but the original errors in order recording, which are unaffected by the invoicing method, are usually more frequent, especially when orders are telephoned. This argument is reversed when it is . maintained that data conversion for pre-invoicing needs to be as accurate as that for post-invoicing. Errors in data conversion in a pre-invoicing system lead to discrepancies between goods ordered and goods delivered; these discrepancies lead to customer dissatisfaction, to returned or refused deliveries, and hence, via many credit notes and other amendments, to increased processing cost. Perhaps cynically, the author suspects that, when items are slow-moving or distinct, e.g. require separate, limited storage, correspondence between delivery and order may be extremely important, as for machinery spare parts; but when there are frequent deliveries of high-turnover items which may use the same stock space and may even be sold as substitutes for one another, as with many items of food and drink, precise correspondence may be relatively unimportant; indeed, moderate lack of correspondence between order and delivery note may only rarely be detected.

Within the depot and warehouse one of the primary demands made on the data processing system is that journey plans and load summaries be available by a fixed time, so that assembly of loads can be started as soon as warehousemen are available. In many companies, the commercial pressure to allow customers to order as late as possible has often resulted in the time available for journey planning and load assembly being reduced to a point not far from the physical limitations of the present plant and system, usually to the point where any further reduction would be extremely expensive. This is almost inevitable, since the costs of rushing the journey planning and load assembly procedures, which occurs mainly in terms of transport inefficiency resulting from poor journey plans, is so

hard to recognize, while the pressures for customer service and the costs
of the clerical and administrative system are obvious. The design of a
computer based administrative system will naturally be subject to cost
limitations, but the time limitations imposed by the depot turn-round
requirements could be even more severe, especially if one computer were
used to cope with several depots, each working to the same internal
schedule.

Chapter 41

Computer system design for wholesale distribution by manufacturing companies

Computer systems for wholesale distribution by manufacturers must be designed to fit into the commercial background described in the last chapter. Clearly, there are many possible designs, and in this chapter an attempt will be made to explore and outline only some of these possibilities. Some of the discussions that follow may appear to be pre-occupied with somewhat trivial details. Unfortunately, seemingly trivial details can be of vital importance in systems design. Failure to pay sufficient attention to such detail is one of the most important reasons for difficulties in the design and implementation of computer systems. Similar phenomena are met in many other fields of endeavour. The design of any novel construction has to be taken to considerable detail; detail often dictates the form of the final design, whether detail of structure in itself, or of construction sequence. In this attempt to sketch some standard computer systems in outline, some attention to, and consideration of, apparently trivial detail is as necessary and desirable as in the design of any other complex and relatively novel system.

Selling, or order taking, and dispatch of goods is usually locally based. Designs for a local system therefore have some natural, logical appeal, and, when they are based on telephone contacts with customers, they appeal also to managers anxious to control self-contained facilities. Computers which meet the calculation speed and direct access storage requirements, with elementary input and output facilities, are available at a price which could be justified at a large depot.

In a locally based manual system it is normal to maintain a file of information about regular customers, e.g. on addressograph plates, to facilitate the preparation of delivery notes. Similar files could serve as a course of permanent customer information, e.g. about location, for a computer system. Filed pre-punched customer data, e.g. key punched cards, or a paper tape equivalent, would be selected at the start of the telephone call for ordering, and inserted into a reader connected to the computer. The computer would utilize a controlled typewriter to print a sequence number and the fixed customer data, e.g. address, for a delivery note, and simultaneously punch a copy; the order taker would type the items and quantities ordered, a copy would be punched, as also would the total requirements of the order, e.g. for vehicle capacity in terms of such factors as weight, which would have been calculated by the computer during receipt of the order. With simple pricing formulae, even if corrections had to be made occasionally in subsequent statements, it would often be possible to prepare a combined delivery note and invoice, and, if so, the details would also be incorporated into the punched copy.

When all orders had been taken, the punched copies of the orders would be submitted to the computer, from which it would extract the data required for planning journeys, the sequence number for identification purposes, customer location, delivery restrictions, and order dimensions relevant to vehicle restrictions such as weight and volume. Data concerning such factors as vehicle availability would also be required. The main printed output of the journey planning process would be a list of the order sequence numbers allocated to each journey in the suggested delivery sequence. The combined invoice and delivery notes would be sorted by their sequence numbers into the suggested delivery sequence within journeys.

When loads are assembled as separate deliveries in correct sequence, the bundles of delivery notes representing journeys would be sent to the warehouse for assembly. If goods are assembled and loaded by item, with the driver assembling deliveries on arrival at the customers' premises, load summaries, lists of the total requirements of each item for each journey, would be prepared by computer after reading the punched copy of the orders again; possibly, if there are many journeys and many items (i.e. if the number of items multiplied by the number of journeys exceeds the computer store space available) the punched copy of the orders might need to be read several times. The load summaries would be printed and sent to the warehouse for assembly, while the bundles of combined invoice and delivery notes, with duplicates, representing journey plans, would be retained as drivers' instructions. The punched copy of the orders would, typically, be sent to a central computer system, where it would be used as the basic source of input data to the sales accounting system. Any alterations resulting from refused or returned items and empties would be recorded on the receipted combined invoice and delivery notes, and introduced into the main data-processing system as amendments.

Each order-taker, the number depending upon peak load requirements, would therefore require a slow punched card, or paper tape, reader and punch, and a typewriter linked to the computer, and, in addition, a file of

pre-punched cards or tape containing permanent customer information.
The computer might also need a fast card or tape reader, with spare, for
reading the order copies for the journey planning and load summarizing
procedures.

If the order information is not recorded on a keyboard at the time of
ordering, an extra function would be required to convert it. Conversion, as
mentioned earlier, is liable to be expensive, and requires some care to
achieve accuracy. The personnel required for efficient conversion need
special training. One aim of the system design proposed here has been to
avoid the need for specialists, with specialized training, to avoid additional
tasks, and to reduce scope for error to a minimum. Little training would be
required to enable typists to record order information received over the
telephone directly, providing their sales and marketing talents were
satisfactory, thus avoiding the need both for special training and for a
special conversion process. The main sources of error not under computer
control would be those of recording the order, which could, and would
normally, be checked by reading back the order to the customer.

There are other methods of arranging for relatively unskilled people to
introduce data into computer systems. Two methods which are currently
being exploited are techniques based on visual display units, especially
those using branching questionnaires, and techniques utilizing specially
designed input terminals. Visual display units are relatively expensive,
although that may change, and tend to require faster, and therefore more
expensive, communication facilities. Special input terminals are also more
expensive, although the design may make fast communication lines
unnecessary. Exploitation of these methods may well lead to better
systems than those based on typewriters. However, the systems described
will be confined to those employing basic typewriter facilities.

The local system described has been oriented towards telephone selling
or order taking. Salesmen often work locally, taking orders in person, but
integrating them into a local system is less straightforward. A delay may be
imposed between the order being taken and its receipt into the dispatching
system, during which it may be in the salesman's hands awaiting attention.
The order document, as prepared by the salesman, or the information on
it, has to be transported to the data processing centre and converted into a
form suitable for machine input. Data conversion at a local centre is
unlikely to be of adequate volume to justify any complex or automatic
conversion equipment, including machine reading. If transport were
provided by the salesman in person, a large batch would have to be carried
at one time if it were not to be unduly expensive, and even then the cost

of this form of transport might well restrict the area dealt with by the centre. The natural batch would be the orders for one complete day, but by the earliest time of delivery to the centre, the late afternoon or early evening, staff for data conversion are likely to be difficult to find, unreliable, and expensive. Even if staff were available to convert the data, the warehousing operations would have to take place overnight or early the following morning if orders were to be delivered the next day.

Consequently, a system that includes order taking by salesmen is only likely to achieve dispatch of orders on the day after orders are taken, if salesmen telephone orders to the processing centre, the remainder of the system following that described already for telephone selling. If delivery on the next day is relinquished as a target, then the first class postal service is probably the cheapest and most convenient form of transport, and, since, within limitations, the postal service achieves overnight transit times over substantial distances, there is no necessity for the system to be locally based. Since data conversion is best carried out in bulk, some degree of concentration is probably less costly. The strongest case for a local system depends upon the use of telephones for receiving order information. The telephone charging tariff will be of importance in determining the economic radius of such a system.

To describe a possible depot based computer system, it has been assumed that the machine would be within the depot. The same basic system could, however, be used with a computer situated outside the depot, with communication via telephone or telex systems; such a computer could be a multi-access machine, and could be owned and operated by the company, or by a computer service bureau organization.

The imposition of remote processing between two locally based activities such as order taking and vehicle dispatching can only be justified on the basis of the reduced cost of obtaining desired standards of service. Data processing systems, whether clerical or based on computers or other machinery, tend to show some economies of scale. In the case of computer based systems these economies of scale arise not only from the better performance to cost ratios of larger machines, or from processing economies of all types, but also, at least notionally, from development and systems maintenance economies.

In a large system one development should be sufficient. While in theory one developed system can be duplicated many times in many different places, in practice it is almost impossible to avoid modifications which take into account special local circumstances or to utilize accumulating experience to improve the system as it is installed in different places.

Systems maintenance is a substantial and continuing expense which is
aggravated if many versions with minor variations are in existence. Further,
in general, larger computers have better languages for program writing and
compilers with better facilities for the detection and correction of errors.
That it may be cheaper overall to use a more expensive computer, simply
to obtain better facilities, is not just a computer salesman's slogan; indeed,
on occasion salesmen conceal this factor to avoid drawing attention to the
size of the expenditure required for, and problems of, development and
maintenance of systems; while many potential customers fix a ceiling to
machinery cost, without interest in, or knowledge of, the possible trade-
offs between different types of expenditure.

In the local system already described, data was transcribed direct from
a telephone call. As a typewritten copy of each order was produced
simultaneously it was possible to check visually, and also by reading back
to the customer. Typing during telephone calls was reduced, and accuracy
increased, by using a pre-punched tape of the customer's name and
address from a customer file; pricing, it was suggested, could often be
done by the computer at the same time with stored information. It was
pointed out that with the development of computing and communication
facilities now becoming available, the precise physical location of a
computer was less important, and that the same system could be
employed with remote machines, whether owned by the organization or
by a service bureau. The system as described, however, has a number of
features which could be improved.

1 Printing a customer's name and address from a pre-punched tape or card
involves procedural difficulties. The time taken to select a record, and
place it in the reader, is not insignificant, and, if it has to be completed
during the telephone call, is likely to lead to an increase of its duration; if
it is carried out after the finish of the telephone call, the checking
procedures are less secure, and, either the name and address will be printed
at the bottom of the order, or the printer has to be back-spaced to print the
address, and then run forward over the order again before the next order
is taken. The analogy between addressograph plates and printing from a
tape given earlier is not entirely sound because, using a plate, there is no
difficulty about stamping the address on the top of an order form detached
from its fellows.

2 Item identification numbers, descriptions, and the associated pricing
procedures, could be too large to be held in the store of a computer that
could be justified at a depot, especially if the pricing procedure should
include adjustments, e.g. special contract prices or discounts, associated

with particular customers. If the order-taker types an item identification number and description, there is a possibility that these will not correspond, and that incorrect unit weights, volumes and prices will be used; in contrast, to deduce these from the descriptions is both very demanding, and prone to error owing, for example, to spelling mistakes, and is definitely not recommended.

3 Various cards or paper tapes were to be punched to store information for later sales accounting procedures on a larger machine, and for the load summarizing and journey planning procedures; occasional disasters with these files would be inevitable.

4 Many data entry errors arise in some organizations because of incompatibility between the customer and his order, e.g. the order may be above the customer's credit limit, or goods may be ordered which the customer does not handle; these errors may be due to the orders placed, or to errors in the recording of order information; in either case, the cost of corrections may be significant.

It is possible that a system designed to utilize remote access to a larger machine shared with other users, either internal or external to the organization, would enable all these difficulties to be overcome. The customer name and address, together with all the associated information about delivery restrictions, credit status, permitted or preferred items and limits, and special pricing or contract terms, could be retrieved from the computer backing store in response to the customer number being typed; the customer name and address could be typed under computer control within a few seconds of the identification number being entered; the system would be faster and more secure, since the typed customer name and address could be verified with the customer. Similarly, with a large computer, it would be possible to retain the item identification numbers, descriptions and pricing information within the immediate access store; the item identification number would act as the key for the item description to be typed under computer control, again facilitating verification with the customer. Incompatibility between order details and stored customer information could be detected and comments or warnings initiated. Data for the journey planning, load summarizing and sales accounting procedures could all be transferred directly to the computer's backing store, eliminating the chance of disasters due to loss or damage of the paper tapes or cards, and reducing the scope for disasters due to errors of operation or malfunctioning of the computer or data transmission system. It is technically feasible to take precautions of various degrees of elaboration, and cost, to secure protection against these factors.

Such is the prospective cost structure of multi-access computers that, whether a company-owned or bureau computer is used, the actual processing cost is likely to be less than with a depot-based computer whenever the local computer could be justified, and be financially attractive in many depots which would be too small for a local computer to be justified. In addition a more elegant system is offered by the larger computer.

However, it is as well to emphasize that the particular contribution of the real-time facilities of a computer system of this type would be to enable the data to be recorded for computer processing to a high level of accuracy by personnel with moderate typing ability, thus avoiding data conversion and its cost. At the same time the order-taker would be able to concentrate on personal contact with the customer. The cost of a real-time, remote system includes the cost of terminals and links to a computer. The cost of these should be compared with the cost of alternative recording systems and of data conversion.

The costs of equipment for different methods of manual data recording and conversion, while not identical, are unlikely to be so different as to force any serious degree of discrimination between them. The particular cost of remote processing is that associated with direct connection and data transmission between the depot terminal and computer throughout the duration of telephone calls for placing orders. The cost of this connection is a function of the tariff of charges, and either the average call duration, or, if a line is hired, the number of orders taken per day per terminal. It is quite possible for connection costs to exceed data conversion costs; according to existing (1969) G.P.O. tariffs, the connection cost for 100 orders per day transmitted 100 miles over a hired telegraph line would be approximately 4.5d. per order, but would be less than 1d. per order for 600 orders per day transmitted over 400 miles. The possibility that connection charges could exceed data conversion costs is greater the longer the connection, and if the line is hired, the fewer the orders. Similarly, connection costs are sufficient, and increase sharply enough with distance, to make it possible for computer service bureaux located near the depot to compete with a distant company owned machine.

Two factors which have been ignored in this simple review are
1   that one line to the computer could serve several active terminals simultaneously with appropriate concentrator equipment, thus reducing transmission cost, and
2   telephone conversations with customers might be prolonged by reading back orders for full checking purposes, which might add significantly to

the costs of these local calls.

The quantity of data transmitted over a connection between a terminal and a computer during the receipt of a telephoned order is likely to be very small in comparison with the data transmission capacity of the connection. Quite apart from concentration, which involves channelling information transfers between several terminals and the computer along a single line, it is possible to make alternative arrangements to transmit data in batches, which would result in a much greater utilization of the capacity of the connection, at the cost, however, of some of the simplicity. Orders could be typed while they are being received by telephone to the extent described earlier, i.e. customer number and quantities and numerical identification of the items ordered; typed and punched copies could be produced. If there were no direct connections with the computer, the customers' names and addresses, and item descriptions, could not be supplied by the computer while orders are received; hence, some loss of accuracy of recorded order information would be expected, because only abbreviated information could be repeated to customers for verification; to compensate, and at the cost of extra typing, which might imply extra typing skill, some alphabetic information could be typed for additional verification purposes. Punched copies of the orders could be transmitted to the computer, and combined delivery notes and invoices could be transmitted back from the computer, in batches. In this way, utilization of the connection between terminals and computer would be increased several times over; the main disadvantages would be a deterioration in security of the order information, additional manipulation of punched copies, and incidental production of an extra typed copy of the order on relatively cheap paper, which would not be needed with a fully on-line system.

These disadvantages may have been exaggerated. On the one hand the G.P.O. are to experiment with a data storage and forwarding service, which might remove the need for storage of data on punched copies, and manipulation of these. On the other hand, the decline in security of information would only be a decline in comparison with what could probably be achieved with a fully on-line system; the decline would almost certainly not be sufficient to reduce the accuracy of order recording below that achieved in a manual system; it could be reduced to some extent, at the expense of some extra typing of alphabetic information about the customer and item identifications, by a manual comparison of the original order and the combined invoice and delivery note.

It has already been emphasized that efficient journey planning is essentially a batch process. Now the economy of a batch process in achieving better utilization of data transmission facilities has been described. Batch processing may also be cheaper both in actual computer utilization and in information retrieval. Keeping the program and information for the receipt and processing of orders, as they are received, permanently in computer store, or transferring them into the computer store every time a connection is made for an order to be received, entails the reservation of a substantial proportion of the immediate access computer storage which would only be fully utilized during peak ordering periods, even if the design of the system had made full utilization of the computer storage possible at any time.

Retrieval of customer and other information in random sequence and in a brief response time can be a relatively expensive process, even when so-called random access equipment is used. Random access storage space is often limited and expensive, and is difficult to utilize very fully if random access is required to records containing variable quantities of information. This is because random access storage is designed to provide access to standard units; similarly, the storage space of an indexed, bound, note-book is difficult to use very fully. Further, the process of identifying the particular record to which access is required is not so straightforward as is often imagined. It is frequently desirable to pass through two or three separate stages of indexing, or access. The use of a card index of a library may serve as an analogy; first of all the correct drawer is identified by the range of the contents recorded on the outside, then projecting tabs identify the section of the drawer which needs to be examined in detail.

There are many random access equipments available, and the ideal way of using each depends upon details of its performance characteristics and of the tasks to be undertaken. Nevertheless, some generalizations are possible: if searches are batched, it is possible to obtain better utilization of the machinery; conversely, acceptance of purely random requirements is more expensive than if there are some restrictions; simple random access backing storage devices are available with extremely large storage capacities, but limited capacity for retrieval and transfer of information; while retrieval and transfer capacity can be increased by an effective increase in the number of storage devices and communication channels to the computer, nevertheless, this is a relatively expensive way of purchasing transfer capacity even if the total storage capacity is not increased.

Besides accuracy of order recording, other examples of the improved service that can be obtained from random, immediate processing, are more up-to-date notional stock levels and constant knowledge of the goods ordered so far; this information may be particularly valuable in some circumstances, e.g. knowledge of the availability of seats in particular aircraft for particular journeys, or of specific spare parts and components. But in the majority of distribution systems as, for example, those involved in the distribution of food and drink, where the emphasis is upon bulk distribution of a relatively small number of distinct items, rather than slow movements of each of a very large number of distinct items, there is a decline in the marginal value of obtaining information which is correct to the hour, minute, or second.

In most wholesale distribution administrative systems, the extra expense of a fully on-line real time system should be justified, if possible, by a reduction in the costs of data conversion and of correcting the associated errors, relative to the reduced processing costs obtainable with a degree of batch processing.

So far, remote systems have been treated as if orders were always collected into a local office. The functions of local offices are to provide a system for personal contact by telephone, to take orders, and to enable delivery to be made soon after ordering. If the extra cost is considered commercially justifiable, salesmen or representatives provide more direct personal contact with customers; but, as has been mentioned already, it is difficult to provide delivery the day after orders are taken unless salesmen communicate orders to local offices by telephone. If next day delivery is not considered essential, orders taken during one day can be posted to the computer centre for processing the next. Equally, if personal contact at the time of ordering is either impossible or unimportant, then customers could post orders to the computer centre, if delivery is not required the following day, or transmit them by telex or telephone if delivery is required urgently.

When orders are received as documents at the computer centre, the existence and size of the data conversion problem can be painfully obvious; it is so easy to spend as much on conversion of data to a computer readable form as on the remainder of the system. Even with good document and system design, the output of a team of two, punching and verifying independently, may be less than 400 orders per day, and will rarely exceed 800 orders per day; thus, between 12 and 25 teams (with equipment) might be required to deal with order data for 10,000 customers per day; this number could easily be doubled by associated processes such as recording payments from customers, as well as making adequate provision for supervision, sickness, holidays, and training. Hence the concentration so far on avoiding a specific conversion task, particularly at local offices where it would be even more expensive.

Bulk conversion of information to computer input may enable automatic reading machinery to be used. On price and performance grounds, machines for reading marks on forms with a relatively flexible format, e.g. the I.C.L. Autolector, probably offer the best value. However, human beings are not used to conveying information by mark codes, and consequently there is considerable interest in the development of machines for reading alphanumeric information. Unfortunately, both mark and character reading machines require, at present, rigid control of the marks of characters used, and their position; it is often considered unlikely that orders could be satisfactorily completed by customers for reading by machines; schemes in which salesmen mark pre-printed order forms for machine reading are, however, working successfully.

When, and if, machines capable of reading a very wide range of type founts are available at the right price, then it may be possible to use customer prepared documents for automatic input; unfortunately, at least from the point of view of designing cheap systems, hand-writing is likely to survive for a long time, and to be very expensive to read automatically. Advantages of machines for reading documents can include direct conversion of the information from the document into a form which can be stored directly on a magnetic backing storeage medium, thus avoiding the process of reading large quantities of punched paper tape or cards, both of which are relatively slow procedures which demand a substantial amount of handling by, and attention from, machine operators.

Once data has been stored on a magnetic backing storage medium, the processing would follow normal batch processing techniques, accessing records serially. This does not necessarily imply that magnetic tape units, as the archetypal serial access machines, would necessarily be preferred to random access devices; many random access devices have excellent serial access performance characteristics.

Orders would be sorted into customer number sequence, and compared with the customer file for the preparation of invoices, recording of customer debits, and conversion of order data into a form suitable for journey planning. The result of the journey planning procedure would be a list of customer numbers, with indicators for the journey, and sequence within the journey, assigned to each. This data would be merged with the invoice information, and the invoices sorted into the sequence given by the assigned journey and sequence numbers. Load summaries could be prepared most conveniently from the invoices in journey sequence by a simple passage of the information, and accumulation of the total quantity

of each item required for each journey. (It would be possible to summarize
loads as soon as the journey and sequence numbers had been associated
with the invoice information, but it would be slightly more complex, and
might require more than a single passage of the information). Completed
load summaries would then be transmitted to warehouses for assembly,
and invoices would be printed in the appropriate journey sequence, either
at the centre, or after transmission to the appropriate depot.

Printing has offered an unusual relationship between quantity and unit
cost. Unit cost appears to be approximately constant over the range of
speeds of the relatively slow machines which print characters sequentially;
unit costs only decline significantly when machines capable of printing
a line of characters at a time are reached, but at most depots there will be
insufficient work either to utilize the capacity offered by these machines,
or to match, in practice, the unit costs of the slower machines. Even if as
many as 500 combined delivery notes and invoices are to be printed daily
at one depot, teleprinter terminals are likely to be cheapest, but printing
will take several hours, requiring attendance and possible inconvenience.
The economies and convenience of faster printing, are, in general, only
available when the printing requirements are very large. In many systems
the only place where sufficient demand is likely to arise is at computer
centres. To exploit faster printers, invoices and delivery notes could be
printed at centres and dispatched to depots by some means of transport.
This might be a particularly cheap and convenient method if a computer
centre were to coincide with a central warehouse from which goods were
sent by trunk haulage overnight for delivery from local distribution centres
the following day.

Errors in input data are inevitable, although the system design can
influence the frequency and type of occurrence. If the order-taker is
connected on-line to a computer, the computer can be used to query odd
data, e.g. an unknown customer or item number, or an exceptionally large
order quantity, while the order is being received. Although this checking is
one of the functions normally performed by the order-taker, for example,
by reading back orders to customers for verification, nevertheless, some
errors always creep through. Orders recorded and collected into batches
for transmission would be expected to be less reliable than orders recorded
on-line, because of reduced checking facilities. Orders recorded, either by
salesmen, or by customers, and converted into a computer input medium,
either by automatic reading machinery, or by manual punching, are likely
to contain a higher error rate, due to the combined effect of the two
procedures.

With all the techniques suggested, it is desirable to use the computer to vet input data by testing its feasibility and consistency, and to make provision for querying unusual information and for its correction. The longer the chain of procedures between customer and computer input the more desirable this scrutiny. Consequently, processing methods should always be designed to enable input data to be scrutinized in more than one batch, and usually in more than two. A typical arrangement would be that the first batch of data submitted would be scheduled to take as much bulk as early as possible, so that errors detected in that batch of data could be corrected while there is plenty of time; amendments would be submitted with the bulk of the later orders, and amendments to correct errors in this batch would be submitted with the last orders; doubtful data in the final batch would either be rejected, and processing deferred until the following day, or accepted, even if unlikely; many systems contain both rejection and provisional acceptance procedures which are called into play by different categories of query. The system described is not obligatory, but a system without explicit provision for possible error detection and correction is unlikely to prove satisfactory in practice.

To summarize, a number of major factors largely determine the choice between distinctly different integrated systems for order taking, dispatching, and sales accounting. These major factors are:
1 the mode of order taking, which is usually determined for marketing reasons; orders are usually taken by a salesman in person, by a telephone salesman or saleswoman contacting customers or receiving customers' calls, or by an order clerk receiving written orders:
2 the acceptable period between order and delivery, which is also usually fixed for marketing reasons; to arrange for delivery within 3 days of the order being determined, it is necessary either for the order processing prior to delivery to be carried out locally, or for some stages of information transfer to be carried out by wire, in person, or by special conveyance:
3 whether there is a policy, as opposed to cost, preference for pre- or post-invoicing; most companies use post-invoicing procedures, which are divorced from the depot procedures of load summarizing and vehicle dispatching; pre-invoicing procedures appear to be less favoured, two significant reasons for this being the rather lengthy minimum period before delivery which can be obtained with pre-invoicing methods and centralized processing, together with the strain to which the system is subjected in order to maintain rapid service.
When these factors are determined, many of the major features of the system are also determined.

A significant proportion of orders is only likely to be communicated by telephone, whichever party initiates the contact and bears the immediate charge, if order offices are situated locally, because of the cost of longer distance telephone calls. If much data has to be sent over long distances very rapidly to deliver quickly, despite the use of a distant computer, a method of transfer that makes more efficient use of the information transfer capacity of the channel than a telephone conversation between a salesman and a customer is likely to be preferred.

If orders are initially entered on documents by salesmen or by customers, then these documents will usually be transmitted to a distant order processing office by post; in which case there is no immediate requirement for orders to be processed locally, and no processing barrier to a pre-invoicing system. In these circumstances the advantages of larger scale batch processing, including data conversion and printing, are such as to give an economic incentive to a larger centralized system; however, such a system tends to be associated with the longer minimum delivery delay. The minimum delivery delay, if measured from the reception of the order at the centre, can be reduced to delivery the next day, if processed delivery notes or invoices are dispatched to the depot by a rapid means of communication, for example, by data transmission systems or by physical conveyance of the documents, possibly along with the goods to be delivered if these are warehoused centrally.

Although the main characteristics of a computer system for wholesale distribution may be a selection from the options as outlined, it has frequently been found necessary, or at least convenient, to include several of the options at each stage. Thus, the order system may allow for both local order taking and central acceptance of orders, some of which may have been taken by representatives: locally received orders may be processed by a post-invoicing system, and the centrally received orders by a pre-invoicing system. Superficially such duplication of systems may appear expensive, and may need very careful arrangement to avoid confusion between the two processing systems. But, for example, while an organization may prefer to use a local post-invoicing system, some large multiple customers with a central ordering system for many outlets may insist on sending a single order with instructions for delivery to many outlets; it may be impossible in practice to refuse to accept orders in this form and expensive, slow, and tedious to convert them into a form suitable for the local post-invoicing system; providing a subsidiary central pre-invoicing system may be the best alternative.

A system without a large range of options may be simpler and cheaper to design and implement in the short term. But such a simple system will often be inflexible, and an inflexible system may wrap the organization in a strait-jacket which will prove to be a serious limitation in the long run. The lower design and implementation costs may be accompanied by a series of special provisions made to deal with various exceptions; whether such exceptions are dealt with by a manual parallel system, or by progressive modification and adaptation of a computer system, provision for them is likely to be expensive and disruptive. Even more seriously, investment in an inflexible computer system is likely to increase the time and expenditure required to enable the organization to be adapted to major changes in the environment.

Consequently, many computer systems, while they may be biased in particular directions, embody a variety of options if they are intended to be in any way comprehensive. The most viable alternative is to use a computer system to save money on any special bulk flow, but maintain manually based systems to provide both for exceptions and flexibility. Major objections to the limited use of computers for only the main stream of processing, while retaining parallel systems, are that:

a   much of the important information, e.g. 'book stock' figures, calculated from withdrawals, that arise as a by-product of a computer system may have little value if the scope of the system is limited;
b   linkage of successive procedures, e.g. invoicing with order and delivery note preparation, may be more difficult if each procedure is split into two processing streams and the split is not the same in each procedure;
c   the relative costs of preparing data for computer input tend to be so large that, unless data is used for several procedures, conversion may not be justified;
d   if, as is believed, there are economies of scale in computer usage and even in manual systems, then divided systems may be relatively expensive.

Thus, there is, or, as they are implemented, there will be, a large degree of overlap between many of the computer based administrative systems serving the wholesale distribution function. It would be expected that substantial economies of scale in the design, implementation and maintenance of such systems would arise from the concentration for wholesaling facilities if individual firms could be persuaded to exchange some of their unique detailed requirements, e.g. of layout and presentation, and accept a degree of standardization. If, however, the minute differences are maintained then any attempt to provide common systems might run into diseconomies of scale of design, implementation and maintenance, due to the problems of distinguishing between, and making provision for,

the many streams requiring to be processed in parallel. The marginal
cost of maintaining minor distinctions between systems for the same
function may already be high, preventing the use of general purpose
systems, and in an environment in which wholesale distribution facilities
were concentrated, might be even more expensive.

A further feature of the discussion in this chapter is the extent to which
computer system design may depend upon detail. Yet many of the features
of any design have been ignored as being too detailed. Thus, for example,
the design of some data checking facilities (e.g. check digits) has not been
discussed although, normally, such facilities should be designed into every
system. To a large extent the considerations governing the design of
checking facilities are internal to the computer system, but some inter-
actions with people outside the system is inevitable and the design may
influence the choice of equipment, particularly peripherical and data
conversion equipment, or the design may itself be influenced by the
availability of equipment with special features.

Although this discussion of systems design problems has been presented
in a particular context, many of the general conclusions are applicable to a
very wide range of design problems. In particular, the problems of detail,
system inflexibility and scale are general.

Chapter 42

Costs and benefits

It has been shown that, while efficient journey planning is fundamental to transport operating efficiency, it must be intimately associated with the administrative system, and, therefore, that the actual function of journey planning should not be considered in isolation. It has also been shown that the transport requirements which have to be satisfied by journey plans may be extremely complicated, and also that the problem of preparing efficient journey plans may be extremely complex computationally. Finally, it has been shown that efficient journey planning depends upon accurate estimation of journey duration. Because of the complexity of these three aspects of the journey planning procedure, it is probable both that there is a limit to the efficiency that is obtainable from manual journey planning methods, and that the maximum efficiency obtainable by manual methods could be surpassed if it were possible to plan journeys by computer. This chapter is intended to throw light on some of the financial aspects of introducing journey planning by computer, with particular reference to wholesale distribution.

The main potential advantages to be anticipated from planning journeys by computer, without a major revision of the basic organizations, are as follows:

1 the transport cost may be reduced if the planned routes are better because better computation results in shorter or quicker routes being incorporated in the journey plans;

2 the cost of the administrative system may be reduced;

3 the speed of the administrative system might be increased, making it possible to achieve alternative benefits, e.g. to improve the distribution service to customers, to improve sales forecasting, and therefore stock and production control, or to invoice customers earlier and thereby possibly reduce the total outstanding debtors' accounts;

4 the transport cost may be reduced due to increased utilization of the total time available, resulting from better estimation of journey duration.

Whether explicitly or implicitly, most discussion of the benefits of journey planning by computer have assumed that the primary, or only, benefit would result from better planned routes produced by more powerful and sophisticated calculation procedures (**42.1-42.6**). For the sake of illustration it will generally be assumed here that typical savings resulting from the production of better routes will be of the order of 10% of the transport cost (**42.4-42.6**). It is doubtful whether journey plans prepared manually would be more than 15% worse than plans prepared for the same task by computer to the same restrictions, so long as the manual task is not so large that it has to be skimped or artifically segmented. The little evidence available suggests that men can produce tolerably good solutions to relatively straightforward combinatorial problems (e.g. **42.7**).

Transport cost reductions are likely to be closely proportional to the number of vehicles 'saved', the reduction in the number of vehicles required to carry out a given task. On the other hand, the cost of planning journeys by computer is likely to be a function of the number of deliveries planned. It is possible to draw some conclusions as to the characteristics of transport fleets, and their tasks, for which it may be possible to justify planning journeys by computer because the resulting saving of transport cost due to the use of better planned routes is expected to exceed the computational costs.

Both vehicle and computer costs vary greatly according to the facilities required and the conditions under which they are obtained. Any choice of particular figures for these costs is bound, therefore, to be arbitrary, and may also be misleading. However, adjustments for particular circumstances can easily be made if desired. Figure 42.1 shows the transport cost, in d. per delivery, plotted against the number of deliveries per day, for vehicles of different annual operating cost. Figure 42.2 shows the value, in d. per delivery, of various levels of gross saving relative to the delivery cost. If the possible range of computational cost, including the cost of preparing the data in machine readable form, achievable at present is assessed as being between 2d. and 6d. per delivery (these figures are arbitrary, but not absurd), which is indicated by the shaded area, the vertical difference between the lines in figure 42.2 and the shaded area is an indication of the potential difference, per delivery, between the transport saving and the computational cost.

It has sometimes been argued that, as the number of deliveries per vehicle per day increases, the driving distance and time decreases, and therefore that any reduction in this resulting from the use of better computational methods in planning journeys becomes less likely. This argument depends upon an assumption that the main part of the reduction of transport cost will be due to a reduction in the driving

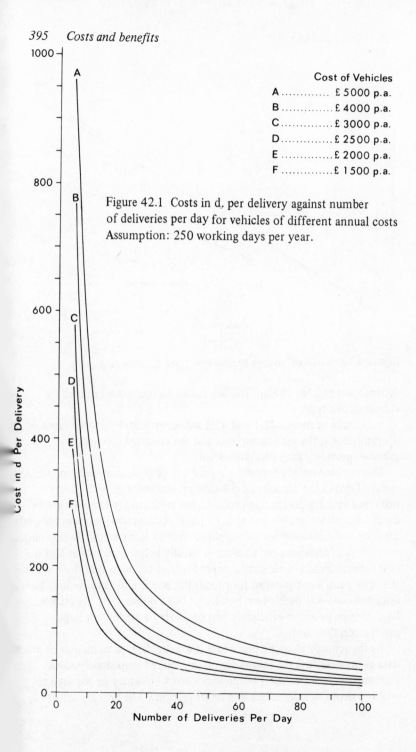

Cost of Vehicles
A .... £ 5000 p.a.
B .... £ 4000 p.a.
C .... £ 3000 p.a.
D .... £ 2500 p.a.
E .... £ 2000 p.a.
F .... £ 1500 p.a.

Figure 42.1 Costs in d, per delivery against number
of deliveries per day for vehicles of different annual costs
Assumption: 250 working days per year.

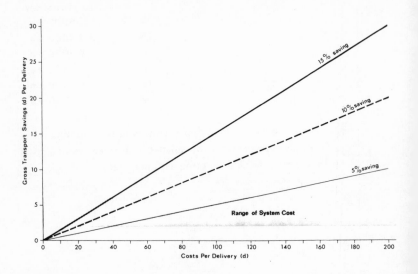

Figure 42.2 Value of savings against costs per delivery (d.)

distance or time. No attempt has been made to introduce or illustrate
effects of this type.

Inspection of figures 42.1 and 42.2 will show that, for a wide range of
operating costs, the break-even level and the potential savings show
promise, providing the assumptions hold.

This application of computers requires, in general, computing power and
storage beyond the capacity of the smallest machines. Slightly larger
machines have the computing capacity, but their storage facilities are too
small for a simple and elegant system design. Computers that have adequate
capacity and flexibility for this application tend to be subject to substantial
economies of scale; one big machine is usually better than two at half the
cost each; indeed, a commonly accepted rule of thumb is that, by doubling
the price paid, a computer of four times the power and capacity may be
obtained (called Grosch's Law by Sharpe (**42.8**)). Very few depots are
large enough to utilize efficiently and profitably a medium or large
machine on their own.

As the journey planning procedure is usually delayed to include as much
data as possible, and the results are often required immediately, data
transmission facilities using telephone or telex links may be required to
enable a depot to have access to a larger machine. The primary effect of

this requirement may be to impose a lower limit on the size of the depot which can profitably be connected to a computer system for journey planning, since the minimum cost of transmitting relatively small quantities of data may be set by the cost of the terminal equipment. Telex equipment is normally the cheapest mode for the transmission of small quantities of data, and the tariff of telex charges contains a number of options, each of which is attractive under some conditions. The picture is simplified here, and the cost for some situations exaggerated, by assuming that the data transmission expenses for each depot are fixed by the use of a hired terminal and line, at charges which in Britain in 1969 were between £400 (for telex terminal and five mile private line rental, although lower charges are made for shorter lines), and £1,000 per annum according to the distance of the connection. Small amounts of data can be transmitted at lower cost by paying for transmission time rather than line hire. For large amounts of data it is advantageous to use faster transmission systems and telephone lines.

If potential transport savings justified an expenditure of as much as 5% or 10% of transport costs on data transmission, the minimum annual depot transport expenditure which would support the data transmission facilities alone would be between £4,000 and £20,000 per annum depending upon the distance of transmission.

Figure 42.3 shows the break-even curves between depot transport cost and number of deliveries per day, for an assumed 10% transport saving, a fixed data transmission cost of £1,000 per annum, and a computational cost, including data conversion but excluding data transmission, of 4d. per delivery. Attention should be drawn to the assumptions, and to the likelihood that they will not apply in any particular case. The transmission cost assumption rests on a very tenuous basis; the cost of an individual terminal and line is likely to vary between £400 and £1,000 per annum according to distance as already mentioned, but the capacity of line depends upon the pattern of transmissions and the length of each. If used for the transmission, and throughout the duration, of orders received by telephone, particularly if it is left to customers to initiate orders, the capacity might be less than 100 orders per line per day. More concentrated methods of use are possible and have been discussed briefly in the last chapter; they might affect terminal and line costs to different extents. Taking into account the data transmission costs, many depots are too small to justify the use of data transmission for journey planning only.

At one time (1968) the computer bureaux in Britain offering a journey planning service on a casual basis appeared to have standardized on a charge

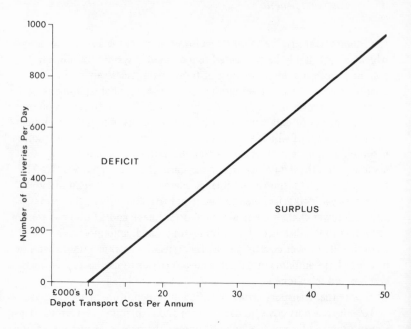

Figure 42.3 No. of deliveries per day to break even for different levels of dep transport costs. Assumptions: 10% saving of expenditure, data-transmission costs £1,000 p.a., computation costs (including data preparation) 4d./deliver

for preparing a journey plan of £15 basic plus 3d. per delivery. If this charge were to be applied to the preparation of journey plans at one depot, and the savings were 10% of transport costs, then transport costs would need to be nearly £50,000 per annum to cover the fixed costs. Very few depots would offer scope for a potentially profitable application on the basis of these charges. It may be that these charges do not bear a close relationship to the charges which bureaux might be able to make for profitable operation of work of this type on a daily basis under a long term contract. But, if so, it is the basic charge of £15 which would need to be drastically reduced. This charge, however, is intended to represent, to some extent, the administrative cost associated with the reception and return of a job, together with the cost of setting up jobs on batch-processin computers.

The cost of administration and set-up for relatively small jobs is a significant proportion of the total cost when the data and results have to be physically handled, and computer operating systems have been designed with the expectation of physical intervention at the start and finish of jobs, or batches of jobs. These job overheads could be, theoretically at least, substantially diminished by the operating systems designed for multi-access computers with direct connection to data transmission lines. Consequently, a substantial reduction in the fixed costs associated with a job may be anticipated with the advent of multi-access computing systems, large enough for this task, into computer bureau use; the reduced costs, however, may only be passed on as reduced charges if there is likely to be sufficient demand for this type of service. Some, at least, of the multi-access bureau systems available in 1970 do not offer adequate facilities, especially storage facilities, for journey planning.

On the basis of these rather crude calculations, some tentative conclusions can be drawn as to the circumstances in which the production of better routes might save more in transport costs than the corresponding computer system operating cost. These conclusions are best summarized as follows:

1 the delivery cost should be above £0.25 per delivery; this represents, for example, a vehicle costing £2,000 per annum to operate, carrying out less than 30 deliveries a day;

2 the transport operating cost at the depot to which the system could be applied should be in excess of £20,000 per annum, unless the cost of data transmission systems can be avoided;

3 either a company owned computer, or a multi-access computer operated by a bureau at time-hire rates, should be available.

These conclusions are very tentative and may understate the true requirements. Thus, conditions 1 and 2 together may imply that one or two terminals and lines will be sufficient to handle data transmission requirements for 300 orders per day; whether this is so will depend upon the numbers of orders received by telephone at peak periods.

These conditions are, however, only those for break-even on computing and data transmission costs. There are additional costs associated with the installation and maintenance of the system, while the objective of the exercise would be to make profits rather than cover costs. Only very large depots, operating expensive vehicles performing relatively few deliveries, offer very attractive scope for profitable application if attention is directed at the saving of transport costs by planning shorter or quicker routes, and it is unlikely that the total profits available are very substantial. This general conclusion agrees with the particular conclusion reached by Unwin and Weatherby (**42.4**).

To be profitable, the benefits of journey planning by computer must proposition as part of a comprehensive data processing system than on its own. This observation is hardly surprising, since it applies equally to most are therefore needed, and these may be derived either from incorporation of journey planning into administrative systems, or from the use of journey planning to increase utilization of the available working time. In many fleets there is little prospect of increasing the utilization of the available working time without the explicit co-operation of drivers; however, there is reason to believe that a significant proportion of the available time could be utilized more effectively if suitable arrangements were made.

The cost of preparing journey plans by hand is not inconsiderable, and would be reduced, but not eliminated, by some arrangements for planning journeys by computer. Any such reduction has, however, been ignored in the case so far presented. When the possibility of planning journeys by computer in association with the processing of sales invoices and accounts, stock control, and load summarizing is considered, the financial case is fundamentally altered. Many companies are already processing sales data by computer and at least one company in Britain has installed a computer and data transmission system primarily for summarizing manually planned loads; the cost of extending these systems should be much lower than the cost of establishing a new system solely for the journey planning function, while the data is largely common to both the original system and its extensions. In addition, the data transmission system may already be in existence, or at least may have a partial justification, for other purposes.

A general representation of the net cost of such an extension is even more open to error than the indications already given in the last section. However, a first approximation to the net cost of such an extension to the data processing system is possible by a series of sweeping assumptions.
a The total data preparation cost is not changed, since it is assumed that the data is already being prepared for invoicing and accounting by computer.
b Additional computer processing time used for the extra procedures (e.g. journey planning and load summarizing) is offset by the elimination of the clerical costs of summarizing loads.
c Data transmission costs are offset by the reduced cost of clerical labour for planning journeys.
With these assumptions, the net cost of the extension to the system is zero, and any transport savings, whether from better routes or better use of the available time, are net benefits.

Thus, daily journey planning by computer is a far more attractive

extend substantially beyond 10%, or 15%, of transport costs. It is unlikely
that routes can be shortened by more than 10% or 15%; additional benefits
data processing applications.

However, the fundamental assumption underlying the justification for
the incorporation of journey planning has been as an extension to a
computer system which has already been installed for processing orders.
Whether the basic system is attractive depends very much upon the
circumstances and the point of view of the beholder; on the cost of
alternative data processing systems; on the type, size, and versatility of
computer system envisaged; on the circumstances of the firm, the size of
its catalogue and complexity of its pricing system; on the resources, both
human and financial, available, and on the competing demands for them;
and on whether the prospect is from a rosy pre-installation, or jaundiced
post-installation, vantage point. If one figure is to be used as a guide,
despite all these variations, the author's rule of thumb is that the
situation may be worth careful examination when the numbers of orders
(or deliveries) per day throughout the firm exceeds 2,000, or the number of
item orders exceed 6,000, per day. The justification for this rule is that,
with a computer system, including programming, cost of £75,000 per
annum, the cost of alternative methods of processing would need to be
£0.15 per delivery for each of the 2,000 deliveries per day for break-even.
Many computer systems have been installed to deal with smaller tasks in
the apparent expectation of profit, although the computer bureaux may
offer more attractive prospects financially for many of these.

It might be considered preferable to view the justification of such a
system as a whole rather than, as here, attempting to justify an extension
of the system on the grounds of marginal cost advantages. There are
three reasons for adopting the marginal approach.

1 It corresponds with the situation in many companies; the invoicing and
accounting procedures have been, or are being, converted, and journey
planning, load summarizing, and depot stock control would be an
extension.

2 The capacity for installing computer applications in most companies is
limited; even if the system were considered as a whole, its implementation
would have to take place in stages, each of which would require a marginal
justification.

3 The range of possibilities and situations which arise in practice is so wide
that it would be necessary to introduce a mass of detail irrelevant to the
main theme to cover them in a balanced way; the use of generalizations
less obviously sweeping than those used here would almost certainly prove

to be more misleading.

It has already been mentioned that there are believed to be substantial economies of scale in computers, Sharpe (**42.8**) summarizes and discusses the evidence. Time and time again, in the reviews of the design of systems and of their costs and benefits, questions of size and utilization have had to be introduced. Data preparation or conversion, data transmission, data storage and retrieval, computation and printing may all be performed more cheaply in bulk, or on a large scale. Similarly, the unit cost of activities using highly skilled man-, or woman-, power such as computer system design, programming, implementation and maintenance, whether for the calculation of journey plans, the incorporation of journey plans in an administrative system, or the production of the administrative systems themselves, is likely to be less the more intensively the products are exploited.

Indeed, the balance of costs and benefits for journey planning by computer is unlikely to be a net benefit unless the activity concerned is very large. This is reinforced by opportunity cost arguments concerning the allocation of highly skilled and scarce personnel to alternative activities.

In part 5 it was suggested that the development of advanced communications and computer based journey planning systems would be necessary to enable acceptable transport service to be maintained by an organization attempting to obtain economies of scale in road goods transport through increased vehicle size, facilitated by increased consignment size and density. Here it is suggested that justification for the development and installation of computer based journey planning and communications systems may only rarely be found in existing fleets, but would become very strong in large, concentrated fleets, such as would be expected to evolve if economies of scale in road goods transport were realized.

It appears probable that dramatic reductions in the cost of transport and associated activities could be achieved if comprehensive changes, designed to this end, were made. Much development work remains to be done, but there are no obvious reasons, given adequate support, why it should not be successful.

References and notes

CHAPTER 2

2.1 Ministry of Transport. *Highway Statistics 1968*. London, H.M.S.O., 1969. Table 55.

Ministry of Transport. *Highway Statistics 1967*. London, H.M.S.O., 1968. Table 52.

2.2 Central Statistical Office. *National Income and Expenditure 1968*. London, H.M.S.O., 1968. Table 27.

2.3 *National Income and Expenditure 1968* (as 2.2). Table 53.

2.4 *National Income and Expenditure 1968* (as 2.2). Table 1.

2.5 *National Income and Expenditure 1968* (as 2.2). Table 17.

2.6 *National Income and Expenditure 1968* (as 2.2). Table 15.

2.7 *Highway Statistics 1968* (as 2.1). Tables 49 and 33.

2.8 British Road Federation. *Basic Road Statistics 1968*. London, British Road Federation, 1968. Section I, p.5.

2.9 Central Statistical Office. *Annual Abstract of Statistics 1968*. London, H.M.S.O., 1968. Table 229.

2.10 Ministry of Transport. *Survey of Road Goods Transport 1962: Final Results, Part I*. London, H.M.S.O., 1964. p.9.

2.11 *Annual Abstract of Statistics 1968* (as 2.9). Table 242.

2.12 Commercial Motor. *Tables of Operating Costs*. (1967 edition). London, Newnes, 1967.

2.13 *Basic Road Statistics 1968* (as 2.8). Section I, p.7.

2.14 Economic Commission for Europe. *Annual Bulletin of Transport Statistics for Europe 1967*. New York, United Nations, 1968. Table 30.

CHAPTER 3

3.1   Ministry of Transport. *Survey of Road Goods Transport 1962. Methodological Report.* London, H.M.S.O., 1964. p.25.

3.2   H. Hunter. *Soviet Transport Experience.* Washington D.C., The Brookings Institution, 1968. Ch. III.

3.3   *National Income and Expenditure 1968* (as 2.2). Table 11.

3.4   *Survey of Road Goods Transport 1962: Commodity Analysis* (as 3.1). Table (v), p.11.

3.5   *Survey of Road Goods Transport 1962: Commodity Analysis* (as 3.1). Table 1.

3.6   *Survey of Road Goods Transport 1962: Final Results, Part I* (as 2.10). Table (vi), p.9.

3.7   *Survey of Road Goods Transport 1962: Final Results, Part I* (as 2.10). Table (v), p.8.

3.8   Until the recent Transport Act 1968, carriers' licences were of four types:

'A' licensed vehicles could be used for the carriage of goods for hire or reward, and for carriage in connection with the operator's business as a carrier of goods;

Contract 'A' licensed vehicles could be used only under a contract, extending over a continuous period of not less than one year, made by the holder with some person other than a carrier, for the exclusive carriage of that person's goods, which had to be connected with the person's trade or business;

'B' licensed vehicles could be used for the carriage of goods either in connection with the trade or business of the licensee, or (subject to any special conditions attached to the licence) for hire or reward;

'C' licensed vehicles could be used only for the carriage of goods in connection with the trade or business of the licensee.

3.9   *Survey of Road Goods Transport 1962: Final Results, Part I* (as 2.10). Table 28.

3.10 *Survey of Road Goods Transport 1962: Final Results, Part I* (as 2.10). Table 33.

3.11 *Survey of Road Goods Transport 1962: Final Results, Part I*

(as 2.10). p.18.

3.12   *Survey of Road Goods Transport 1962: Final Results, Part I*
(as 2.10). Table 11.

3.13   *Survey of Road Goods Transport 1962: Final Results, Part I*
(as 2.10). Table 30.

3.14   *Survey of Road Goods Transport 1962: Final Results, Part I*
(as 2.10). Table 12a.

3.15   *Survey of Road Goods Transport 1962: Final Results, Part I*
(as 2.10). Table 31a.

CHAPTER 4

4.1   J.H. von Thünen. *Der Isolirte Staat in Beziehung auf Landwirtshaft
und Nationalökonomie.* Hamburg, 1826. Translation – Edited by
P. Hall. *Von Thünen's Isolated State.* Oxford, Pergamon Press,
1966.

4.2   E.M. Hoover. *The Location of Economic Activity.* New York,
McGraw-Hill, 1948.

4.3   W. Isard. *Location and Space Economy.* New York, Wiley, 1956.

4.4   K.F. Glover and D.N. Miller. 'The outlines of the road goods
industry'. *Journal of the Royal Statistical Society, Series A,*
vol. 117, 1954, p.297.

4.5   K.F. Glover. 'Statistics of the transport of goods by road',
Journal of the Royal Statistical Society, Series A, Vol.123,
1960, p.107.

4.6   Ministry of Transport. *The Transport of Goods by Road: Report
of a Sample Survey made in April 1958.* London, H.M.S.O.,
1959.

4.7   *Tables of Operating Costs* (as 2.12).

4.8   *Survey of Road Goods Transport 1962: Final Results, Part I*
(as 2.10). Table 5.

4.9   National Board for Prices and Incomes Report No. 48.
*Charges, Costs and Wages in the Road Haulage Industry. Cmnd.
3482.* London, H.M.S.O., 1967.

4.10   *Annual Bulletin of Transport Statistics for Europe 1967*
(as 2.14). Table 30.

4.11   S.L. Edwards. 'Transport Costs in the Wholesale Trades'.
        Journal of Transport Economics and Policy, Vol. III, 1969, p.272.

4.12   R.T. Eddison in
        D.B. Hertz and R.T. Eddison. *Progress in Operations Research.*
        New York, Wiley, 1964. Ch. 4.

4.13   A. Fletcher and G. Clarke. *Management and Mathematics.*
        London, Business Publications, 1966.

4.14   S. Eilon and D.P. Deziel. 'Siting a distribution centre: an
        analogue computer application'. *Management Science,* Vol. 12,
        1966, p. B-245.

4.15   F.E. Maranzana. 'On the location of supply points to minimize
        transport costs'. *Operational Research Quarterly,* Vol. 15, 1964.
        p. 261.

4.16   K.B. Haley, 'The siting of depots'. *International Journal of
        Production Research,* Vol. 2, 1963. p. 41.

4.17   D.O. Griffiths. 'The use of regression analysis in a depot location
        exercise'. *Applied Statistics,* Vol. 17, 1968. p. 57.

4.18   M.H.J. Webb. 'Cost functions in the location of depots for
        multiple-delivery journeys'. *Operational Research Quarterly,*
        Vol. 19, 1968. p. 311.

4.19   N. Christofides and S. Eilon. 'Expected distances in distribution
        problems'. *Operational Research Quarterly,* Vol. 20, 1969.
        p. 437.

4.20   B.T. Bayliss. *Private communication.* 1969.

CHAPTER 5

5.1   R.F.F. Dawson. 'Estimating road goods transport expenditure'.
        Journal of the Royal Statistical Society, Series A, Vol. 125, 1962.
        p. 462.

5.2   *Tables of Operating Costs* (as 2.12). p. 31.

5.3   *Charges, Costs and Wages in the Road Haulage Industry. Cmnd.
        3482* (as 4.9). p. 25.

5.4   Greater London Council. *Greater London Development Plan
        Report of Studies.* London, Greater London Council, 1969.
        pp. 186-7.

5.5   *Highway Statistics 1968* (as 2.1). Table 33.

5.6   *Highway Statistics 1968* (as 2.1). Table 36.

5.7   *Greater London Development Plan Report of Studies* (as 5.4).
        p. 172.

5.8   *Highway Statistics 1968* (as 2.1). Table 33.

5.9   P.G. Gray. *Private Motoring in England and Wales.* (Government
        Social Survey). London, H.M.S.O., 1969, p. 35.

5.10   Ministry of Transport. *The Transport of Freight. Cmnd. 3470.*
        London, H.M.S.O., 1967. pp. 17-18.

5.11   Ministry of Transport. *Transport Policy. Cmnd. 3057.* London,
        H.M.S.O., 1966. p. 23.

5.12   Ministry of Transport. *Carriers' Licensing: Report of the
        Committee. (The Geddes Report).* London, H.M.S.O., 1965.
        paras. 1.3, 1.4.

5.13   *The Transport of Freight. Cmnd. 3470* (as 5.10). Ch. V.

5.14   Economic Development Committee for the Distributive Trades.
        Planning Warehouse Locations. London, N.E.D.O., 1967.

CHAPTER 6

6.1   *Transport Policy. Cmnd. 3057* (as 5.11). pp. 1-2.

6.2   A. Fischer. *L'Organisation des Transports dans le Cadre de
        L'Europe des Six.* Leiden, Sijthoff, 1968. p. 212.

6.3   P.J. Kapteijn. 'Rapport fait au nom de la Commission des
        transports sur la Coordination des Transports Européens'.
        Quoted by Fischer (as 6.2). p. 209.

6.4   E.C.E. Comité des Transports Intérieurs. 'La coordination des
        Transports'. Doc. W. Trans/247. p. 1. Quoted by Fischer (as 6.2).
        p. 209.

6.5   P. Michelet. *Les transports au sol et l'Organisation de l'Europe.*
        Paris, Payot, 1962. p. 173.

6.6   A. Fischer (as 6.2). p. 210.

6.7   Quoted from *The Geddes Report* (as 5.12). p. 10.

6.8   *The Geddes Report* (as 5.12). pp. 29-31.

6.9 *The Geddes Report* (as 5.12). pp. 41-3.

CHAPTER 7

7.1 Ministry of Transport. *Proposals for a Fixed Channel Link. Cmnd. 2137.* London, H.M.S.O., 1963.

7.2 A. Sauvy. *Les Quatre Roues de la Fortune.* Paris, Flammarion, 1968. p. 139.

7.3 Greater London Council. *Movement In London.* London, Greater London Council, 1969. Table 4.2.

7.4 London Transport. *The Victoria Line.* London, London Transport, 1969.

7.5 P. Hall. 'Transportation'. *Urban Studies,* Vol. 6, 1969. p. 415.

7.6 Road Research Laboratory. *Research on Road Traffic.* London, H.M.S.O., 1965. Ch. 5.

7.7 J.C. Tanner. *An Economic Comparison of Motorways with Two and Three Lanes in Each Direction.* Road Research Laboratory Report LR203. Crowthorne, Road Research Laboratory, 1968.

7.8 R.J. Smeed. 'Traffic studies and urban congestion'. *Journal of Transport Economics and Policy,* Vol. II, 1968. p. 33.

7.9 H. Hunter (as 3.2). p. 63 and Table 11.

7.10 *Highway Statistics 1968* (as 2.1). Tables 33 and 49.

7.11 Ministry of Transport. *Roads in England and Wales.* Report by the Ministry for the year ended 31st March 1964. London, H.M.S.O., 1964.

7.12 D.L. Munby. *The Economics of City Traffic,* in T.E.H. Williams. *Urban Survival and Traffic.* London, Spon, 1962. p. 211.

7.13 Cahiers de L'Institut D'Aménagement et D'Urbanisme de La Région Parisienne. *Les Transports Urbains: Investissement et Tarification des Transports Urbains,* Vols. 17-18, 1969. Part 4, p. 5.

7.14 *Movement in London* (as 7.3). Appendix C.

7.15 Greater London Council. *Owners of blighted property may get new deal.* London, G.L.C. Press Office, 13 March 1969.

7.16 Greater London Council. *Joint report of the Planning and*

Transportation Committee and the Strategic Planning Committee: approved by the Council on Tuesday 22nd July, 1969. London, Greater London Council, 1969.

7.17   Greater London Council. *G.L.C. To Revise Spending Programme.* London, G.L.C. Press Office, 21 January 1970.

7.18   J.M. Thomson. *Motorways in London.* London, Duckworth, 1969. p. 147.

7.19   London Transport. Letter dated 22 May 1969.

7.20   *Financial Times.* '£70M. London Fleet Line Tube Proposed'. 5 July 1969.

7.21   *The Times.* 'London Transport Plans Third New Tube Line'. 2 January 1970.

7.22   A. Stone. 'The future of road transport in our cities'. *Journal of the Institute of Transport,* Vol. 31, 1966. p. 272.

7.23   Manchester, The Corporation. *Manchester Rapid Transit Study,* Vol. 3, Manchester, The Corporation, 1968. Tables 5.3.2 and 6.1.

7.24   A. Sauvy (as 7.2). p. 126.

7.25   H. Hunter (as 3.2). Tables D-2 and D-6.

7.26   A. Sauvy (as 7.2). p. 191.

7.27   *Basic Road Statistics 1968* (as 2.8). p. 23.

7.28   *Highway Statistics 1968* (as 2.1). Table 50.

7.29   *Highway Statistics 1968* (as 2.1). Table 52.

7.30   *Annual Abstract of Statistics 1968* (as 2.9). Tables 132 and 242.

7.31   *Movement in London* (as 7.3). p. 8.

7.32   *Annual Abstract of Statistics* (as 2.9). Table 245.

7.33   *Annual Abstract of Statistics* (as 2.9). Table 235.

7.34   *Highway Statistics 1968* (as 2.1). Tables 33, 52 and 55.

7.35   *Tables of Operating Costs* (as 2.12).

7.36   J.R. Meyer, J.F. Kain, and M. Wohl. *The Urban Transportation Problem.* Cambridge, Massachusetts, Harvard University Press, 1965. pp. 299-306.

7.37   Llewelyn-Davies, Weeks, Forestier-Walker and Bor. *Milton Keynes*

Plan: Interim Report to the Milton Keynes Development
Corporation. London, 1968.

CHAPTER 8

8.1   National Board for Prices in Incomes Report No.72. *Proposed
Increases by British Railways Board in Certain Country-wide
Fares and Charges. Cmnd. 3656.* London, H.M.S.O., 1968.
Appendix D.

8.2   *Annual Abstract of Statistics 1968* (as 2.9). Table 242.

8.3   *Highway Statistics 1968* (as 2.1). Tables 52 and 55.

8.4   *Tables of Operating Costs* (as 2.12).

8.5   *Greater London Development Plan Report of Studies* (as 5.4).
pp. 153 and 156.

8.6   *Research on Road Traffic* (as 7.6). Ch. 5.

8.7   Ministry of Transport. *Road Pricing: the economic and technical
possibilities (The Smeed Report).* London, H.M.S.O., 1964. p. 49.

8.8   National Board for Prices and Incomes Report No. 112.
*Proposals by the London Transport Board for Fares Increases.
Cmnd. 4036.* London, H.M.S.O., 1969. Appendix 3.

CHAPTER 9

9.1   *Basic Road Statistics 1968* (as 2.8). pp. 42-5.

9.2   *Highway Statistics 1968* (as 2.1). Tables 53 and 55.

9.3   *National Income and Expenditure 1968* (as 2.2). Tables 27 and
29.

9.4   D.A. Quarmby. 'Choice of Travel Mode for the Journey to Work'.
Journal of Transport Economics and Policy, Vol. I, 1967. p. 273.

9.5   *Proposed Increases by British Railways Board in Certain Country-
Wide Fares and Charges. Cmnd. 3656* (as 8.1). p. 4.

9.6   *Movement in London* (as 7.3). p. 8.

9.7   S. Joy. 'British Railways' track costs'. *Journal of Industrial
Economics,* Vol. 13, 1964. p. 74.

9.8   *Annual Abstract of Statistics 1968* (as 2.9). Tables 132, 242, 243
and 244.

9.9   H. Hunter (as 3.2). Tables D-1, D-2, D-3, D-4 and D-6.

9.10   D.H. Aldcroft. *British Railways in Transition: the economic problems of Britain's Railways since 1914.* London, Macmillan, 1968.

9.11   British Railways Board. *The Reshaping of British Railways. (The Beeching Report).* London, H.M.S.O., 1963. p. 58.

9.12   *The Beeching Report* (as 9.11). pp. 59, 60.

9.13   A. Sauvy (as 7.2). Chapter II.

9.14   A. Fischer (as 6.2). p. 194.

CHAPTER 10

10.1   J.M. Thomson, 'The Value of Traffic Management'. *Journal of Transport Economics and Policy,* Vol. II, 1968. p. 3.
        J.M. Thomson. 'The Value of Traffic Management: A Note on Traffic Capacity in Central London'. *Journal of Transport Economics and Policy,* Vol. II, 1968, p. 242.
        T.M. Ridley and E.D. Turner. 'The Value of Traffic Management: A Reply', and J.M. Thomson. 'The Value of Traffic Management: A Rejoinder'. in *Journal of Transport Economics and Policy.* Vol. II, 1968. p. 367.

10.2   R.J. Smeed (as 7.8).

10.3   Ministry of Transport. *Better Use of Town Roads.* London, H.M.S.O., 1967.

10.4   J.M. Thomson. *Some Characteristics of Motorists in Central London.* London, London School of Economics and Political Science, 1968. p. 13.

10.5   M.A. Taylor. *Studies of travel in Gloucester, Northampton and Reading.* Road Research Laboratory Report LR.141. Crowthorne, Road Research Laboratory, 1968. p. 138.

10.6   Ministry of Transport. *Traffic in Towns. Report of the Steering Group and Working Group (Crowther and Buchanan Reports).* London, H.M.S.O., 1963.

10.7   Ministry of Transport. *Public Transport and Traffic. Cmnd. 3481.* London, H.M.S.O., 1967. p. 1.

10.8   Buchanan (Colin) and Partners. *The Conurbations: a study.*

London, British Road Federation, 1969.

10.9 *Movement in London* (as 7.3). p. 93.

10.10 *Motorways in London* (as 7.18).

10.11 *G.L.C. to Revise Spending Programme* (as 7.17).

10.12 *Movement in London* (as 7.3). Figure 5.5

10.13 *Greater London Development Plan Report of Studies* (as 5.4). paras. 6.240-2.

10.14 *Motorways in London* (as 7.18). pp. 132-9.

10.15 *Movement in London* (as 7.3). pp. 91-3.

10.16 *Motorways in London* (as 7.18). pp. 121-5.

10.17 *Motorways in London* (as 7.18). pp. 114-121.

10.18 *Milton Keynes Plan: Interim Report* (as 7.37).

10.19 *Highway Statistics 1968* (as 2.1). Table 38.

10.20 B.T. Bayliss. *European Transport.* London, Mason, 1965. Chapter III.

10.21 Compare *Movement in London* (as 7.3). paras. 1.34, 1.35, and 1.56

and *Greater London Development Plan Report of Studies* (as 5.4). para. 6.263.

CHAPTER 11

11.1 *The Smeed Report* (as 8.7). p. 49.

11.2 *Proposals by the London Transport Board for Fares Increases* (as 8.8).

11.3 A.A. Walters. 'Track Costs and Motor Taxation'. *Journal of Industrial Economics,* Vol. II, 1954. p. 135.

11.4 M. Beckmann, C.B. McGuire and C.B. Winsten. *Studies in the Economics of Transportation.* New Haven, Yale University Press, 1956. Ch. 4.

11.5 A.A. Walters. 'The Theory and Measurement of Private and Social Costs of Highway Congestion'. *Econometrica,* Vol. 29, 1961.

11.6 *The Smeed Report* (as 8.7).

11.7   A.A. Walters. *The Economics of Road User Charges,* World Bank
        Staff Occasional Papers Number Five Washington D.C.,
        International Bank for Reconstruction and Development, 1968.

11.8   European Economic Community. *Options on Transport Tariff
        Policy.* Transport Series No.1. Brussels, European Economic
        Community, 1965.

11.9   W. Vickrey. 'Optimization of Traffic and Facilities'.
        Journal of Transport Economics and Policy, Vol. 1, 1967. p. 123.

11.10   G.J. Roth. *Paying for Roads: the economics of traffic congestion.*
        Harmondsworth, Penguin, 1967.

11.11   *Transport Policy. Cmnd. 3057.* (as 5.11). p. 13.

11.12   M.E. Beesley. 'The Value of Time Spent Travelling: Some New
        Evidence'. *Economica,* Vol. XXXII, 1965. p. 174.

11.13   N. Lee and M.Q. Dalvi. 'Variations in the Value of Travel Time'.
        The Manchester School, Vol. XXXVII, 1969. p. 213.

11.14   E.J. Mishan. Interpretation of the Benefits of Private Transport.
        Journal of Transport Economics and Policy, Vol. I, 1967. p. 184.

11.15   D.G. Tipping. 'Time Savings in Transport Studies'. *Economic
        Journal,* Vol. LXXVIII, 1968. p. 843.

11.16   A.R. Prest and R. Turvey. 'Cost Benefit Analysis: A Survey'.
        Economic Journal, Vol. LXXV, 1965. p. 683.

11.17   A. Sauvy (as 7.2). Ch. XIV.

11.18   C.H. Sharp. 'Congestion and Welfare: An Examination of the
        Case for a Congestion Tax'. *Economic Journal,* Vol. LXXVI,
        1966. p. 806.

11.19   W. Vickrey. 'Congestion Charges and Welfare: Some Answers to
        Sharp's Doubts'. *Journal of Transport Economics and Policy,*
        Vol. II, 1968, p. 107.

11.20   C.H. Sharp. 'Congestion and Welfare Reconsidered'. *Journal of
        Transport Economics and Policy,* Vol. II, 1967. p. 119.

11.21   J.H. Moore. 'Congestion and Welfare – Comment'. *Economic
        Journal,* Vol. LXXVIII, 1968. p. 157.

11.22   C.H. Sharp. 'Congestion and Welfare – A Reply'.
        Economic Journal, Vol. LXXIX, 1969. p. 407.

11.23   E.J. Mishan (as 11.14).

11.24   D. Wood. 'Interpretation of the Benefits of Private Transport; a Comment'. *Journal of Transport Economics and Policy*, Vol. II, 1968. p. 105.

11.25   E.J. Mishan. 'Interpretation of the Benefits of Private Transport; a Reply'. *Journal of Transport Economics and Policy*, Vol. II, 1968, p. 105.

11.26   *Better use of town roads* (as 10.3). Foreword and p. 35.

CHAPTER 12

12.1   A. Sauvy (as 7.2). p. 123.

12.2   W. Owen in
E.T. Haefele (editor). *Transport and National Goals.*
Washington D.C., The Brookings Institution, 1969. Ch. 3.

12.3   A.A. Walters (as 11.7).

12.4   *Les Transports Urbains* (as 7.13). Part 4.

12.5   C.D. Foster. *The Transport Problem.* London, Blackie, 1963. pp. 29, 30.

12.6   Treasury. *Nationalized Industries: A Review of Economic and Financial Objectives. Cmnd. 3437.* London, H.M.S.O., 1967.

12.7   *Railway Policy. Cmnd. 3439* (as 11.14).

12.8   *The Reshaping of British Railways* (as 9.11).

12.9   *Proposed Increases in British Railways Board in Certain Country-wide Fares and Charges. Cmnd. 3656* (as 8.1). Chapters 6 and 7.

12.10   C.D. Foster and M.E. Beesley. 'Estimating the social benefit of constructing an underground railway in London'. *Journal of the Royal Statistical Society, Series A*, Vol. 126, 1963. p. 46.

12.11   R. Rees. 'Second-Best Rules for Public Enterprise Pricing'. *Economica*, Vol. XXXV, 1968. p. 260.

12.12   *Options on Transport Tariff Policy* (as 11.8). Ch. 22.

12.13   N.W. Mansfield. 'Recreational Trip Generation'. *Journal of Transport Economics and Policy*, Vol. III, 1969. p. 152.

12.14   *Private Motoring in England and Wales* (as 5.9). Table 6.2.

12.15   R. Sherman. 'Club Subscriptions for Public Transport'.
         Journal of Transport Economics and Policy, Vol. I, 1967. p. 237.
         R. Sherman. 'A Private Ownership Bias in Transit Choice'.
         The American Economic Review, Vol. LVII, 1967. p. 1211.

12.16   L. Fishman and J.S. Wabe, 'Restructuring the Form of Car
         Ownership'. *Transportation Research,* Vol. 3, 1969. p. 429.

12.17   Two surveys, in which the complaints ring true even if the
         sources and questions appear biased, have been conducted by the
         Traders' Road Transport Association (quoted by B.T. Bayliss
         (as 10.20). p. 31), and Aims of Industry *(Integration of Freight
         Transport: a survey of users' attitudes:* date probably 1968).

12.18   A typical selection appeared in *The Times* in the first fortnight
         of September, 1969.

12.19   *Transport Policy. Cmnd. 3057.* p. 2.

12.20   Economist Intelligence Unit. 'Mass Merchandising: Shopping
         Centres'. *Retail Business,* Issue 130, December 1968.

CHAPTER 13

13.1   *Tables of Operating Costs* (as 2.12).

13.2   B.T. Bayliss and S.L. Edwards. *Transport for Industry* (Summary
         Report). (Ministry of Transport). London, H.M.S.O., 1968.
         Table 3.

13.3   London County Council and Ministry of Transport. *London Traffic
         Survey,* Vol. 1. London, London County Council, 1964. Tables
         5.7 H.4   and
         Greater London Development Plan Report of Studies (as 5.4).
         Table 4.4.

13.4   *Survey of Road Goods Transport 1962: Final Results, Part I*
         (as 2.10). Table 4.

13.5   *Annual Bulletin of Transport Statistics for Europe 1967* (as 2.14).
         Table 31.

13.6   The Monopolies Commission. *Petrol: A Report on the Supply of
         Petrol to Retailers in the United Kingdom.* (H.C. 264, 1964-5).
         London, H.M.S.O., 1965. Chapter 9 and paras. 319-322.

13.7   *Survey of Road Goods Transport 1962: Final Results, Part I*

(as 2.10). Table (x).

13.8   *Survey of Road Goods Transport 1962: Final Results, Part I*
        (as 2.10). Table 6.

13.9   B.T. Bayliss (as 10.20). p. 71.

13.10   *Charges, Costs and Wages in the Road Haulage Industry.*
        Cmnd. 3482 (as 4.9).

13.11   *Survey of Road Goods Transport 1962: Final Results, Part I*
        (as 2.10). Tables 21 and 22.

13.12   *Survey of Road Goods Transport 1962: Final Results, Part I*
        (as 2.10). Table 28.

13.13   *Survey of Road Goods Transport 1962: Final Results, Part I*
        (as 2.10). Tables 21 and 23.

13.14   *London Traffic Survey*, Vol. I (as 13.3). Table 8.15.

13.15   Ministry of Transport. *Highway Statistics 1965.* London,
        H.M.S.O., 1966. Table 35.

13.16   A. Fischer (as 6.2). p. 83.

13.17   B.T. Bayliss (as 10.20). Table XI, p. 22.

13.18   *Highway Statistics 1965* (as 13.15). Table 40.

13.19   M. Chisholm. 'Economies of Scale in Road Goods Transport?
        Off-Farm Milk Connection in England and Wales'. *Oxford*
        Economic Papers, Vol. II, 1959. p. 282.

13.20   A.J. Harrison. 'Economies of Scale and the Structure of the
        Road Haulage Industry'. *Oxford Economic Papers*, Vol. 15,
        1963, p. 287.

13.21   B.T. Bayliss. Personal communication, 1969.

CHAPTER 14

14.1   P.G. Hollowell. *The Lorry Driver.* London, Routledge & Kegan
        Paul, 1968.

14.2   *Survey of Road Goods Transport 1962: Final Results, Part I*
        (as 2.10). Table 6.

14.3   *The Geddes Report* (as 5.12). p. 26, para. 3.11.

14.4   B.T. Bayliss and S.L. Edwards (as 13.2). p.39.

14.5   *The Geddes Report* (as 5.12). pp. 25, 26, paras. 3.8-3.10.

14.6   H.C. Kuiler in
European Conference of Ministers of Transport. *International Symposium on Theory and Practice in Transport Economics.* Paris, 1965. p. 25.

14.7   *The Geddes Report* (as 5.12). p. 23, paras. 2.53, 2.54.

14.8   Quoted by B.T. Bayliss (as 10.20). p. 31.

14.9   B.T. Bayliss and S.L. Edwards (as 13.2).

14.10   B.T. Bayliss and S.L. Edwards (as 13.2). Table 18.

14.11   *Survey of Road Goods Transport 1962: Final Results, Part I* (as 2.10). Table 21.

14.12   *Survey of Road Goods Transport 1962: Final Results, Part I* (as 2.10). Table 27.

CHAPTER 15

15.1   Derivation explained later in this chapter.

15.2   *London Traffic Survey,* Vol. I (as 13.3). Table H.4, and *Greater London Development Plan Report of Studies* (as 5.4). Table 4.4.

15.3   B.T. Bayliss and S.L. Edwards (as 13.2). p. 55.

15.4   *National Income and Expenditure 1968* (as 2.2). Table 68.

15.5   *Survey of Road Goods Transport 1962: Final Results, Part I* (as 2.10). p. 7.

15.6   A.J. Merrett and A. Sykes. 'Return on Equities and Fixed Interest Securities: 1919-1966'. *District Bank Review,* No. 158, 1966. p. 29.

15.7   A.T. Kearney & Co. 'A survey of British industrial distribution practices and costs'. Quoted in reference 15.8.

15.8   *Planning Warehouse Locations* (as 5.14).

15.9   *Board of Trade Journal* 26th July, 1968.

15.10   *Survey of Road Goods Transport 1962: Final Results, Part I* (as 2.10). Table 11.

15.11   *Survey of Road Goods Transport 1962: Final Results, Part I*

(as 2.10). Table 27.

15.12   *London Traffic Survey,* Vol. I (as 13.3). Tables 8.15, 8.24.

15.13   *Tables of Operating Costs* (as 2.12).

15.14   *Charges, Costs and Wages in the Road Haulage Industry. Cmnd. 3482* (as 4.9).

15.15   S.L. Edwards (as 4.11).

15.16   F.H. Gruen. 'Trends in Food Marketing'. *Australian Journal of Agricultural Economics,* Vol. 12, 1968. p. 24.

15.17   *Greater London Development Plan Report of Studies* (as 5.4). para. 4.51.

15.18   P. Mathias. *Retailing Revolution.* London, Longman's, 1967. Chapters 6-9.

15.19   *Survey of Road Goods Transport 1962: Final Results, Part I* (as 2.10). Table 30.

15.20   The total length of the journeys between deliveries is assumed to be approximately equal to the circumference of the area within which the load is delivered.

15.21   *London Traffic Survey,* Vol I (as 13.3). p. 4.

15.22   *London Traffic Survey,* Vol I (as 13.3). Table 8.24.

15.23   *Survey of Road Goods Transport 1962: Final Results, Part I* (as 2.10). Table 5.

15.24   *Survey of Road Goods Transport 1962: Final Results, Part I* (as 2.10). Tables 12a, 31a.

15.25   *Petrol: A Report on the Supply of Petrol to Retailers in the United Kingdom* (as 13.6). Chapter 9, and paras. 319-322.

CHAPTER 16

16.1   The Monopolies Commission. *Beer: A Report on the Supply of Beer (H.C. 216).* London, H.M.S.O., 1969. para. 176.

16.2   Economist Intelligence Unit. 'Stock Control'. *Marketing in Europe.* Annual Supplement 1969.

16.3   Economist Intelligence Unit. 'Marketing Review'. *Retail Business,* Issue 145, March 1970.

16.4   *Group Grocer*, May, 1968. Quoted in reference 16.5.

16.5   Economist Intelligence Unit. 'The Future for the Independent
        Retailer'. *Retail Business*, Issue 126, August 1968.

16.6   *The Times*, 'NCL plans regional storage expansion'. 18 March
        1970.

16.7   For example, Eldonwall Industrial Estates Ltd. were granted
        planning permission in 1968 for a 34½ acre warehousing site for
        a 'local distribution centre' at Crick near the junctions of the
        M1, M45 and M6 motorways. This site, which could be extended,
        could serve as a base for as many as 500 vehicles.

16.8   Economist Intelligence Unit. 'Annual Review of Retailing'.
        Retail Business, Issue 145, March 1970.

16.9   Economist Intelligence Unit. 'Marketing Review'. *Retail
        Business*, Issue 140, October 1969.

CHAPTER 17

17.1   Economist Intelligence Unit. 'Mass Merchandising: Discount
        Stores'. *Retail Business*, Issue 131, January 1969.

17.2   Economist Intelligence Unit. 'Mass Merchandising: Supermarkets'.
        Retail Business, Issue 133, March 1969.

17.3   Economist Intelligence Unit. 'Marketing Review'. *Retail
        Business*, Issue 135, May 1969.

17.4   Economist Intelligence Unit. 'Mass Merchandising: Shopping
        Centres'. *Retail Business*, Issue 130, December, 1968.

17.5   Economist Intelligence Unit. 'Marketing Review'. *Retail
        Business*, Issue 136, June 1969.

17.6   Economist Intelligence Unit. 'Marketing Review'. *Marketing in
        Europe*, Issue 78, May 1969.

17.7   Economist Intelligence Unit. 'Marketing Review'. *Retail
        Business*, Issue 128, October 1968.

17.8   *London Traffic Survey*, Vol. I (as 13.3). Table 6.16A.

17.9   M.A. Taylor (as 10.5). Table 48.

17.10   M.A. Taylor (as 10.5). Fig. 47.

17.11   *London Traffic Survey*, Vol. I (as 13.3). Table 7.5.

A similar, more recent, table may be found in *Les Transports Urbains* (as 7.13). Part I, table 22.

17.12   Quoted from Economist Intelligence Unit. 'Marketing Review'. *Retail Business,* Issue 140, October 1969.

17.13   National Board for Prices and Incomes Report No. 46. *The Remuneration of Milk Distributors (Final Report). Cmnd. 3477.* London, H.M.S.O., 1967.

17.14   Post Office. *Report and Accounts 1967/8* (H.C. 349, 1967-8). London, H.M.S.O., 1968. p. 56.

17.15   Economist Intelligence Unit. 'Door-To-Door Selling'. *Marketing in Europe.* Annual Supplement 1969.

CHAPTER 18

18.1   B.T. Bayliss and S.L. Edwards (as 13.2).

18.2   Aims of Industry. *Integration of Freight Transport: a Survey of Users' Attitudes.* London, Aims of Industry, 1968.

18.3   B.T. Bayliss and S.L. Edwards (as 13.2). pp. 42-7.

CHAPTER 19

19.1   B.T. Bayliss and S.L. Edwards (as 13.2). Table 10.

19.2   N.A. Dudley. *Work Measurement: Some Research Studies.* London, Macmillan, 1968. Chapter 4.

CHAPTER 20

20.1   *Survey of Road Goods Transport 1962: Final Results, Part I* (as 2.10). Table 27.

20.2   *Survey of Road Goods Transport 1962: Final Results, Part I* (as 2.10). Tables 18-20.

20.3   B.T. Bayliss (as 10.20). p. 92.

20.4   *Highway Statistics 1965* (as 13.15). Table 35.

20.5   *Survey of Road Goods Transport 1962: Final Results, Part I* (as 2.10). Table 21.

20.6   *The Geddes Report* (as 5.12). paras. 1.3, 1.4.

20.7   *Survey of Road Goods Transport 1962: Final Results, Part I*
(as 2.10). Tables 4, 27, 29.

20.8   *Survey of Road Goods Transport 1962: Final Results, Part I*
(as 2.10). Tables 21, 23, 25.

20.9   *Survey of Road Goods Transport 1962: Final Results, Part I*
(as 2.10). Table 22.

20.10   *Survey of Road Goods Transport 1962: Final Results, Part I*
(as 2.10). Table 13.

CHAPTER 22

22.1   The details quoted are those given in H.G.M. Pullen and M.H.J.
Webb. 'A computer application to a transport scheduling problem'.
The Computer Journal, Vol. 10, 1967. p. 10.

CHAPTER 23

23.1   *Charges, Costs and Wages in the Road Haulage Industry.*
Cmnd. 3482 (as 4.9).

23.2   The average duration would normally refer to the average of a
number of observations of repetitions of the same journey. If
conditions remained unchanged the expected duration of the next
performance of this journey might be the average of the previous
observations (the conditional is used because this would not be
true if the observed durations were not grouped symmetrically
about the average). Often, however, particular journeys are
rarely repeated; consequently averages of these journeys are
rarely observed. It is, nevertheless, possible to expect one
duration more than others.

23.3   These are statistical terms, and explanations are best sought
elsewhere. For the present, a normal distribution is what would
be expected if differences between the actual and expected
durations occurred randomly and symmetrically; the standard
error is a measure of the size and spread of the differences
between the actual and expected durations.

23.4   R.J. Smeed. *The Traffic Problem in Towns.* Manchester,
Manchester Statistical Society, 1961. p. 13.

23.5   *London Traffic Survey,* Vol. I (as 13.3). Table 8.27.

CHAPTER 25

25.1   R.J. Smeed (as 23.4). pp. 12-13.

25.2   *Research on Road Traffic* (as 7.6). Chapter 3.

25.3   J.M. Thomson (as 10.1).

25.4   E.D. Turner and K. Crawford. *Central London Traffic Survey April-May 1966* Research Report HT/RD-4. London, Greater London Council, Department of Highways and Transportation, 1966.

25.5   Joan K. Turner and J.G. Wardrop. *The Variation of Journey Time in Central London.* Road Research Laboratory. Note No. RN/1511, 1951.

25.6   The unpublished, detailed data was kindly lent by Research and Development Group of the Department of Highways and Transportation of the Greater London Council.

25.7   Unfortunately the term average speed is commonly used with different detailed meanings. The average speed of a journey may be the quotient obtained by dividing the journey distance by the duration for a single performance of this journey; alternatively it may be the average of a number of observations of that quotient. In the section which follows the 'speed' of a journey will be used to refer to the quotient of the journey distance and duration, and the 'average speed' to the average of a number of observations of the speed.

25.8   *Research on Road Traffic* (as 7.6). Chapter 5.

25.9   *Research on Road Traffic* (as 7.6). Chapter 6.

25.10   E.D. Turner and K. Crawford (as 25.4). Table 2.

CHAPTER 26

26.1   R.E. Schofer and B.M. Levin. 'The Urban Transportation Planning Process'. *Socio-Economic Planning Sciences,* Vol. I, 1967. p. 185.

26.2   *London Traffic Survey,* Vol. I (as 13.3). para. 2.04. and *Greater London Development Plan Report of Studies* (as 5.4). para. 6.8.

26.3   *London Traffic Survey,* Vol. I (as 13.3). para. 3.15.

CHAPTER 27

27.1   Automobile Association. *Members' Annual Handbook* (1956 edition). London, Automobile Association, 1956.

27.2   Janice A. Timbers. 'Route Factors in Road Networks'. *Traffic Engineering and Control,* Vol. 9, 1967. p. 392.

27.3   *London Traffic Survey,* Vol. I (as 13.3). Tables 8.15 and 8.24.

27.4   M.E. Eliot Hurst. 'The Structure of Movement and Household Travel Behaviour'. *Urban Studies,* Vol. 6, 1969. p. 70. This paper gives references to a number of studies of which the results are summarized.

CHAPTER 28

28.1   *The Remuneration of Milk Distributors (Final Report). Cmnd. 3477* (as 17.13).

28.2   Economic Development Committee for the Distributive Trades. *Newsletter No.5.* London, National Economic Development Office, 1967. Reference has been made to a more recent experiment in Economic Development Committee for the Distributive Trades. *Newsletter No.6.* London, National Economic Development Office, 1968. p. 6. It appears unlikely that a full report will be written.

28.3   Economic Development Committee for the Distributive Trades. *Newsletter No.3.* London, National Economic Development Office. 1966.

28.4   Economic Development Committee for the Distributive Trades. *Newsletter No.6.* London, National Economic Development Office, 1968. p. 3.

CHAPTER 29

29.1   *Members' Annual Handbook* (as 27.1).

CHAPTER 30

30.1   D.J. Wilde and C.S. Beightler. *Foundations of Optimization.* Englewood Cliffs, Prentice Hall, 1967.

30.2   G. Danzig, R. Fulkerson and S. Johnson. 'Solution of a Large
        Scale Travelling Salesman Problem'. *Operations Research,* Vol. 2,
        1954. p. 393.

30.3   M. Held and R. Karp. 'A Dynamic Programming Approach to
        Sequencing Problems'. *SIAM Journal,* Vol. 10, 1962. p. 196.

30.4   J.D. Little, K.G. Murty, D.W. Sweeney and D. Karel. 'An
        Algorithm for the Travelling Salesman Problem'. *Operations
        Research,* Vol. 11, 1963. p. 972.

CHAPTER 31

31.1   G.A. Croes. 'A Method for Solving Travelling Salesman Problems'.
        Operations Research, Vol. 6, 1958. p. 791.

31.2   S. Lin. 'Computer Solution of the Travelling Salesman Problem'.
        Bell System Technical Journal, Vol. 44, 1965. p. 2245.

31.3   R.E. Oberuc. 'A Practical Algorithm for Finding Solutions to the
        Travelling Salesman Problem'. Paper presented to 34th National
        Meeting, Operations Research Society of America, 1968.

31.4   M. Bellmore and G. Nemhauser. 'The Travelling Salesman
        Problem: A Survey'. *Operations Research,* Vol. 16, 1968.
        p. 538.

31.5   A.M. Isaac and E. Turban. 'Some Comments on the Travelling
        Salesman Problem'. *Operations Research,* Vol. 17, 1969.
        p. 543.

CHAPTER 32

32.1   B.W. Boehm. 'Third Generation Computer Trends'. *Rand
        Paper P3903.* August 1968.

32.2   W.F. Sharpe. *The Economics of Computers.* New York, Columbia
        University Press, 1969. Chapter 9.

32.3   S. Lin (as 31.2).

32.4   D. Michie, J.G. Fleming and J.V. Oldfield, 'A Comparison of
        Heuristic Interactive and Unaided Methods of Solving a
        Shortest Route Problem'.
        In D. Michie (Editor) *Machine Intelligence 3.* Edinburgh
        University Press, 1968.

CHAPTER 33

33.1   J.F. Pierce. 'Application of Combinatorial Programming to a Class of All-Zero-One Integer Programming Problems'. *Management Science,* Vol. 15, 1968. p. 191.

33.2   J.D. Little, K.G. Murty, D.W. Sweeney and D. Karel (as 30.4).

33.3   J.F. Pierce and J.S. Lasky. 'An Improved Combinatorial Algorithm for Zero-One Integer Programming'. Announcement in *O.R.S.A. Bulletin,* Spring, 1969, of a paper presented at the 1969 Joint National Meeting of the Operations Research Society of America together with the American Astronautical Society. 'This algorithm solved a truck dispatching problem (1156 variables, 19 constraints) in ½ minute on IBM 7094. A previous algorithm (published in *Management Science,* November 1968) did not solve this problem in 40 minutes.'

33.4   A.J. Scott. 'Combinatorial Programming and the Planning of Urban and Regional Systems'. *Environment and Planning,* Vol. I, 1969. p. 125.

CHAPTER 35

35.1   G.A. Miller. 'The Magical Number Seven, Plus-or-Minus Two, or Some Limits on Our Capacity for Processing Information'. *Psychological Review,* Vol. 63, 1956. p. 81.

35.2   Quite apart from differences inevitably associated with the different data, the programs utilized different searching techniques. Further, although the 'loss' criterion employed to obtain the reported results was the same, the sequence rules were changed for the co-ordinate problems to increase computing speeds.

35.3   J. Beardwood, H.J. Halton and J.M. Hammersley. 'The shortest route through many points'. *Proceedings of the Cambridge Philosophical Society,* Vol. 55, 1959. p. 299.

35.4   M.H.J. Webb. 'Some methods of producing approximate solutions to travelling salesman problems with hundreds or thousands of cities'. *Operational Research Quarterly,* Vol. 22, 1971.

35.5   G. Clarke and J.W. Wright. 'Scheduling of Vehicles from a Central Depot to a Number of Delivery Points'. *Operations Research,* Vol. 12, 1964. p. 568.

35.6   M.H.J. Webb. 'A Study in Transport Routing'. *Glass Technology,* Vol. 5, 1964. p. 172.

35.7   T.J. Gaskell. 'Bases for Vehicle Fleet Scheduling'. *Operational Research Quarterly*, Vol. 18, 1967. p. 281.

35.8   N. Christofides and S. Eilon. 'An algorithm for the vehicle dispatching problem'. *Operational Research Quarterly*, Vol. 20, 1969. p. 309.

35.9   S. Lin (as 31.2).

CHAPTER 36

36.1   The number of savings to be calculated is $N(N-1)/2$; to calculate each straight line distance involves calculating the square root of a sum of squares, and many computers would take milliseconds per saving calculation; for 500 deliveries and 1 millisecond to calculate each saving, the time requirement to calculate all the savings would be 125 seconds. Time reports are rare, probably because so many special factors may alter the time taken. However, in reference 36.2 it states that the preparation of a savings file for a problem in which the area was represented by 300 customer zones, with 20 barriers and 2 congested areas where special allowances were made, took 6¼ hours on a 64K IBM 360 Model 30, while in reference 36.3 finding the shortest time from one origin to each of 2,500 destinations is said to take ½ second on a 64K CDC 3600.

36.2   Presentation of the IBM 360 vehicle scheduling program to the Vehicle Scheduling Working Party of the Transport Study Group of the Operational Research Society on 12th May, 1969, as reported by J. Hargreaves in Operational Research Society circular SG/50/VS/WB/69.

36.3   R.E. Schofer and B.M. Levin (as 26.1).

36.4   For example, if it is necessary to store 3 digits for the saving of each potential link, and there are 500 deliveries, the storage space required for this purpose alone would be 375,000 digits; this assumes that the saving is identified with its potential link by its position, as in a full matrix; if the savings of some potential links were omitted, and identification of each one remaining became necessary, since each remaining potential link, in crude terms, would need 3 digits to identify each end, more than ⅔ of the potential links would have to be discarded before the storage requirement decreased.

36.5   A. Fletcher and G. Clarke. 'A Case Study in Transportation'.
Paper presented to the annual conference of the Operational
Research Society at Nottingham in 1963.

CHAPTER 37

37.1   *Members' Annual Handbook* (as 27.1).

37.2   S.W. Golomb and L.D. Baumert. 'Backtrack Programming'.
Journal of the Association for Computing Machinery, Vol. 12,
1965, p. 516.

CHAPTER 38

38.1   T.J. Gaskell (as 35.7).

38.2   R.G. Greaves. 'Vehicle Routing for Newspaper Distribution'.
Paper presented at the Operational Research Society Annual
Conference at Edinburgh, 1968. Reported briefly in
Operational Research Quarterly, Vol. 20, 1969, Special
Conference Issue. pp. 98-9.

CHAPTER 39

39.1   H.G.M. Pullen and M.H.J. Webb (as 22.1).

CHAPTER 42

42.1   G. Clarke and J.W. Wright (as 35.5).

42.2   T.J. Gaskell (as 35.7).

42.3   N. Christofides and S. Eilon (as 35.8).

42.4   E.G. Unwin and J.D.H. Weatherby (1968). 'Improved Route
Planning'. Paper presented at the Annual Conference of the
Operational Research Society at Edinburgh in 1968, and
reprinted in *Operational Research Quarterly,* Vol. 20, 1969,
Special Conference Issue. p. 103.

42.5   Results claimed for application of the I.B.M. 360 Vehicle
Scheduling Program to an Air Products Ltd. depot in a
presentation (as 36.2).

42.6   Results claimed for application of an I.C.L. Vehicle Scheduling
        Program within Calor Gas in a presentation to the Vehicle
        Scheduling Working Party of the Transport Study Group of the
        Operational Research Society on 21st July, 1969, as reported
        by J.A.T. Pritchard in Operational Research Society circular
        SG/77/T/VS/GS/69.

42.7   D. Michie, J.G. Fleming and J.V. Oldfield (as 32.4).

42.8   W.F. Sharpe (as 32.2).

INDEX